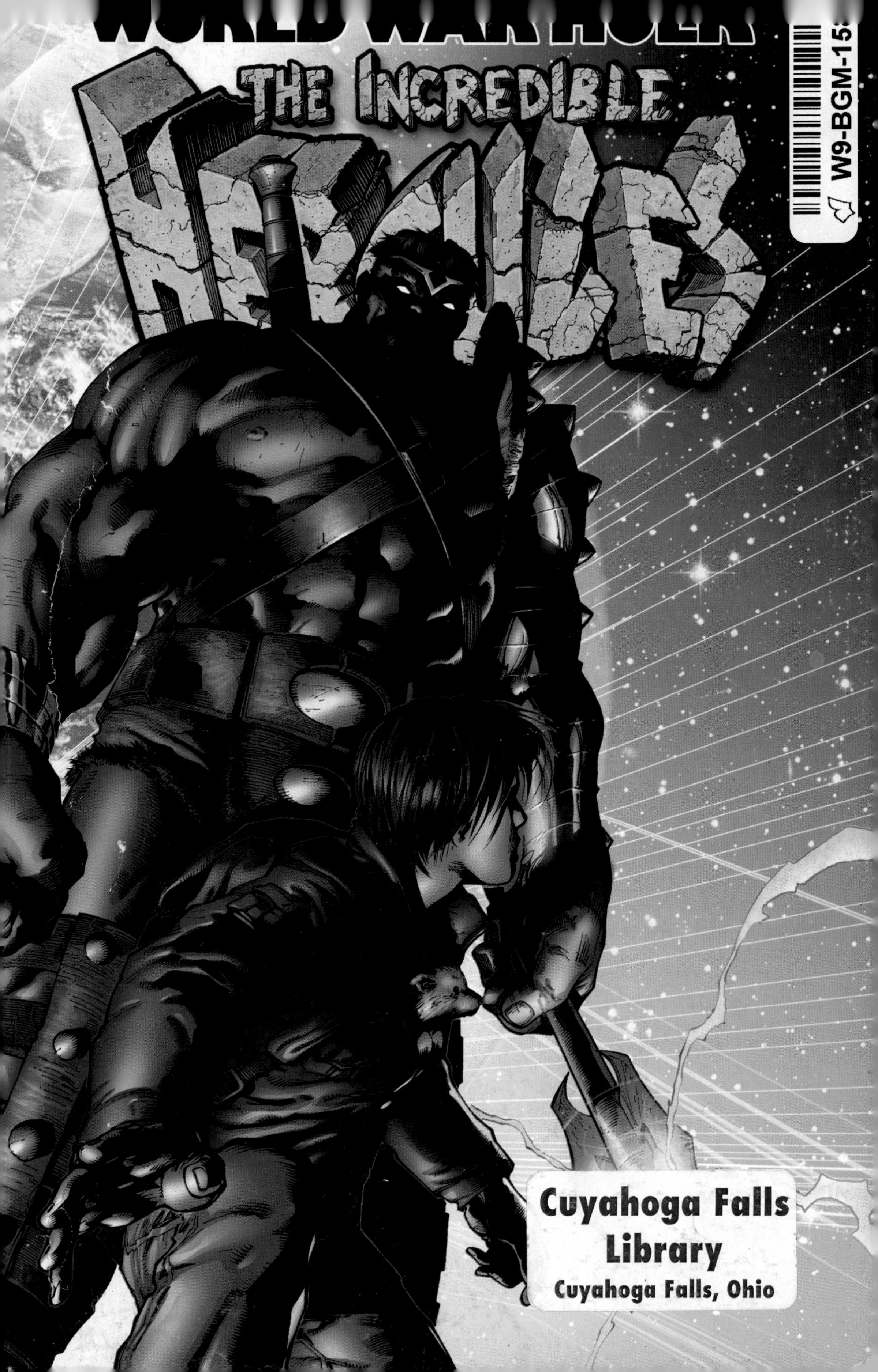
WORLD WAR HULK
THE INCREDIBLE

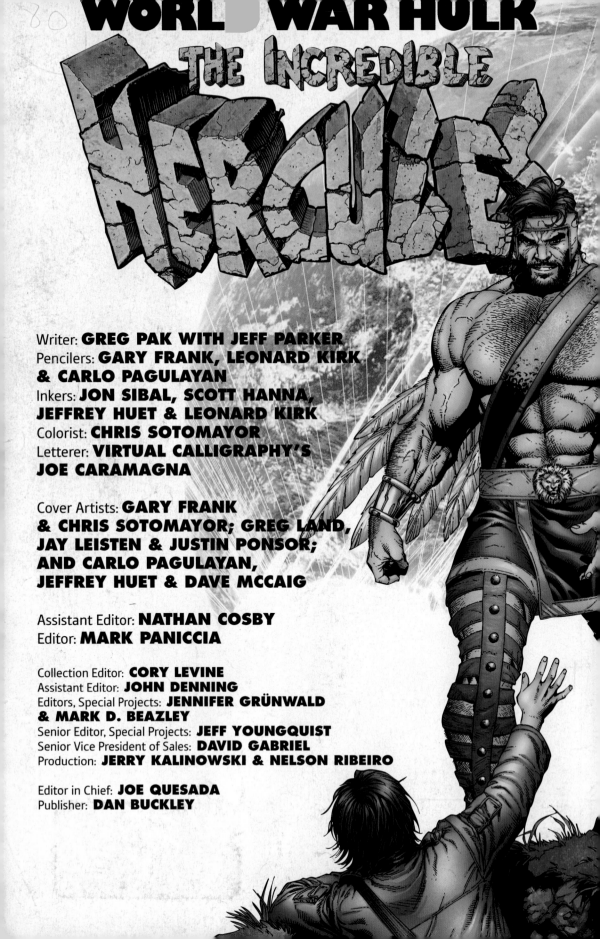

WORLD WAR HULK
THE INCREDIBLE HERCULES

Writer: **GREG PAK WITH JEFF PARKER**
Pencilers: **GARY FRANK, LEONARD KIRK**
& CARLO PAGULAYAN
Inkers: **JON SIBAL, SCOTT HANNA,**
JEFFREY HUET & LEONARD KIRK
Colorist: **CHRIS SOTOMAYOR**
Letterer: **VIRTUAL CALLIGRAPHY'S**
JOE CARAMAGNA

Cover Artists: **GARY FRANK**
& CHRIS SOTOMAYOR; GREG LAND,
JAY LEISTEN & JUSTIN PONSOR;
AND CARLO PAGULAYAN,
JEFFREY HUET & DAVE MCCAIG

Assistant Editor: **NATHAN COSBY**
Editor: **MARK PANICCIA**

Collection Editor: **CORY LEVINE**
Assistant Editor: **JOHN DENNING**
Editors, Special Projects: **JENNIFER GRÜNWALD**
& MARK D. BEAZLEY
Senior Editor, Special Projects: **JEFF YOUNGQUIST**
Senior Vice President of Sales: **DAVID GABRIEL**
Production: **JERRY KALINOWSKI & NELSON RIBEIRO**

Editor in Chief: **JOE QUESADA**
Publisher: **DAN BUCKLEY**

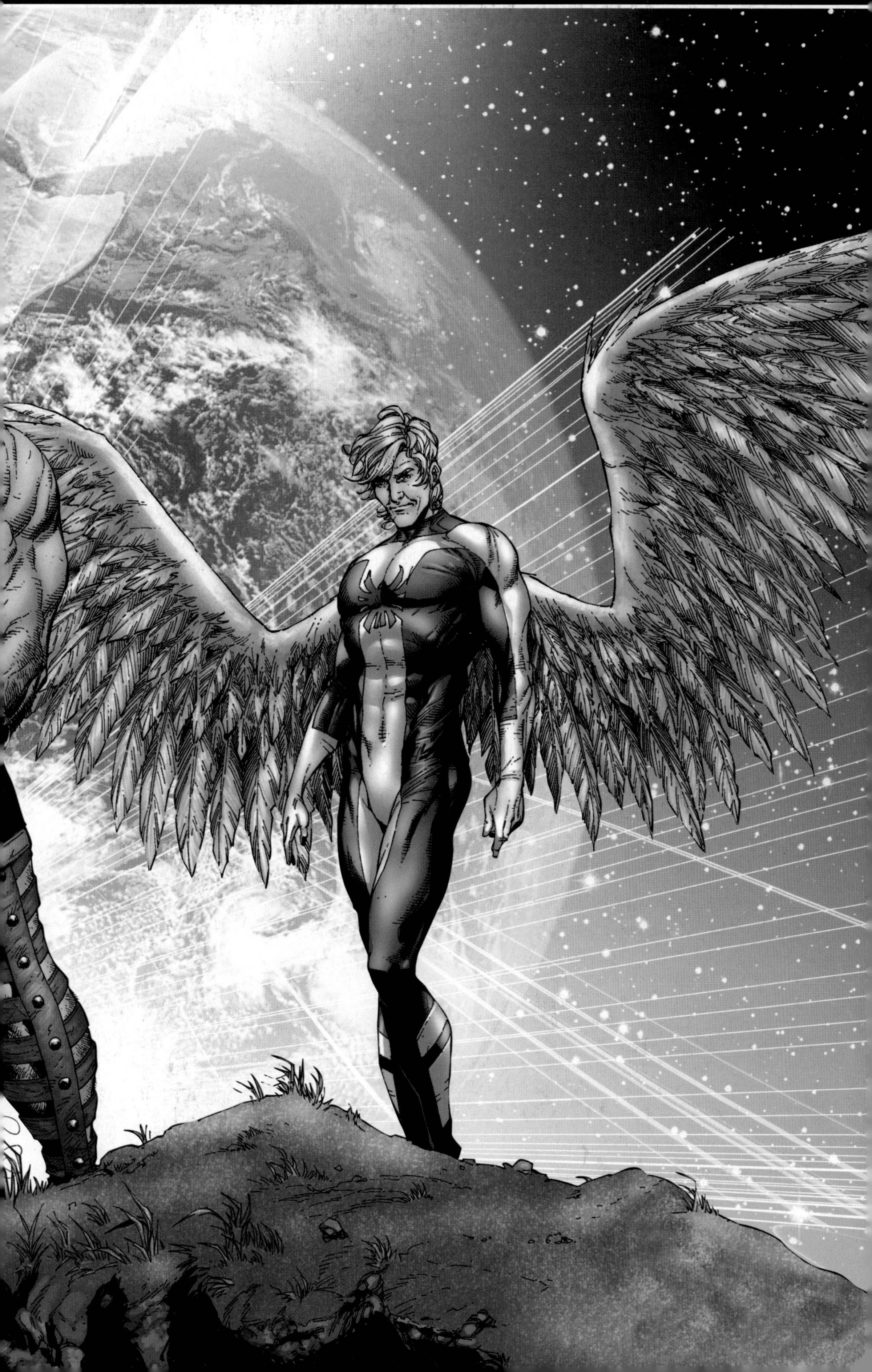

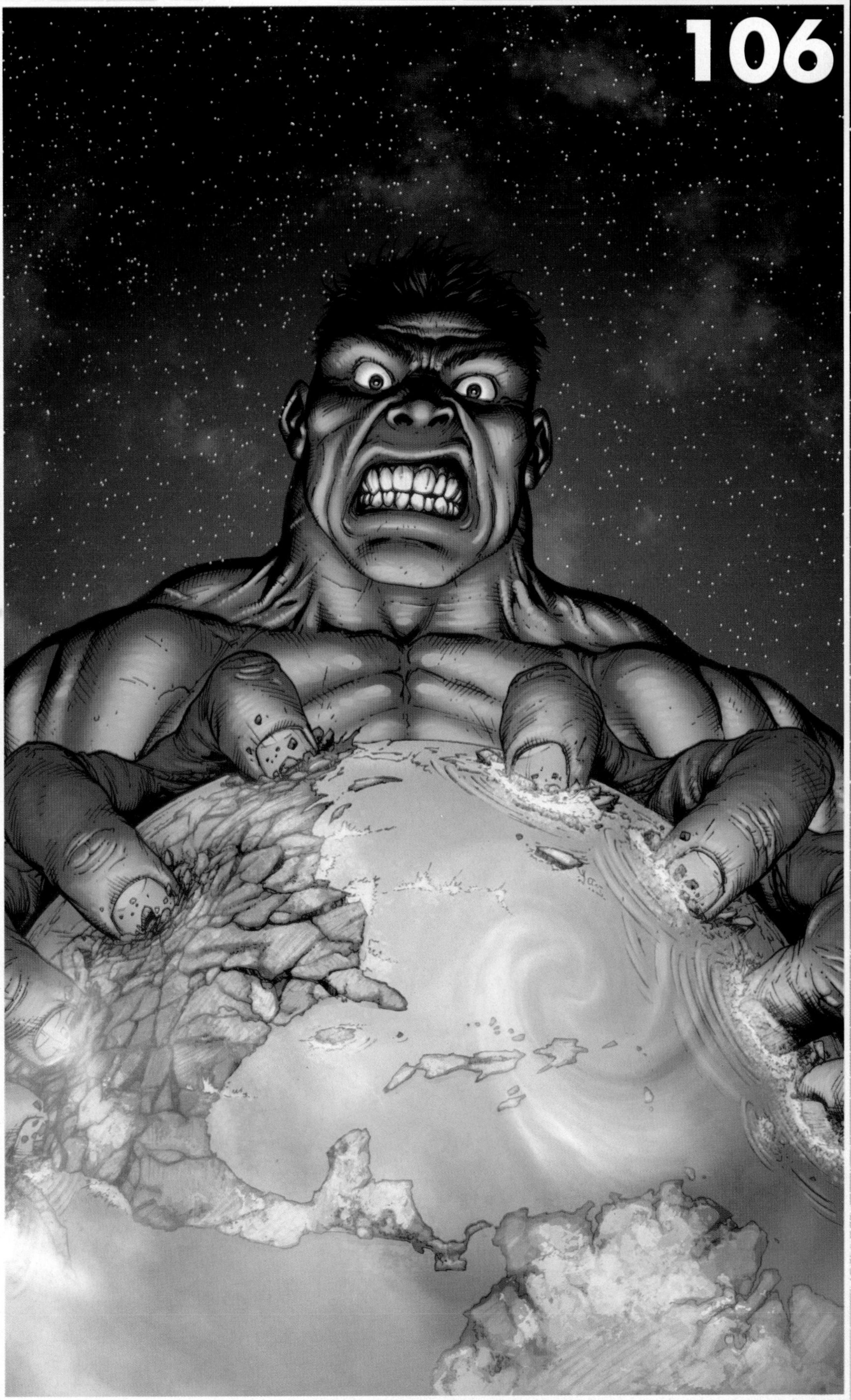
106

While trying to save the life of an innocent, Doctor Bruce Banner was caught in the blast of a gamma bomb and became

THE INCREDIBLE HULK

...a rampaging monster with near-limitless power.

Fearing the threat he posed to humanity, Earth's most powerful heroes shot Hulk into space.

Landing on a faraway planet, Hulk became an Emperor and fell in love.

But the shuttle that sent Hulk away from Earth exploded, killing millions of people, including Hulk's queen and the baby growing inside of her.

Filled with rage, Hulk and his Warbound warriors have set course for Earth, to bring revenge upon those he holds responsible for destroying his world…

WARBOUND

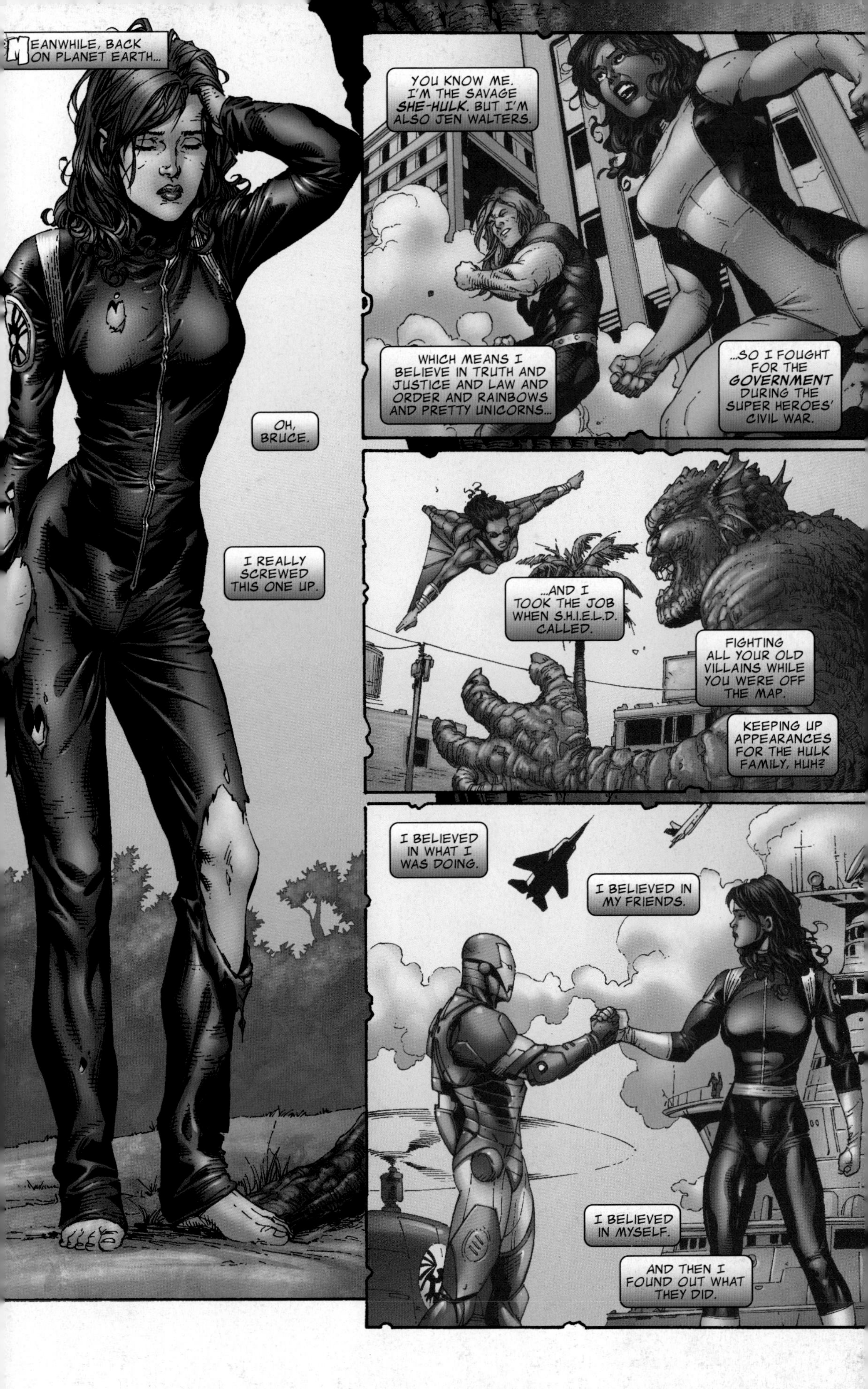
MEANWHILE, BACK ON PLANET EARTH...
OH, BRUCE.
I REALLY SCREWED THIS ONE UP.
YOU KNOW ME. I'M THE SAVAGE SHE-HULK. BUT I'M ALSO JEN WALTERS.
WHICH MEANS I BELIEVE IN TRUTH AND JUSTICE AND LAW AND ORDER AND RAINBOWS AND PRETTY UNICORNS...
...SO I FOUGHT FOR THE GOVERNMENT DURING THE SUPER HEROES' CIVIL WAR.
...AND I TOOK THE JOB WHEN S.H.I.E.L.D. CALLED.
FIGHTING ALL YOUR OLD VILLAINS WHILE YOU WERE OFF THE MAP.
KEEPING UP APPEARANCES FOR THE HULK FAMILY, HUH?
I BELIEVED IN WHAT I WAS DOING.
I BELIEVED IN MY FRIENDS.
I BELIEVED IN MYSELF.
AND THEN I FOUND OUT WHAT THEY DID.

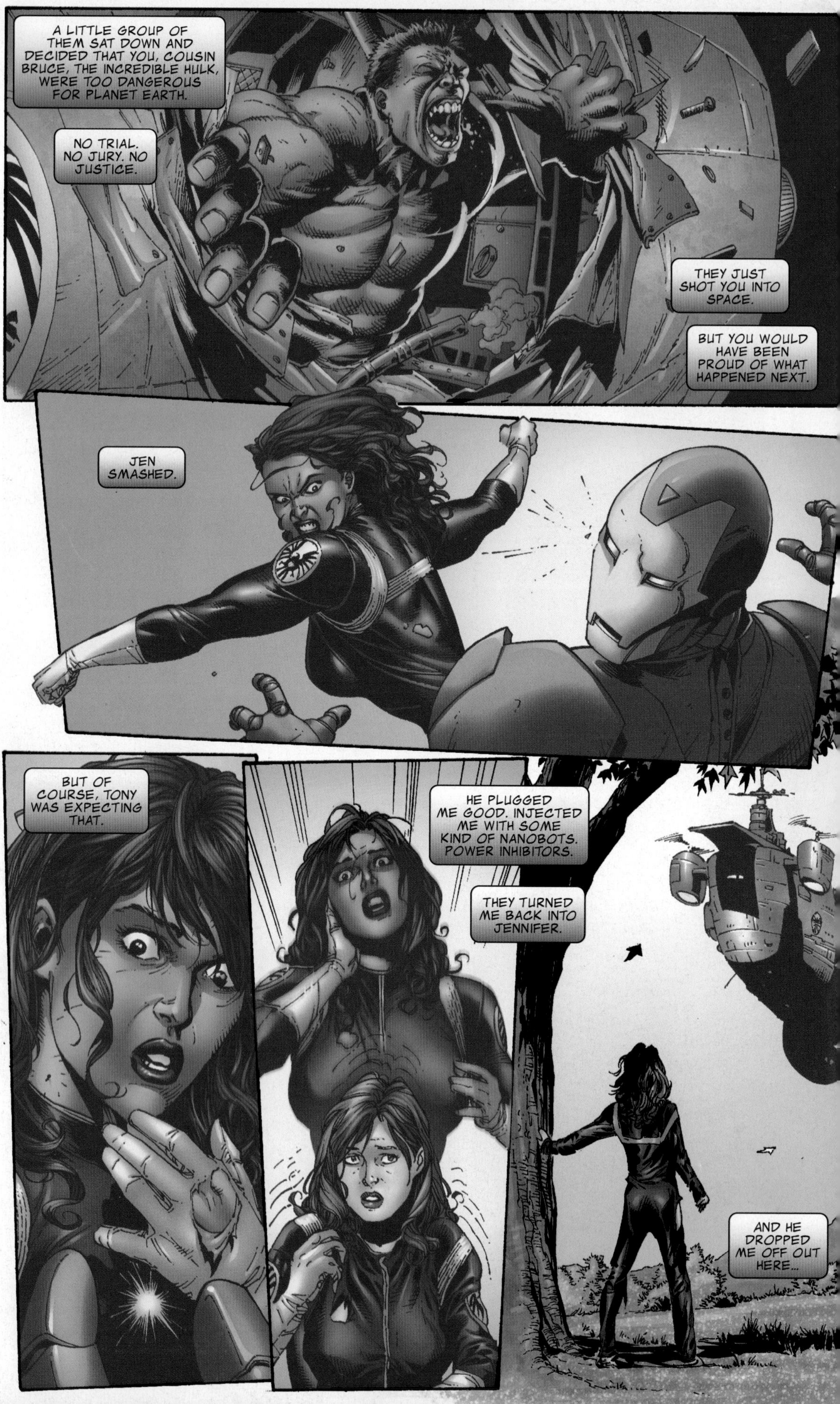
A LITTLE GROUP OF THEM SAT DOWN AND DECIDED THAT YOU, COUSIN BRUCE, THE INCREDIBLE HULK, WERE TOO DANGEROUS FOR PLANET EARTH.
NO TRIAL. NO JURY. NO JUSTICE.
THEY JUST SHOT YOU INTO SPACE.
BUT YOU WOULD HAVE BEEN PROUD OF WHAT HAPPENED NEXT.
JEN SMASHED.
BUT OF COURSE, TONY WAS EXPECTING THAT.
HE PLUGGED ME GOOD. INJECTED ME WITH SOME KIND OF NANOBOTS. POWER INHIBITORS.
THEY TURNED ME BACK INTO JENNIFER.
AND HE DROPPED ME OFF OUT HERE...

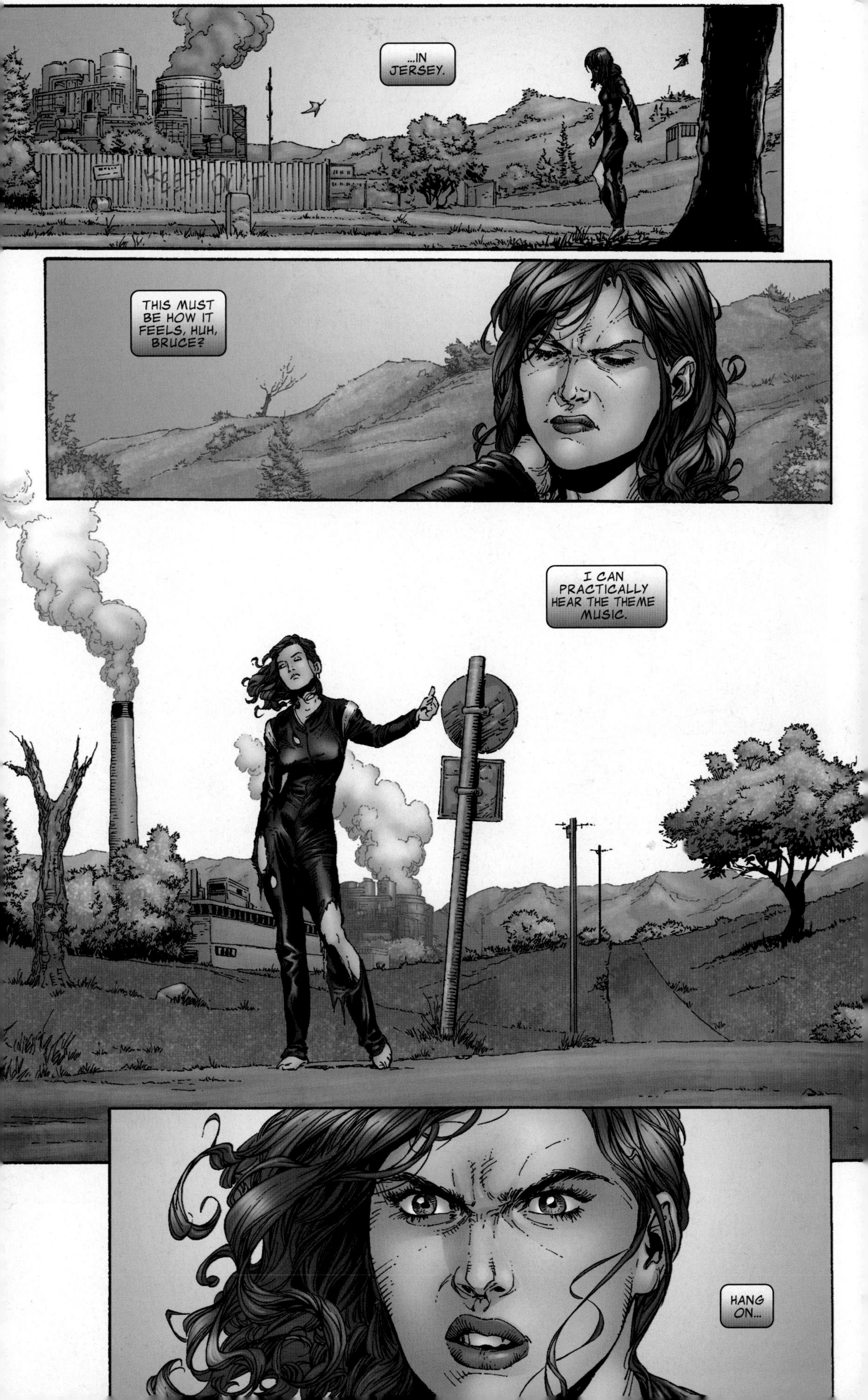
...IN JERSEY.
THIS MUST BE HOW IT FEELS, HUH, BRUCE?
I CAN PRACTICALLY HEAR THE THEME MUSIC.
HANG ON...

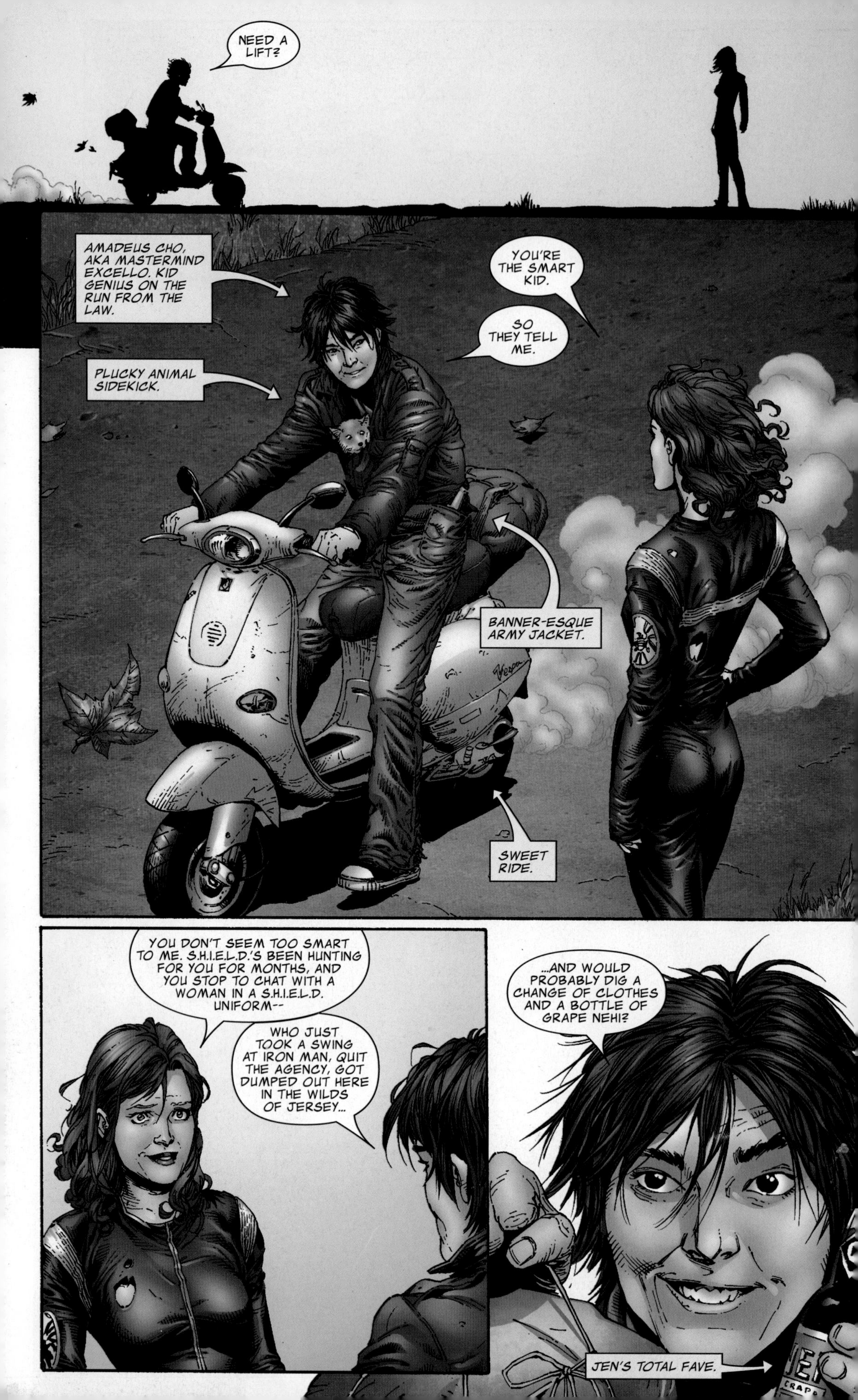

NEED A LIFT?
AMADEUS CHO, AKA MASTERMIND EXCELLO. KID GENIUS ON THE RUN FROM THE LAW.
YOU'RE THE SMART KID.
SO THEY TELL ME.
PLUCKY ANIMAL SIDEKICK.
BANNER-ESQUE ARMY JACKET.
SWEET RIDE.
YOU DON'T SEEM TOO SMART TO ME. S.H.I.E.L.D.'S BEEN HUNTING FOR YOU FOR MONTHS, AND YOU STOP TO CHAT WITH A WOMAN IN A S.H.I.E.L.D. UNIFORM--
WHO JUST TOOK A SWING AT IRON MAN, QUIT THE AGENCY, GOT DUMPED OUT HERE IN THE WILDS OF JERSEY...
...AND WOULD PROBABLY DIG A CHANGE OF CLOTHES AND A BOTTLE OF GRAPE NEHI?
JEN'S TOTAL FAVE.

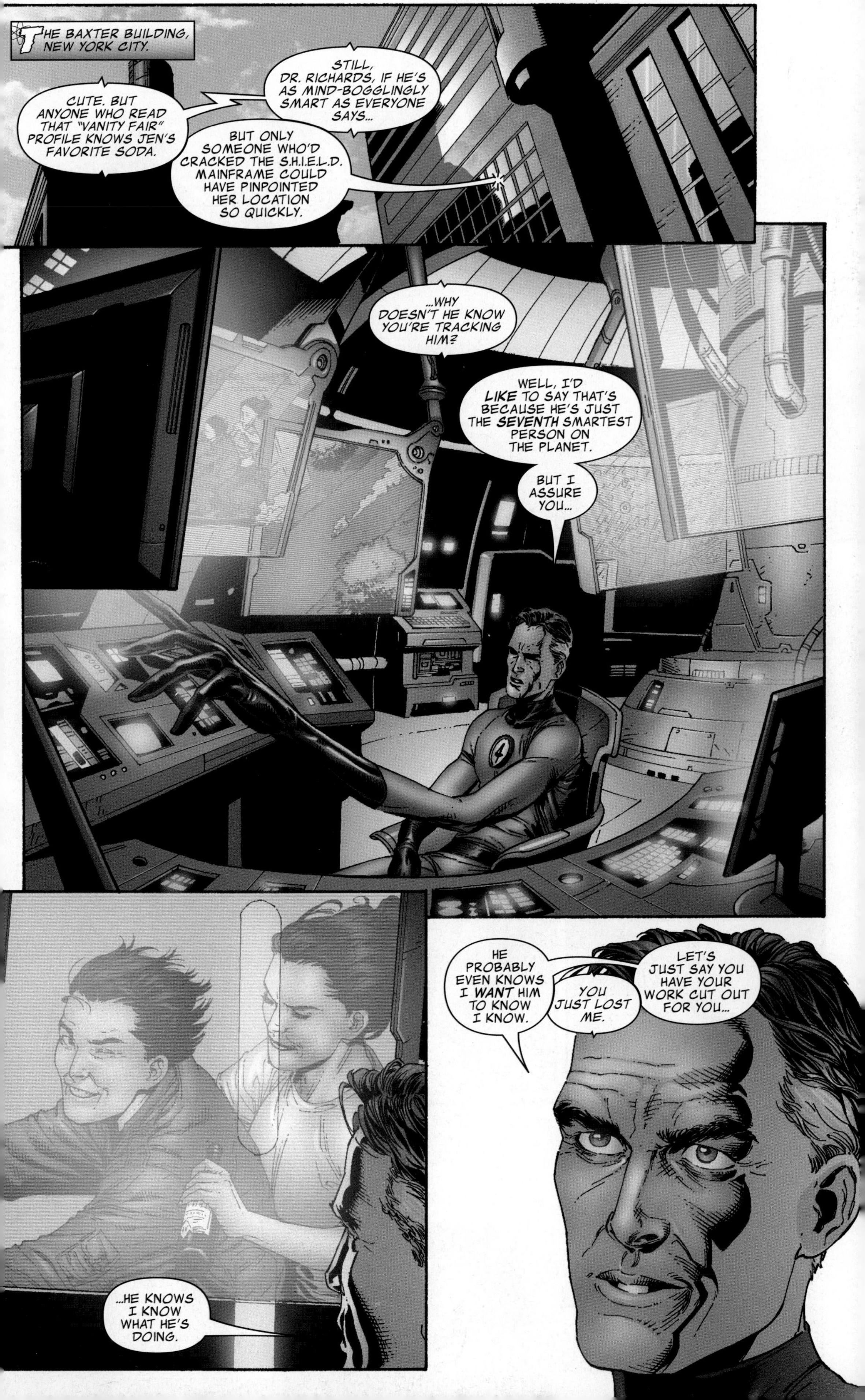
THE BAXTER BUILDING, NEW YORK CITY.
STILL, DR. RICHARDS, IF HE'S AS MIND-BOGGLINGLY SMART AS EVERYONE SAYS...
CUTE. BUT ANYONE WHO READ THAT "VANITY FAIR" PROFILE KNOWS JEN'S FAVORITE SODA.
BUT ONLY SOMEONE WHO'D CRACKED THE S.H.I.E.L.D. MAINFRAME COULD HAVE PINPOINTED HER LOCATION SO QUICKLY.
...WHY DOESN'T HE KNOW YOU'RE TRACKING HIM?
WELL, I'D LIKE TO SAY THAT'S BECAUSE HE'S JUST THE SEVENTH SMARTEST PERSON ON THE PLANET.
BUT I ASSURE YOU...
...HE KNOWS I KNOW WHAT HE'S DOING.
HE PROBABLY EVEN KNOWS I WANT HIM TO KNOW I KNOW.
YOU JUST LOST ME.
LET'S JUST SAY YOU HAVE YOUR WORK CUT OUT FOR YOU...

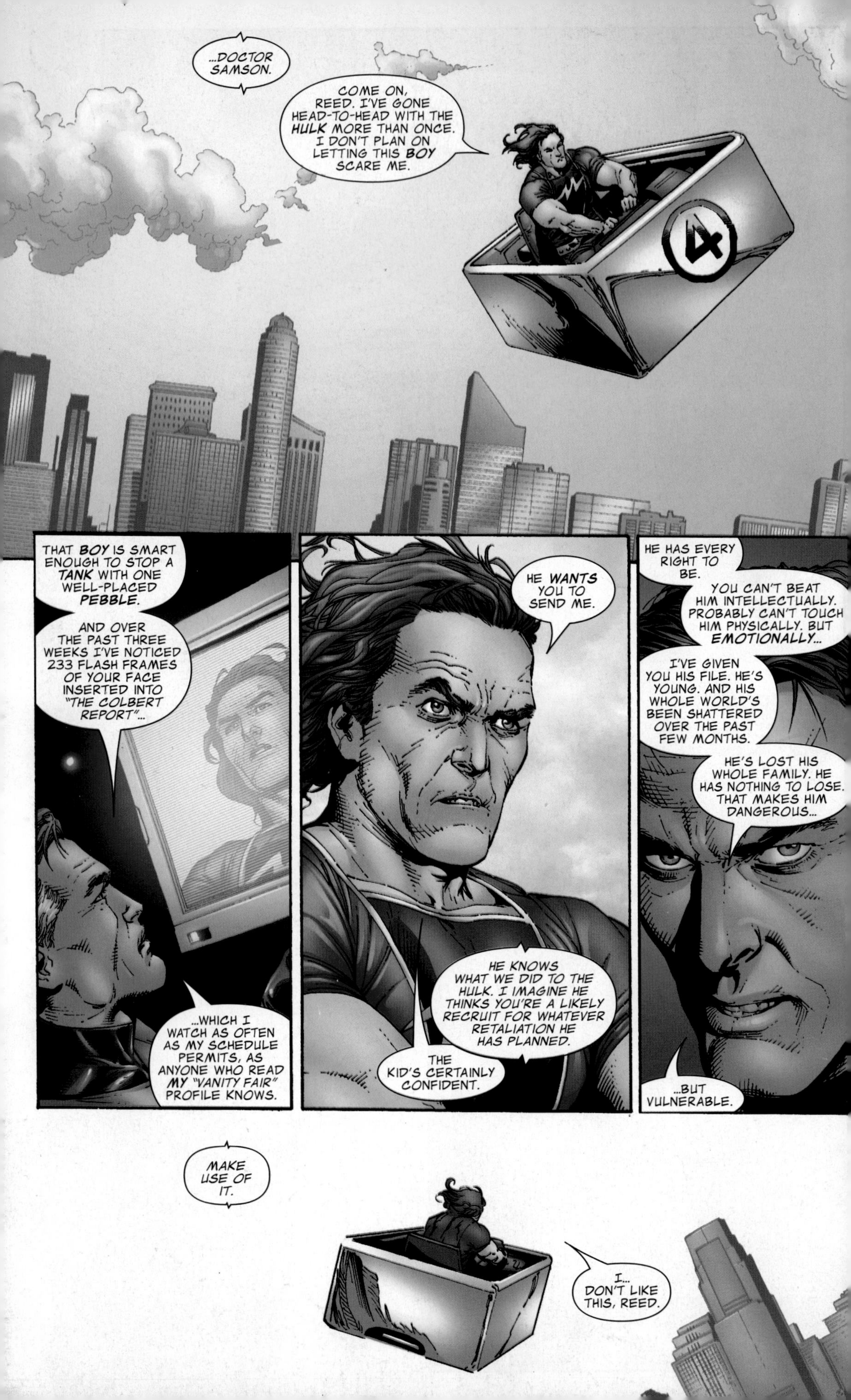
...DOCTOR SAMSON.
COME ON, REED. I'VE GONE HEAD-TO-HEAD WITH THE HULK MORE THAN ONCE. I DON'T PLAN ON LETTING THIS BOY SCARE ME.
THAT BOY IS SMART ENOUGH TO STOP A TANK WITH ONE WELL-PLACED PEBBLE.
AND OVER THE PAST THREE WEEKS I'VE NOTICED 233 FLASH FRAMES OF YOUR FACE INSERTED INTO "THE COLBERT REPORT"...
...WHICH I WATCH AS OFTEN AS MY SCHEDULE PERMITS, AS ANYONE WHO READ MY "VANITY FAIR" PROFILE KNOWS.
HE WANTS YOU TO SEND ME.
HE KNOWS WHAT WE DID TO THE HULK. I IMAGINE HE THINKS YOU'RE A LIKELY RECRUIT FOR WHATEVER RETALIATION HE HAS PLANNED.
THE KID'S CERTAINLY CONFIDENT.
HE HAS EVERY RIGHT TO BE.
YOU CAN'T BEAT HIM INTELLECTUALLY. PROBABLY CAN'T TOUCH HIM PHYSICALLY. BUT EMOTIONALLY...
I'VE GIVEN YOU HIS FILE. HE'S YOUNG. AND HIS WHOLE WORLD'S BEEN SHATTERED OVER THE PAST FEW MONTHS.
HE'S LOST HIS WHOLE FAMILY. HE HAS NOTHING TO LOSE. THAT MAKES HIM DANGEROUS...
...BUT VULNERABLE.
MAKE USE OF IT.
I... DON'T LIKE THIS, REED.

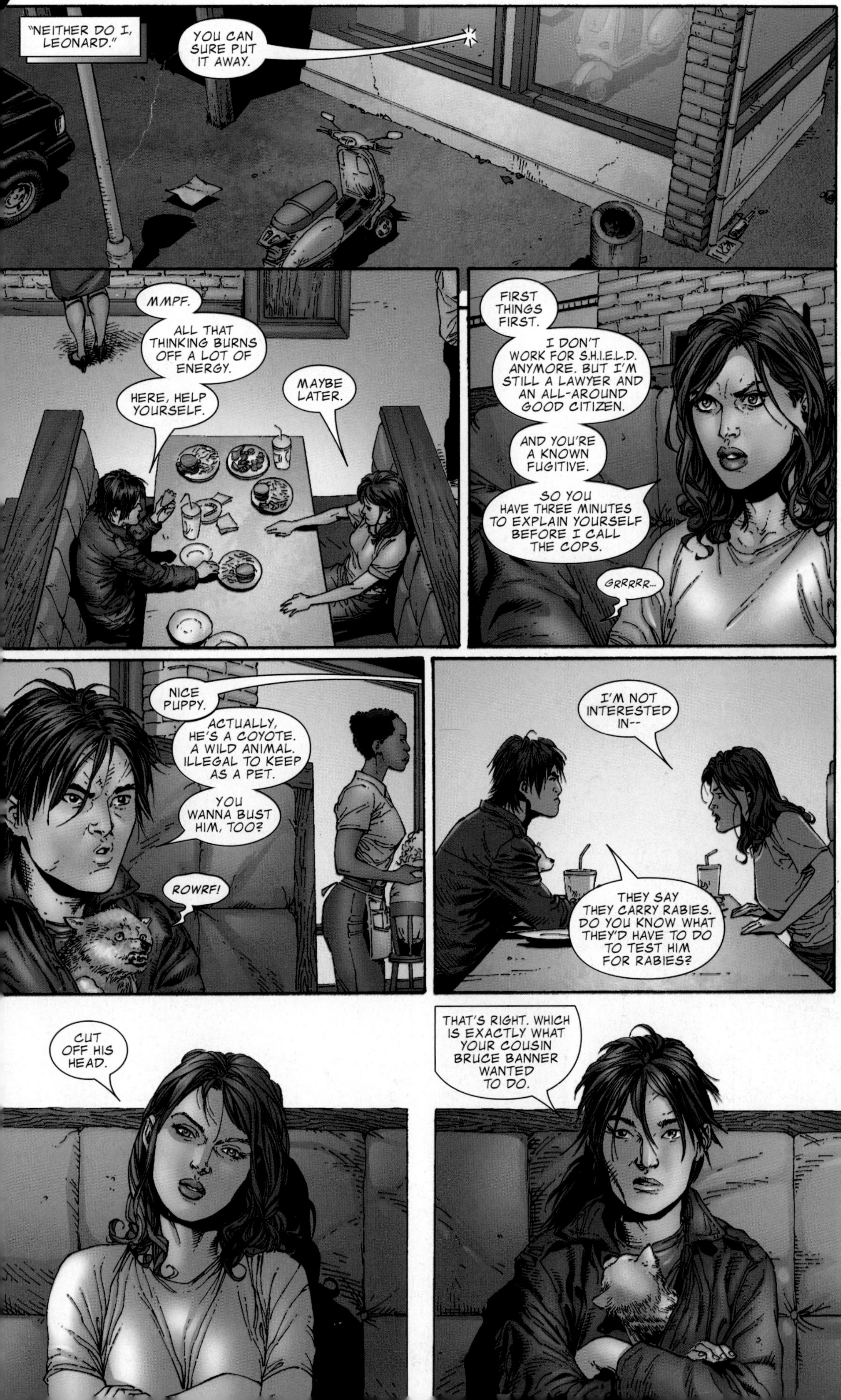
"NEITHER DO I, LEONARD."
YOU CAN SURE PUT IT AWAY.
MMPF.
ALL THAT THINKING BURNS OFF A LOT OF ENERGY.
HERE, HELP YOURSELF.
MAYBE LATER.
FIRST THINGS FIRST.
I DON'T WORK FOR S.H.I.E.L.D. ANYMORE. BUT I'M STILL A LAWYER AND AN ALL-AROUND GOOD CITIZEN.
AND YOU'RE A KNOWN FUGITIVE.
SO YOU HAVE THREE MINUTES TO EXPLAIN YOURSELF BEFORE I CALL THE COPS.
GRRRRR...
NICE PUPPY.
ACTUALLY, HE'S A COYOTE. A WILD ANIMAL. ILLEGAL TO KEEP AS A PET.
YOU WANNA BUST HIM, TOO?
ROWRF!
I'M NOT INTERESTED IN--
THEY SAY THEY CARRY RABIES. DO YOU KNOW WHAT THEY'D HAVE TO DO TO TEST HIM FOR RABIES?
CUT OFF HIS HEAD.
THAT'S RIGHT. WHICH IS EXACTLY WHAT YOUR COUSIN BRUCE BANNER WANTED TO DO.

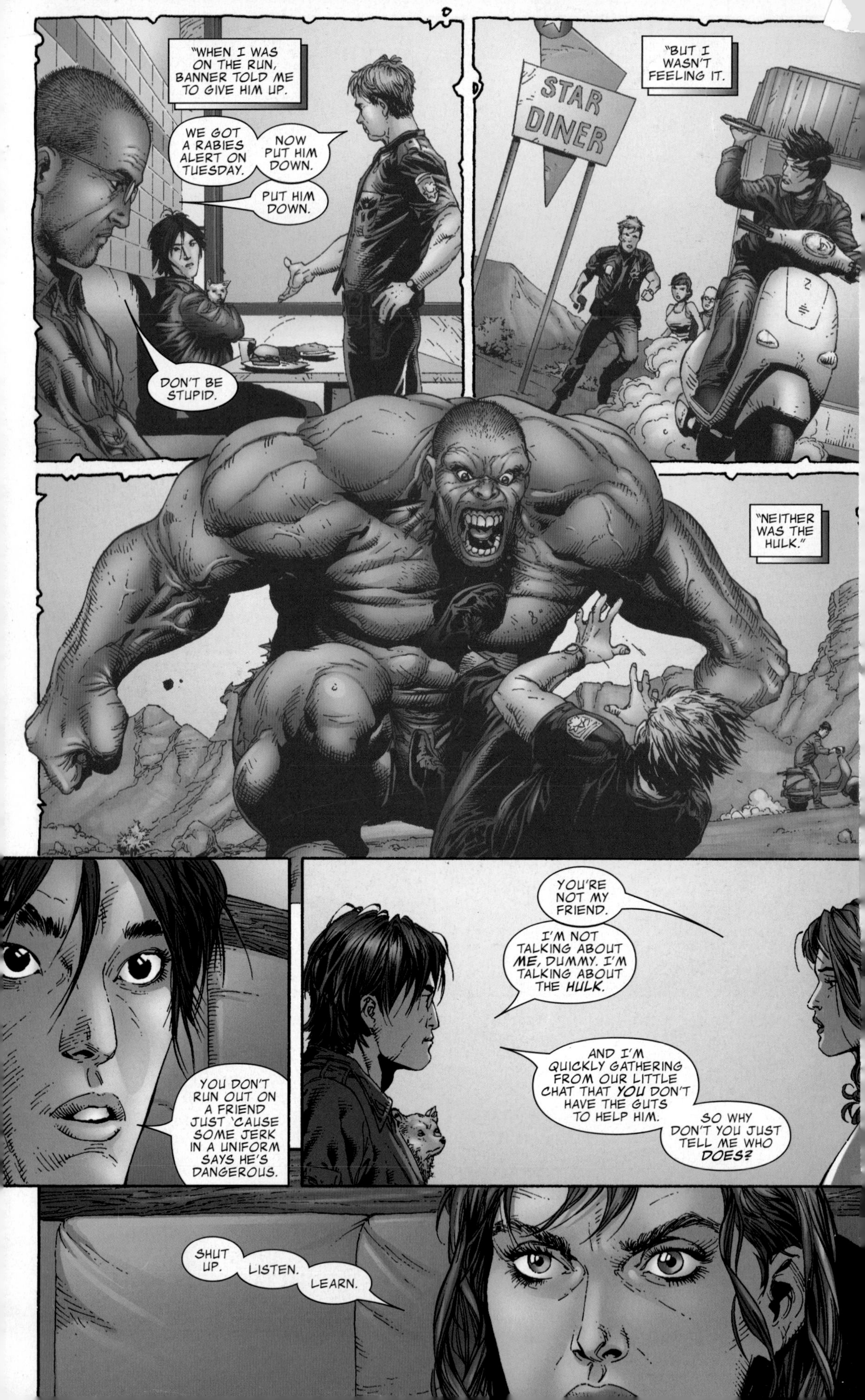
"WHEN I WAS ON THE RUN, BANNER TOLD ME TO GIVE HIM UP.
WE GOT A RABIES ALERT ON TUESDAY.
NOW PUT HIM DOWN.
PUT HIM DOWN.
DON'T BE STUPID.
"BUT I WASN'T FEELING IT.
STAR DINER
"NEITHER WAS THE HULK."
YOU DON'T RUN OUT ON A FRIEND JUST 'CAUSE SOME JERK IN A UNIFORM SAYS HE'S DANGEROUS.
YOU'RE NOT MY FRIEND.
I'M NOT TALKING ABOUT *ME*, DUMMY. I'M TALKING ABOUT THE *HULK*.
AND I'M QUICKLY GATHERING FROM OUR LITTLE CHAT THAT *YOU* DON'T HAVE THE GUTS TO HELP HIM.
SO WHY DON'T YOU JUST TELL ME WHO *DOES?*
SHUT UP.
LISTEN.
LEARN.

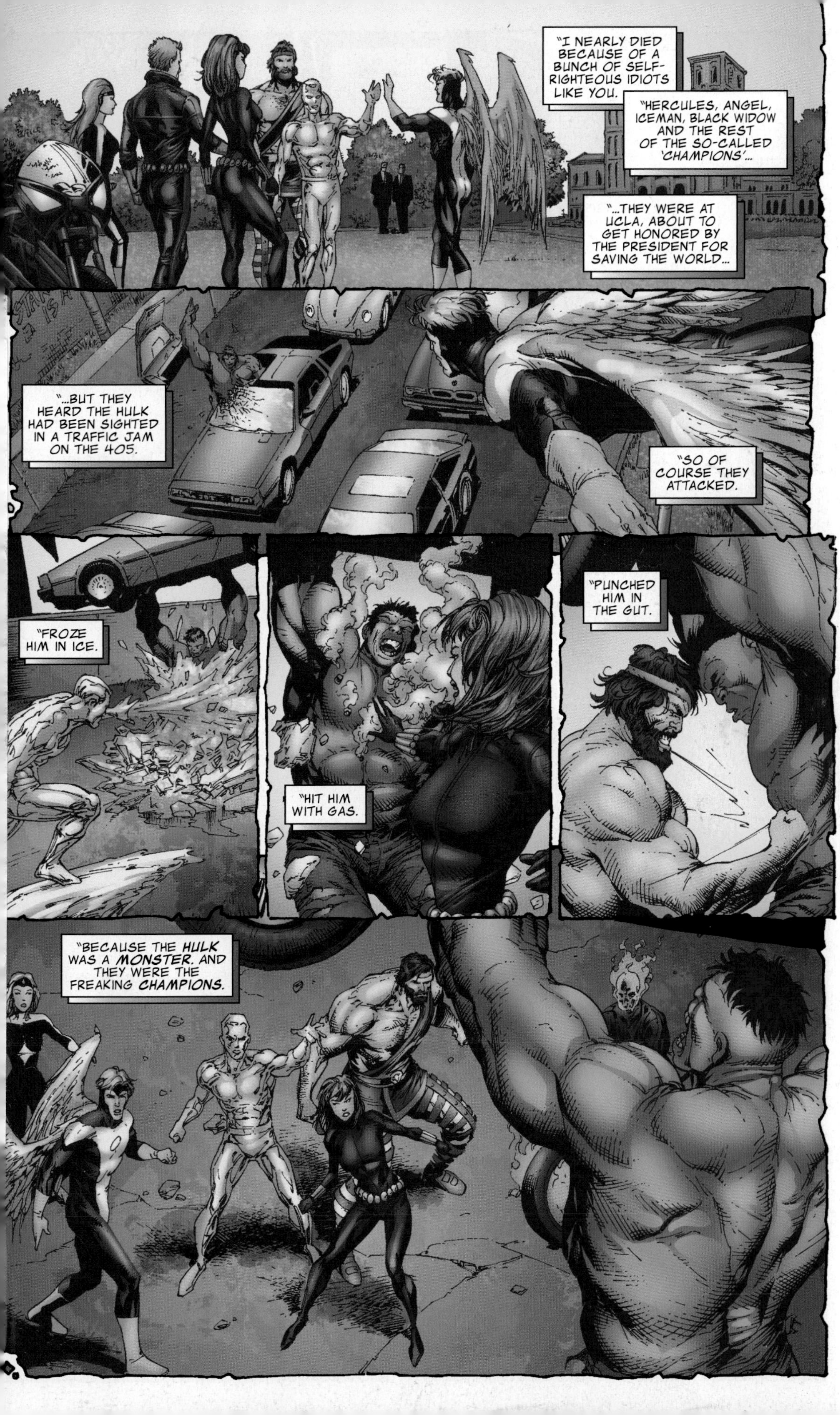
"I NEARLY DIED BECAUSE OF A BUNCH OF SELF-RIGHTEOUS IDIOTS LIKE YOU.
"HERCULES, ANGEL, ICEMAN, BLACK WIDOW AND THE REST OF THE SO-CALLED 'CHAMPIONS'...
"...THEY WERE AT UCLA, ABOUT TO GET HONORED BY THE PRESIDENT FOR SAVING THE WORLD...
"...BUT THEY HEARD THE HULK HAD BEEN SIGHTED IN A TRAFFIC JAM ON THE 405.
"SO OF COURSE THEY ATTACKED.
"FROZE HIM IN ICE.
"HIT HIM WITH GAS.
"PUNCHED HIM IN THE GUT.
"BECAUSE THE HULK WAS A MONSTER. AND THEY WERE THE FREAKING CHAMPIONS.

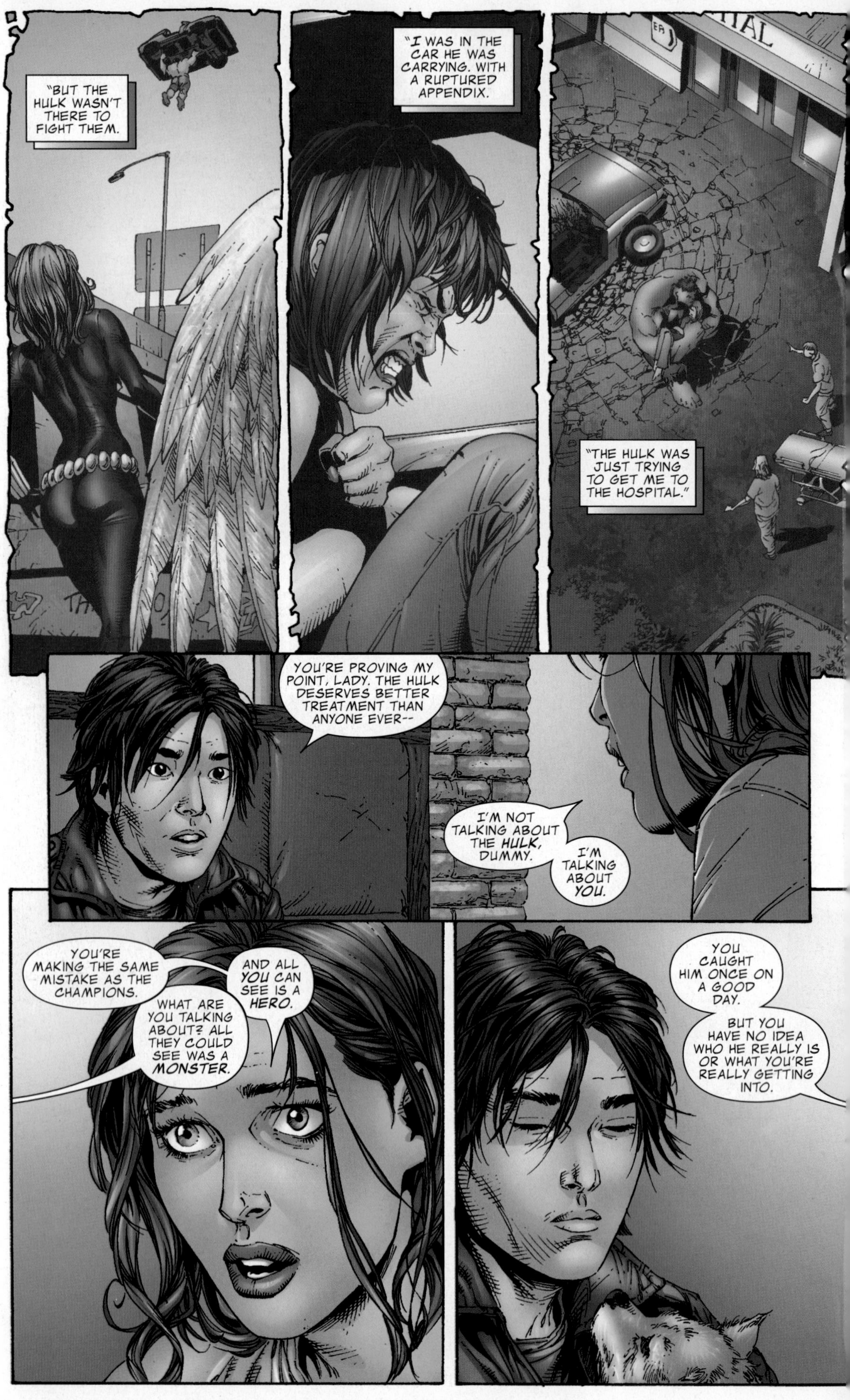
"BUT THE HULK WASN'T THERE TO FIGHT THEM.
"I WAS IN THE CAR HE WAS CARRYING. WITH A RUPTURED APPENDIX.
"THE HULK WAS JUST TRYING TO GET ME TO THE HOSPITAL."
YOU'RE PROVING MY POINT, LADY. THE HULK DESERVES BETTER TREATMENT THAN ANYONE EVER--
I'M NOT TALKING ABOUT THE HULK, DUMMY.
I'M TALKING ABOUT YOU.
YOU'RE MAKING THE SAME MISTAKE AS THE CHAMPIONS.
WHAT ARE YOU TALKING ABOUT? ALL THEY COULD SEE WAS A MONSTER.
AND ALL YOU CAN SEE IS A HERO.
YOU CAUGHT HIM ONCE ON A GOOD DAY.
BUT YOU HAVE NO IDEA WHO HE REALLY IS OR WHAT YOU'RE REALLY GETTING INTO.

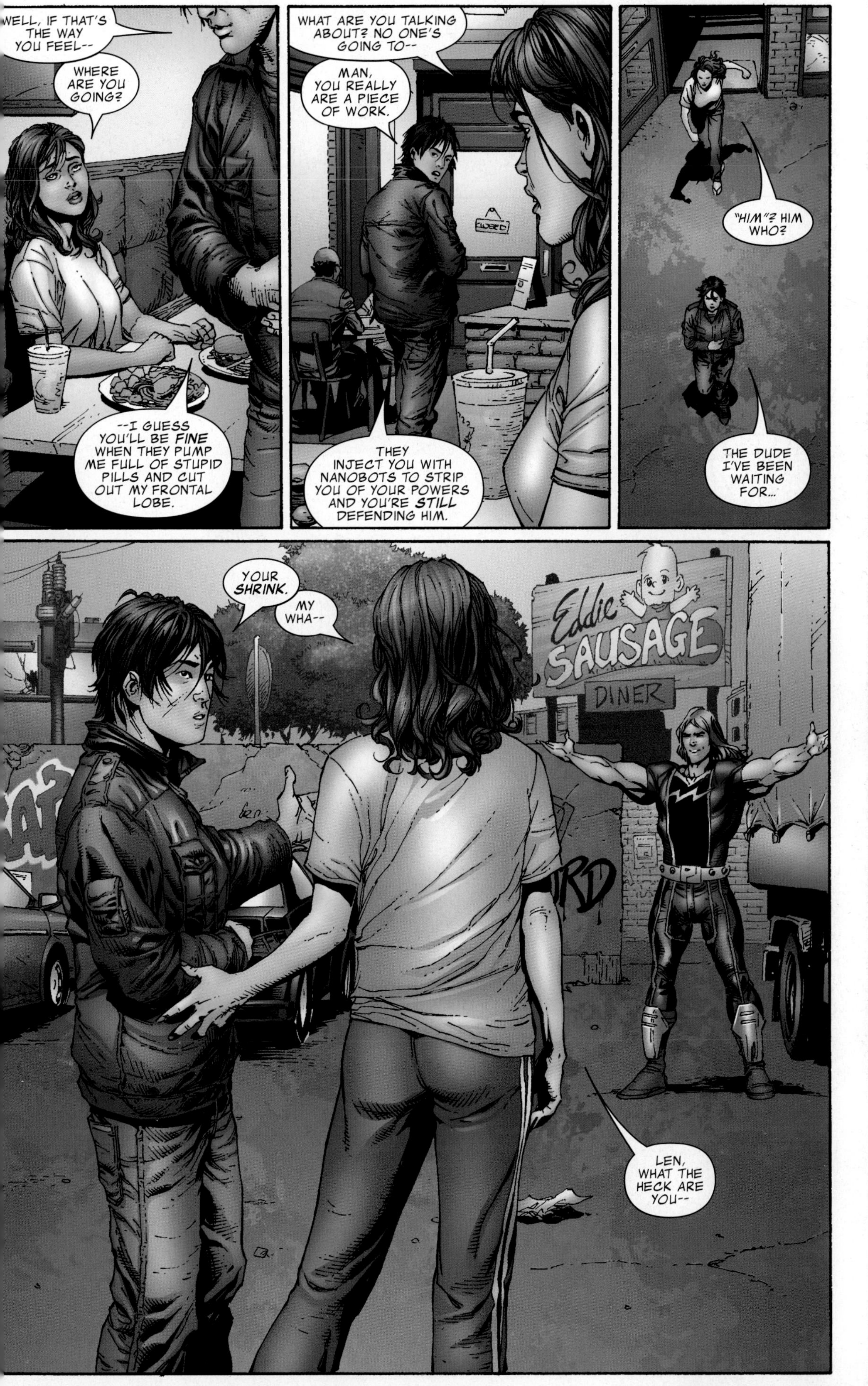
WELL, IF THAT'S THE WAY YOU FEEL--
WHERE ARE YOU GOING?
--I GUESS YOU'LL BE FINE WHEN THEY PUMP ME FULL OF STUPID PILLS AND CUT OUT MY FRONTAL LOBE.
WHAT ARE YOU TALKING ABOUT? NO ONE'S GOING TO--
MAN, YOU REALLY ARE A PIECE OF WORK.
CLOSED
THEY INJECT YOU WITH NANOBOTS TO STRIP YOU OF YOUR POWERS AND YOU'RE STILL DEFENDING HIM.
"HIM"? HIM WHO?
THE DUDE I'VE BEEN WAITING FOR...
YOUR SHRINK.
MY WHA--
Eddie SAUSAGE
DINER
LEN, WHAT THE HECK ARE YOU--

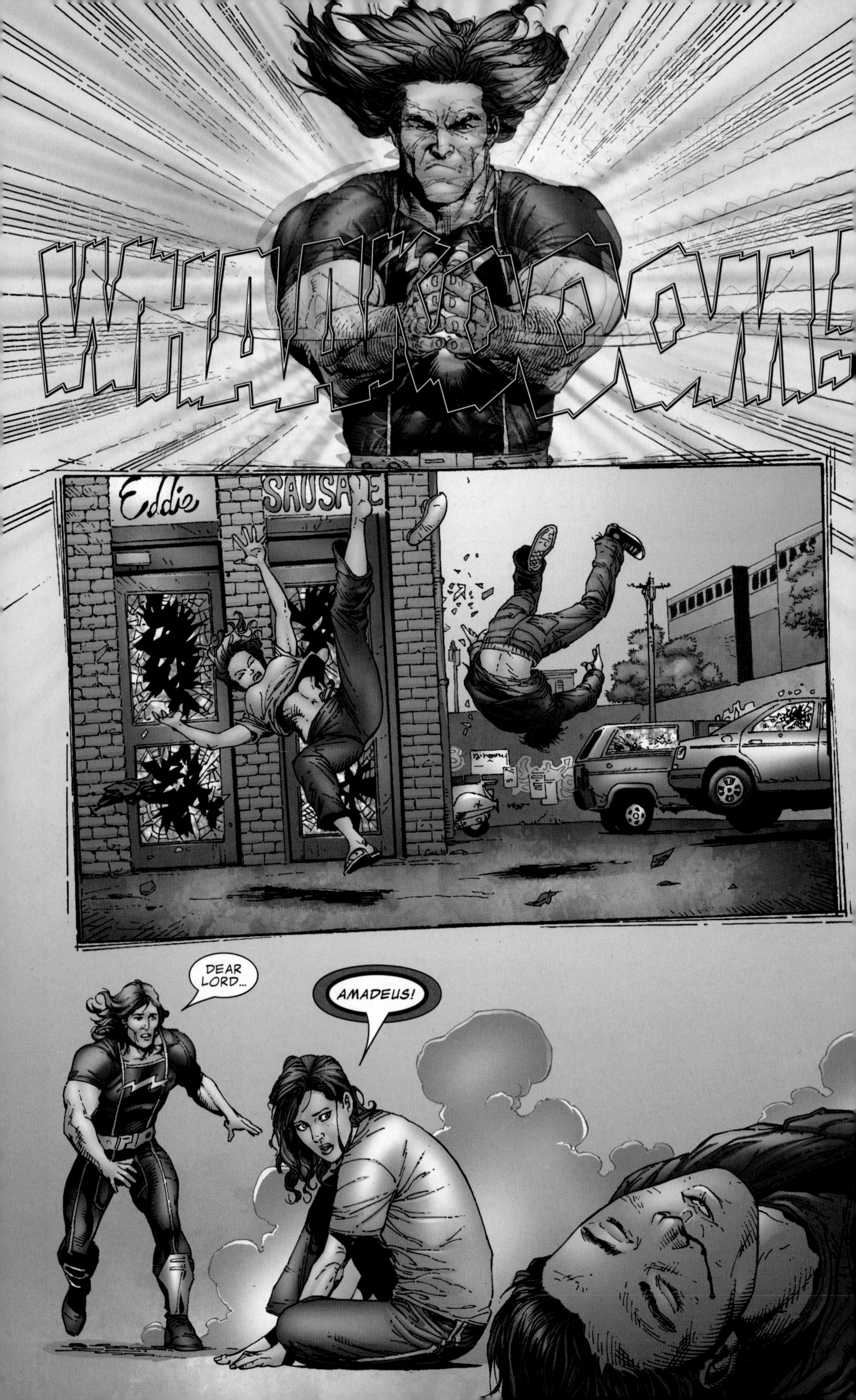
WHAMOOOOM!
Eddie
SAUSA E
DEAR LORD...
AMADEUS!

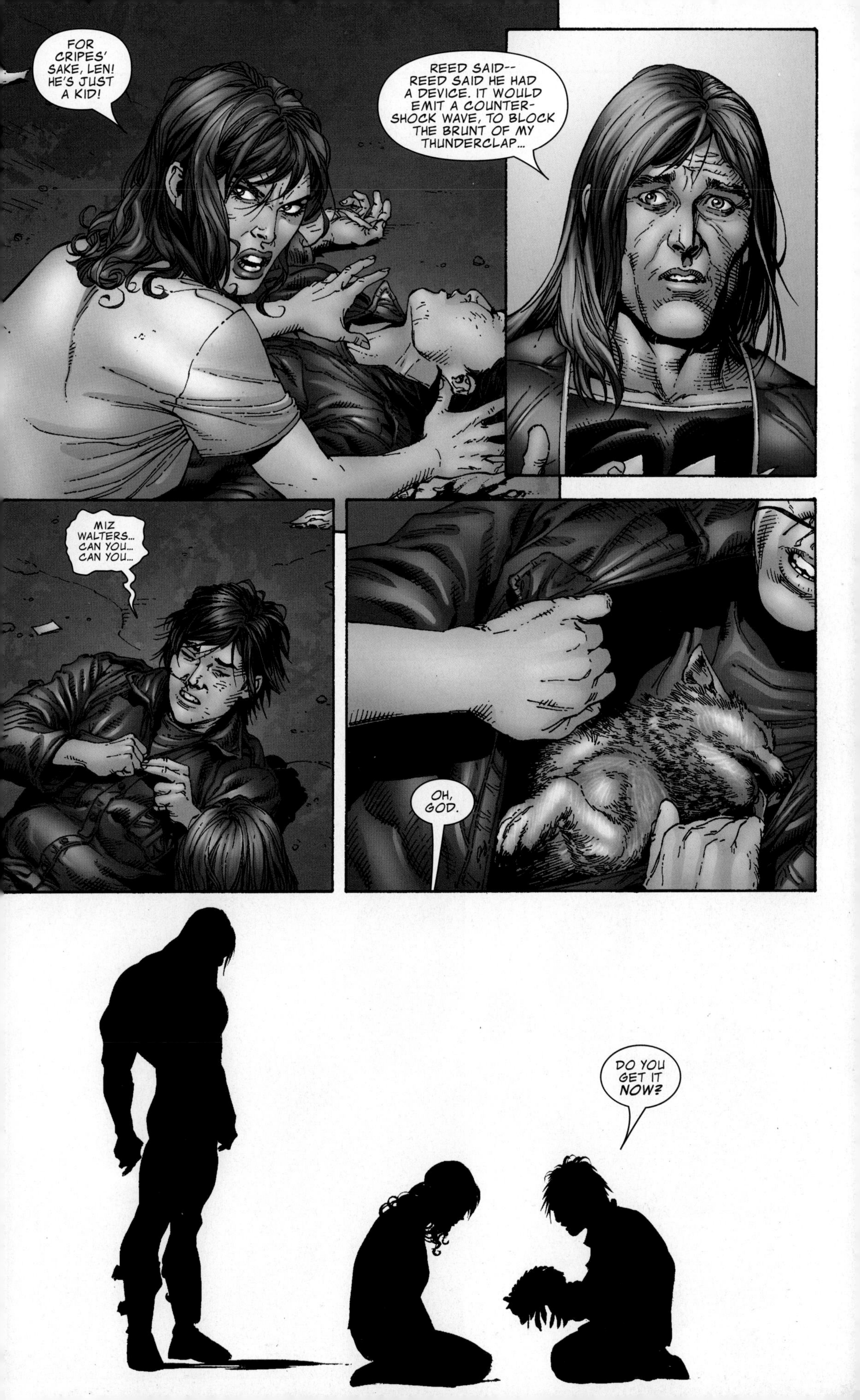
FOR CRIPES' SAKE, LEN! HE'S JUST A KID!
REED SAID-- REED SAID HE HAD A DEVICE. IT WOULD EMIT A COUNTER-SHOCK WAVE, TO BLOCK THE BRUNT OF MY THUNDERCLAP...
MIZ WALTERS... CAN YOU... CAN YOU...
OH, GOD.
DO YOU GET IT NOW?

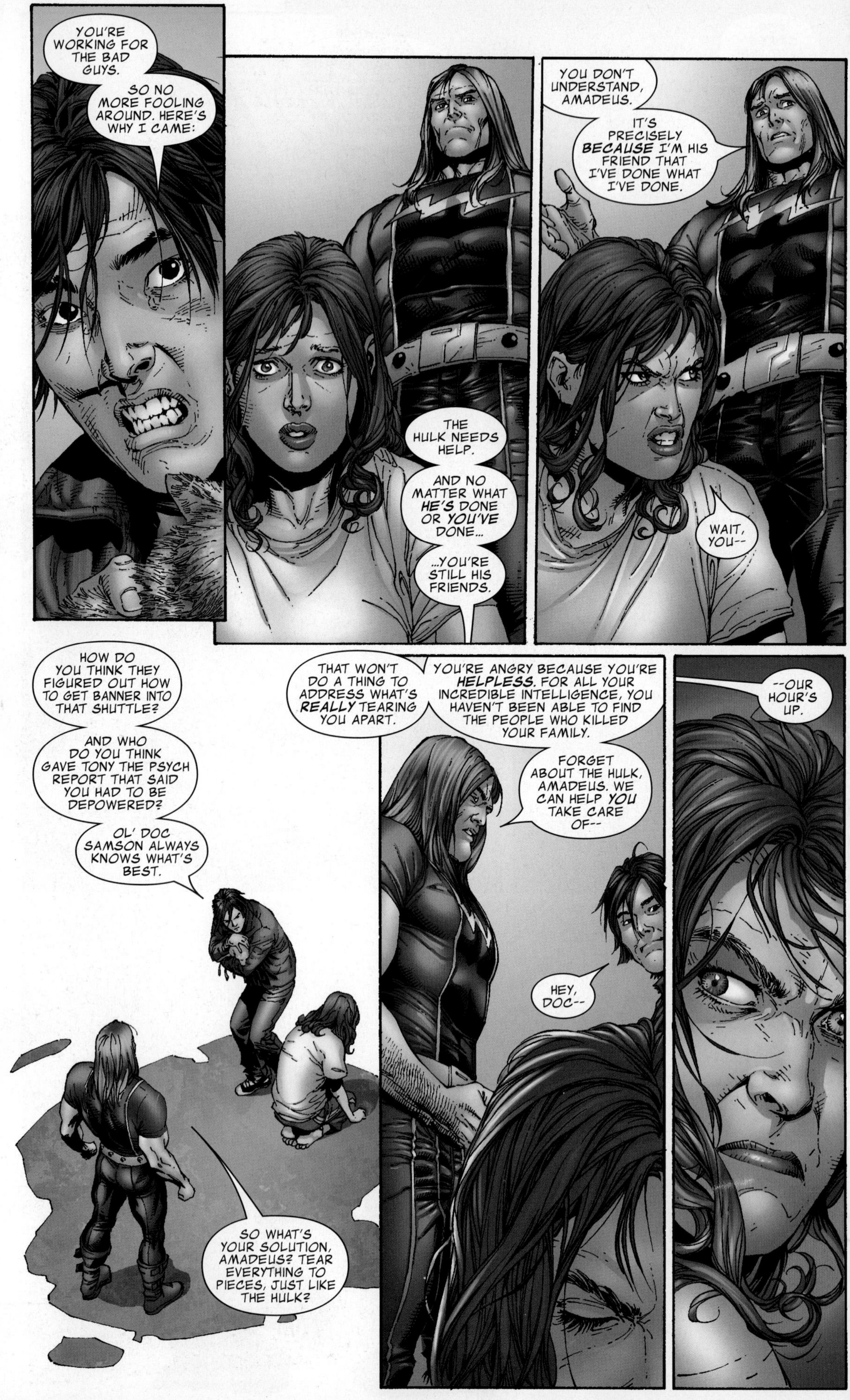
YOU'RE WORKING FOR THE BAD GUYS.
SO NO MORE FOOLING AROUND. HERE'S WHY I CAME:
THE HULK NEEDS HELP.
AND NO MATTER WHAT HE'S DONE OR YOU'VE DONE...
...YOU'RE STILL HIS FRIENDS.
YOU DON'T UNDERSTAND, AMADEUS.
IT'S PRECISELY BECAUSE I'M HIS FRIEND THAT I'VE DONE WHAT I'VE DONE.
WAIT, YOU--
HOW DO YOU THINK THEY FIGURED OUT HOW TO GET BANNER INTO THAT SHUTTLE?
AND WHO DO YOU THINK GAVE TONY THE PSYCH REPORT THAT SAID YOU HAD TO BE DEPOWERED?
OL' DOC SAMSON ALWAYS KNOWS WHAT'S BEST.
SO WHAT'S YOUR SOLUTION, AMADEUS? TEAR EVERYTHING TO PIECES, JUST LIKE THE HULK?
THAT WON'T DO A THING TO ADDRESS WHAT'S REALLY TEARING YOU APART.
YOU'RE ANGRY BECAUSE YOU'RE HELPLESS. FOR ALL YOUR INCREDIBLE INTELLIGENCE, YOU HAVEN'T BEEN ABLE TO FIND THE PEOPLE WHO KILLED YOUR FAMILY.
FORGET ABOUT THE HULK, AMADEUS. WE CAN HELP YOU TAKE CARE OF--
HEY, DOC--
--OUR HOUR'S UP.

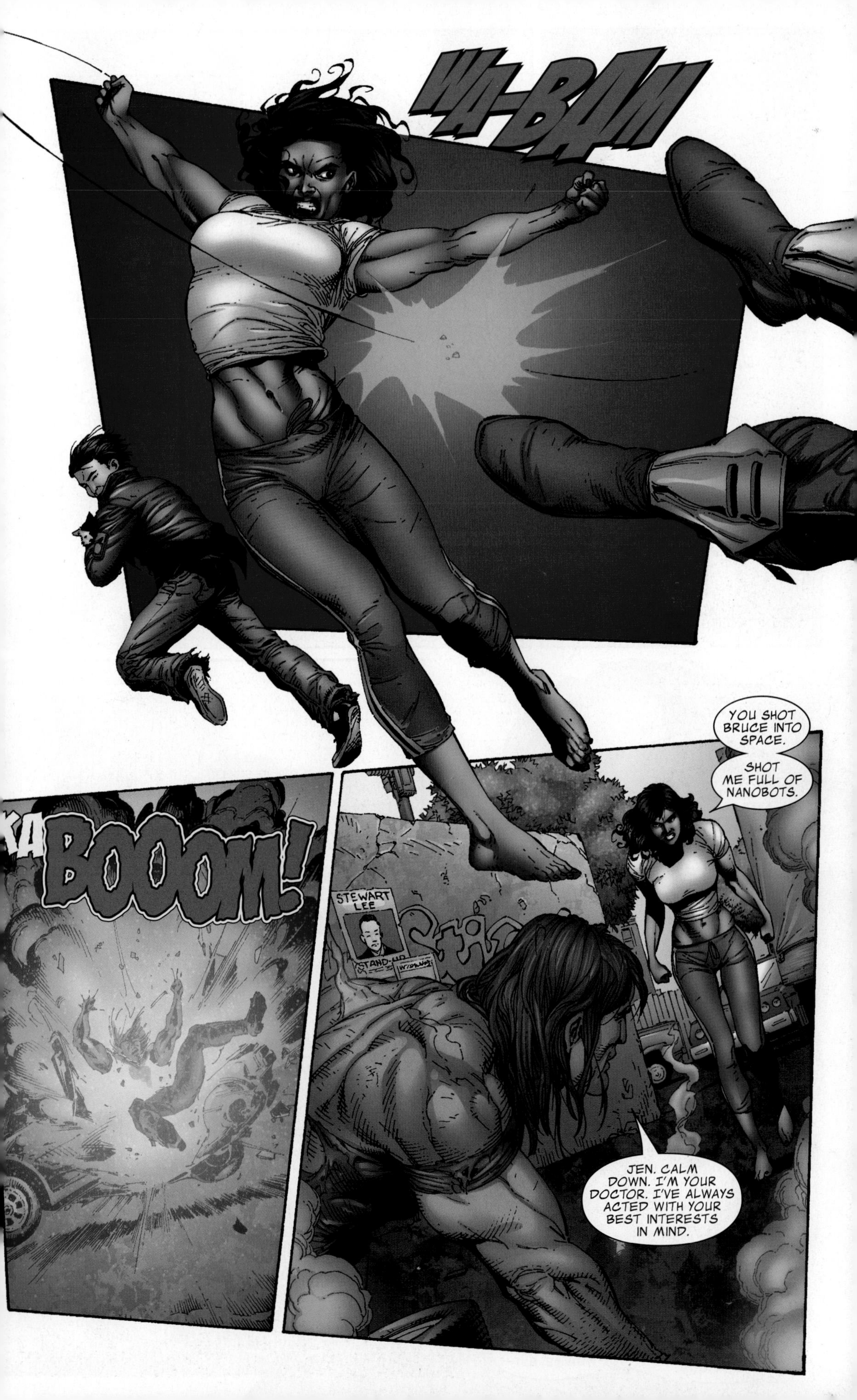
WA-BAM
KA BOOOM!
YOU SHOT BRUCE INTO SPACE.
SHOT ME FULL OF NANOBOTS.
STEWART LEE
STAND-UP
JEN. CALM DOWN. I'M YOUR DOCTOR. I'VE ALWAYS ACTED WITH YOUR BEST INTERESTS IN MIND.

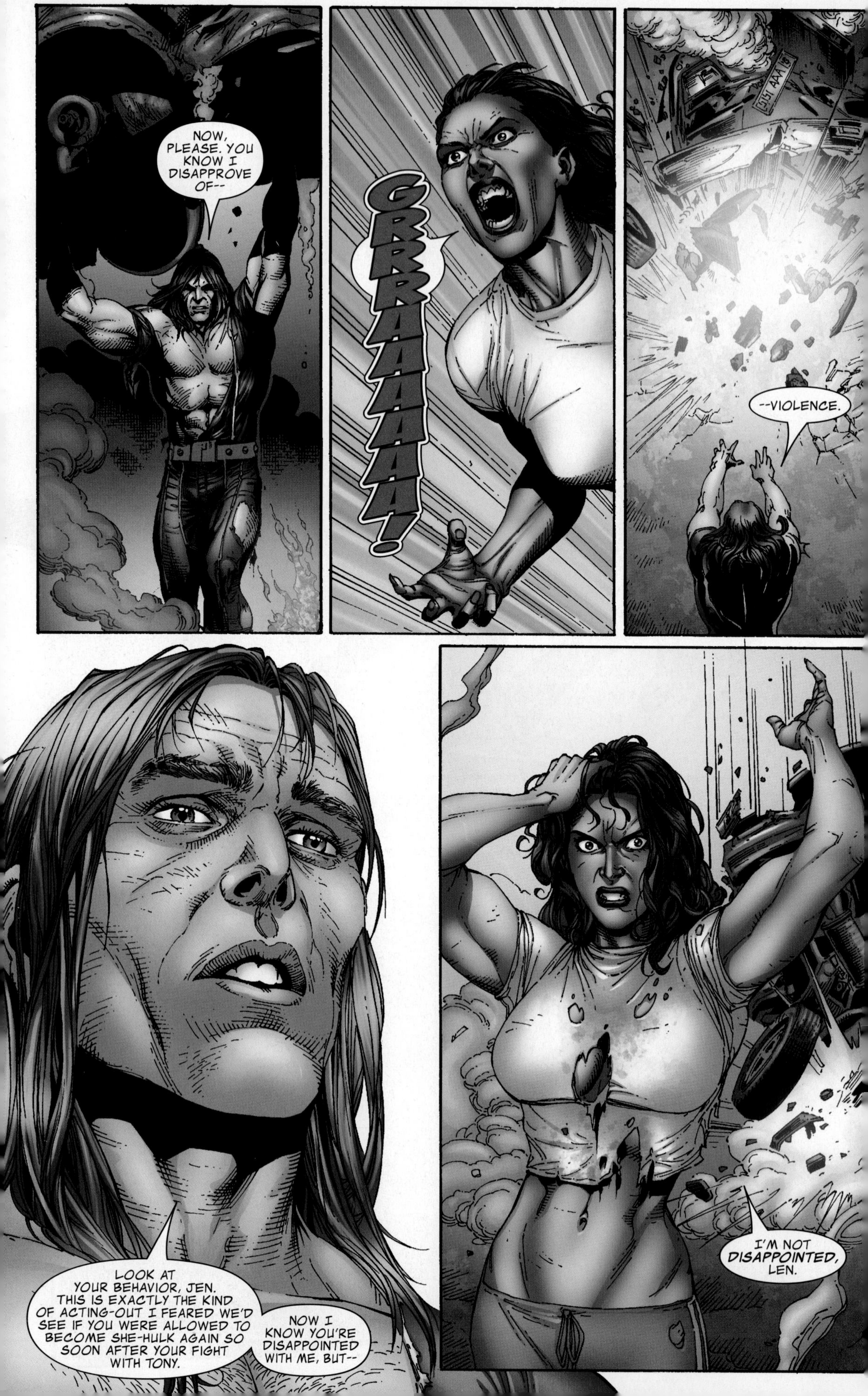
NOW, PLEASE. YOU KNOW I DISAPPROVE OF--
GRRRAAAAAAA!
--VIOLENCE.
LOOK AT YOUR BEHAVIOR, JEN. THIS IS EXACTLY THE KIND OF ACTING-OUT I FEARED WE'D SEE IF YOU WERE ALLOWED TO BECOME SHE-HULK AGAIN SO SOON AFTER YOUR FIGHT WITH TONY.
NOW I KNOW YOU'RE DISAPPOINTED WITH ME, BUT--
I'M NOT DISAPPOINTED, LEN.

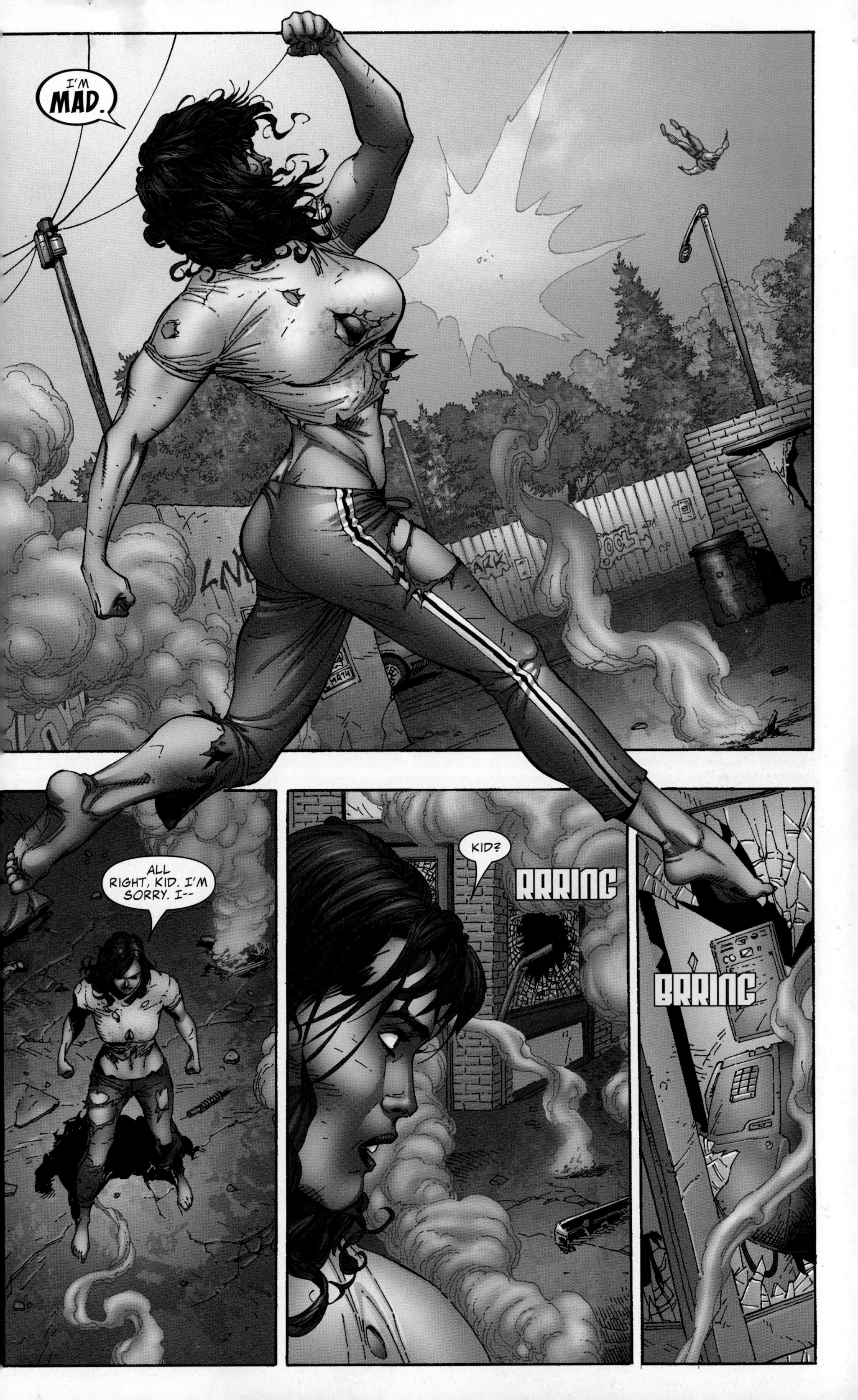
I'M MAD.
ALL RIGHT, KID. I'M SORRY. I--
KID?
RRRING
BRRING

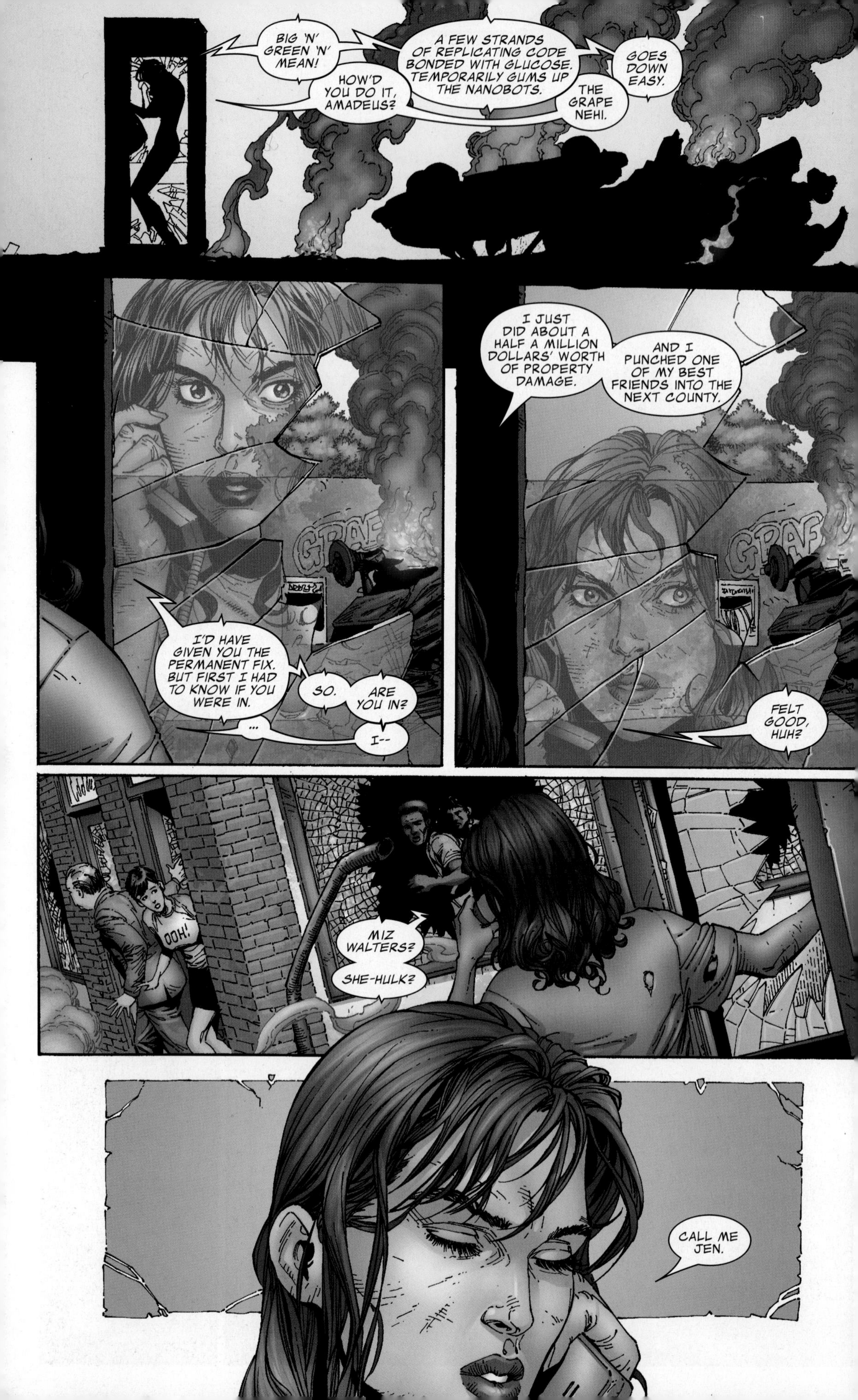
BIG 'N' GREEN 'N' MEAN!
HOW'D YOU DO IT, AMADEUS?
A FEW STRANDS OF REPLICATING CODE BONDED WITH GLUCOSE. TEMPORARILY GUMS UP THE NANOBOTS.
THE GRAPE NEHI.
GOES DOWN EASY.
I'D HAVE GIVEN YOU THE PERMANENT FIX. BUT FIRST I HAD TO KNOW IF YOU WERE IN.
SO.
ARE YOU IN?
...
I--
I JUST DID ABOUT A HALF A MILLION DOLLARS' WORTH OF PROPERTY DAMAGE.
AND I PUNCHED ONE OF MY BEST FRIENDS INTO THE NEXT COUNTY.
FELT GOOD, HUH?
OOH!
MIZ WALTERS?
SHE-HULK?
CALL ME JEN.

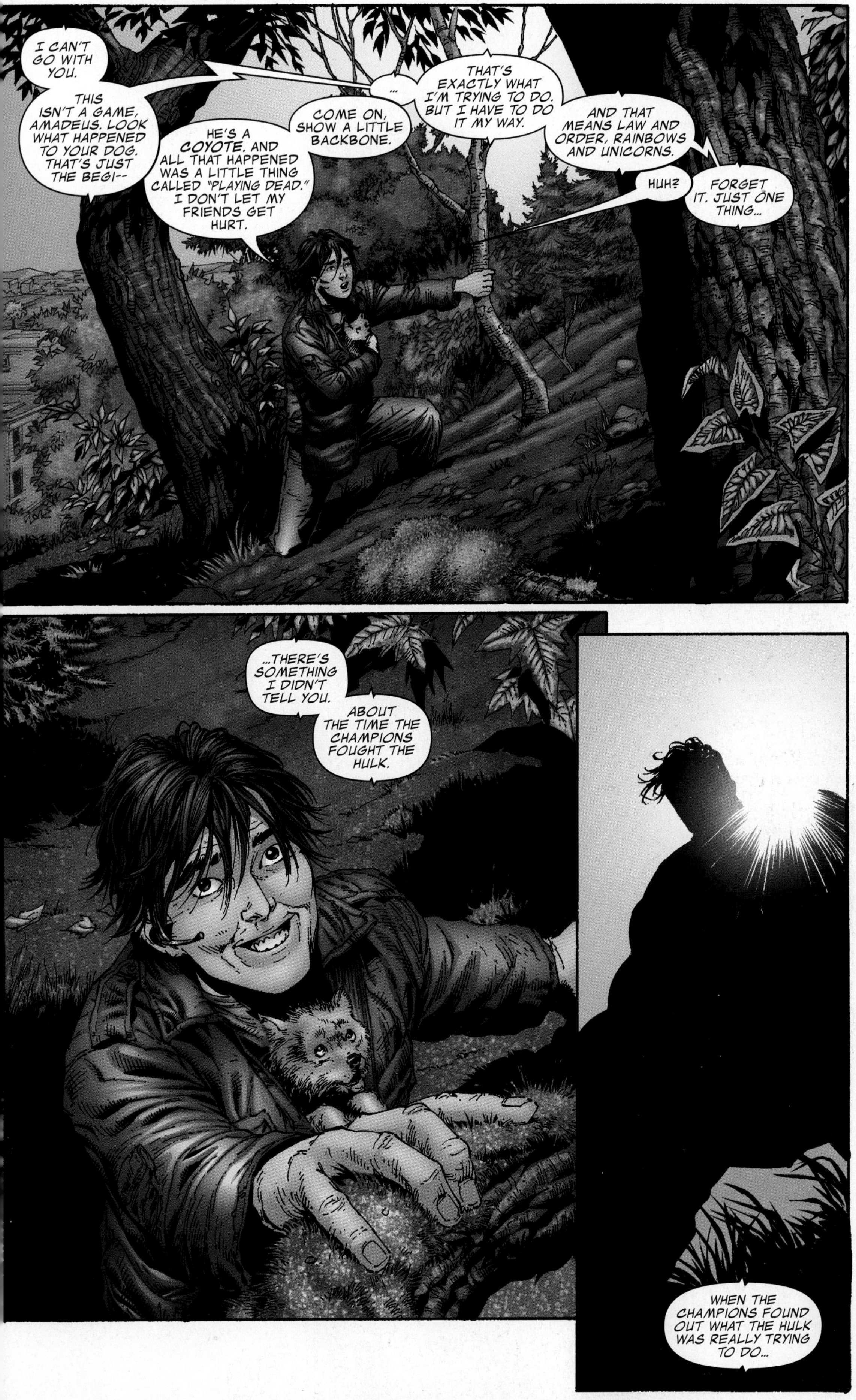
I CAN'T GO WITH YOU.
THIS ISN'T A GAME, AMADEUS. LOOK WHAT HAPPENED TO YOUR DOG. THAT'S JUST THE BEGI--
HE'S A COYOTE. AND ALL THAT HAPPENED WAS A LITTLE THING CALLED "PLAYING DEAD." I DON'T LET MY FRIENDS GET HURT.
COME ON, SHOW A LITTLE BACKBONE.
...
THAT'S EXACTLY WHAT I'M TRYING TO DO. BUT I HAVE TO DO IT MY WAY.
AND THAT MEANS LAW AND ORDER, RAINBOWS AND UNICORNS.
HUH?
FORGET IT. JUST ONE THING...
...THERE'S SOMETHING I DIDN'T TELL YOU.
ABOUT THE TIME THE CHAMPIONS FOUGHT THE HULK.
WHEN THE CHAMPIONS FOUND OUT WHAT THE HULK WAS REALLY TRYING TO DO...

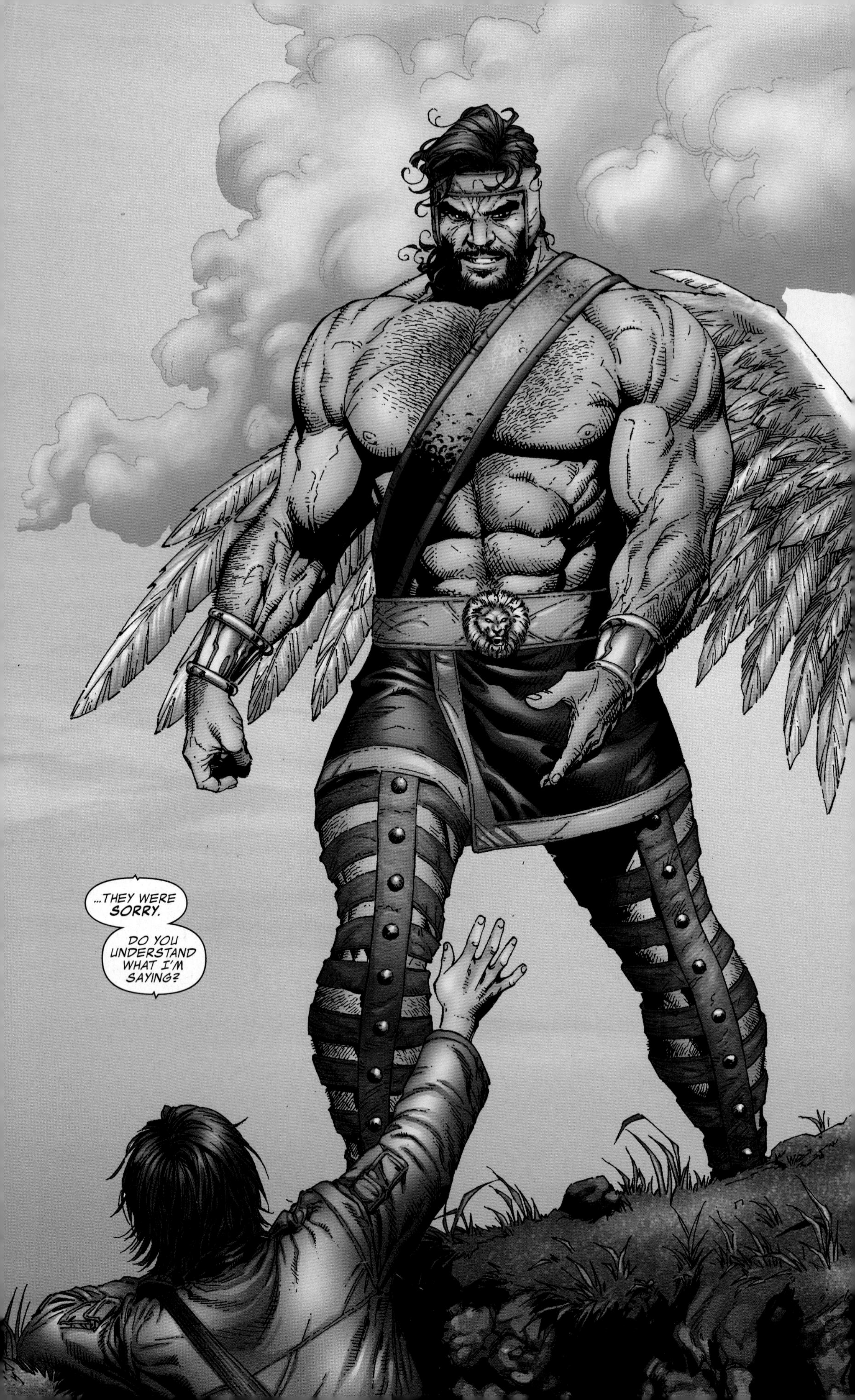
...THEY WERE SORRY.
DO YOU UNDERSTAND WHAT I'M SAYING?

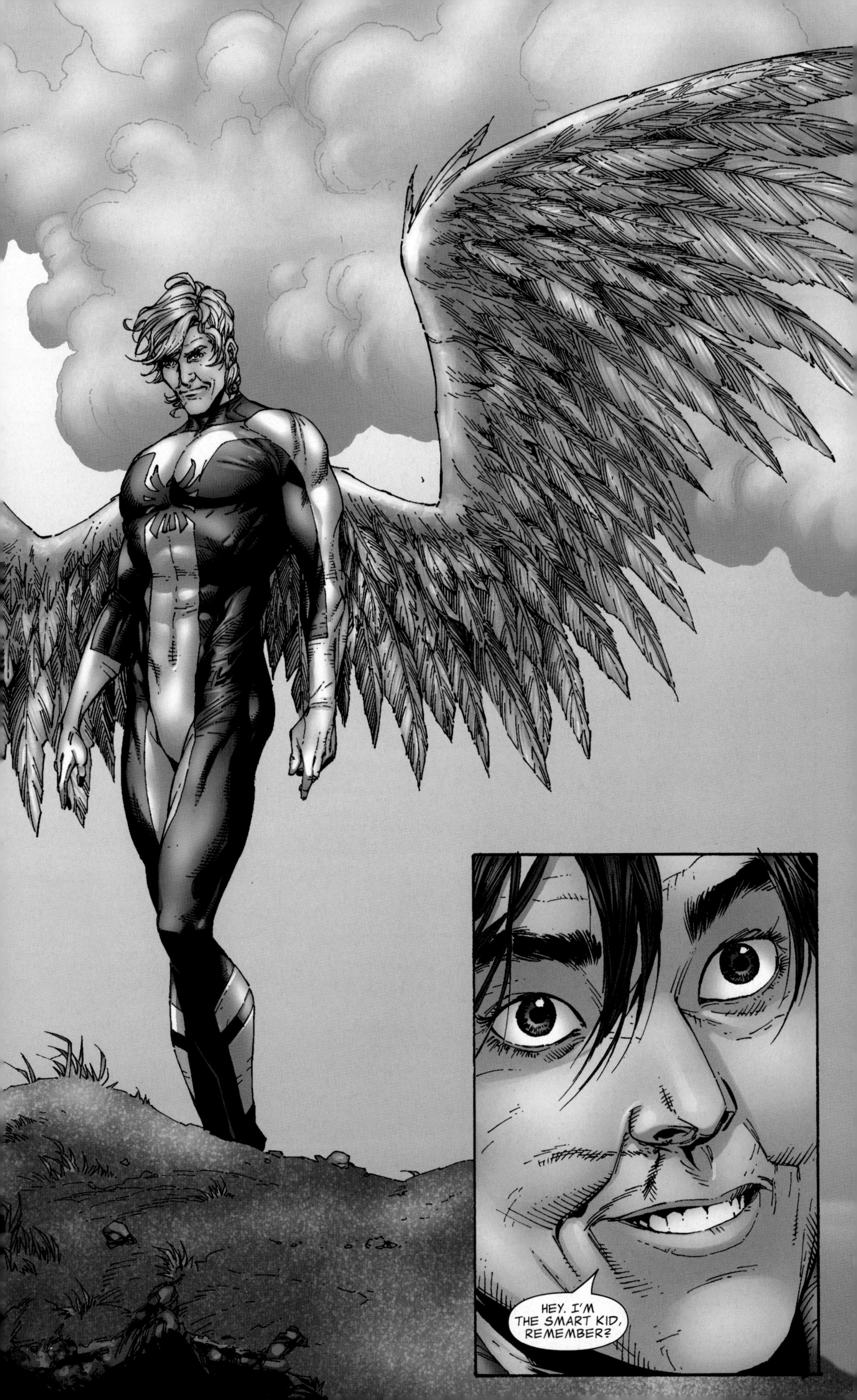
HEY. I'M THE SMART KID, REMEMBER?

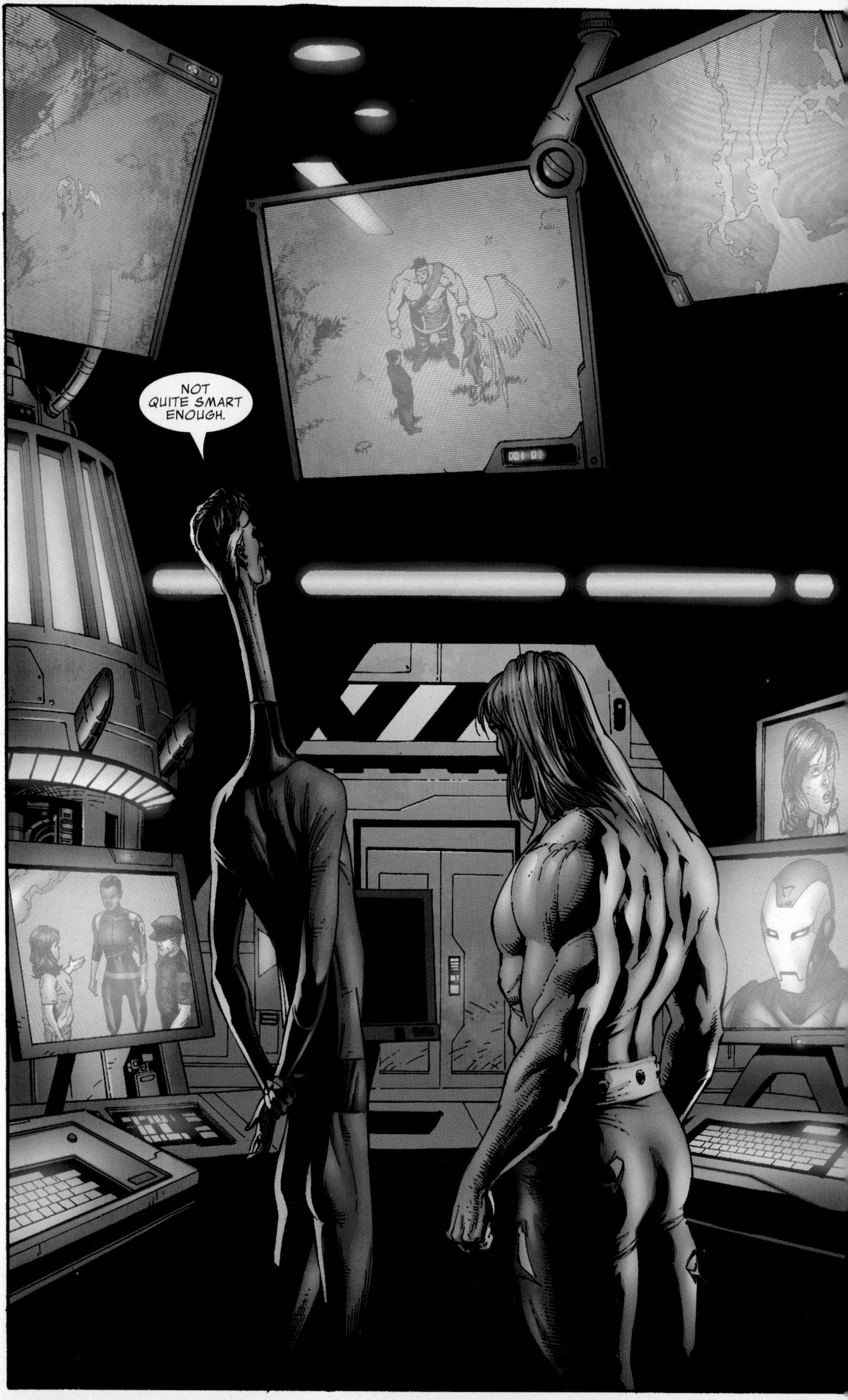
NOT QUITE SMART ENOUGH.

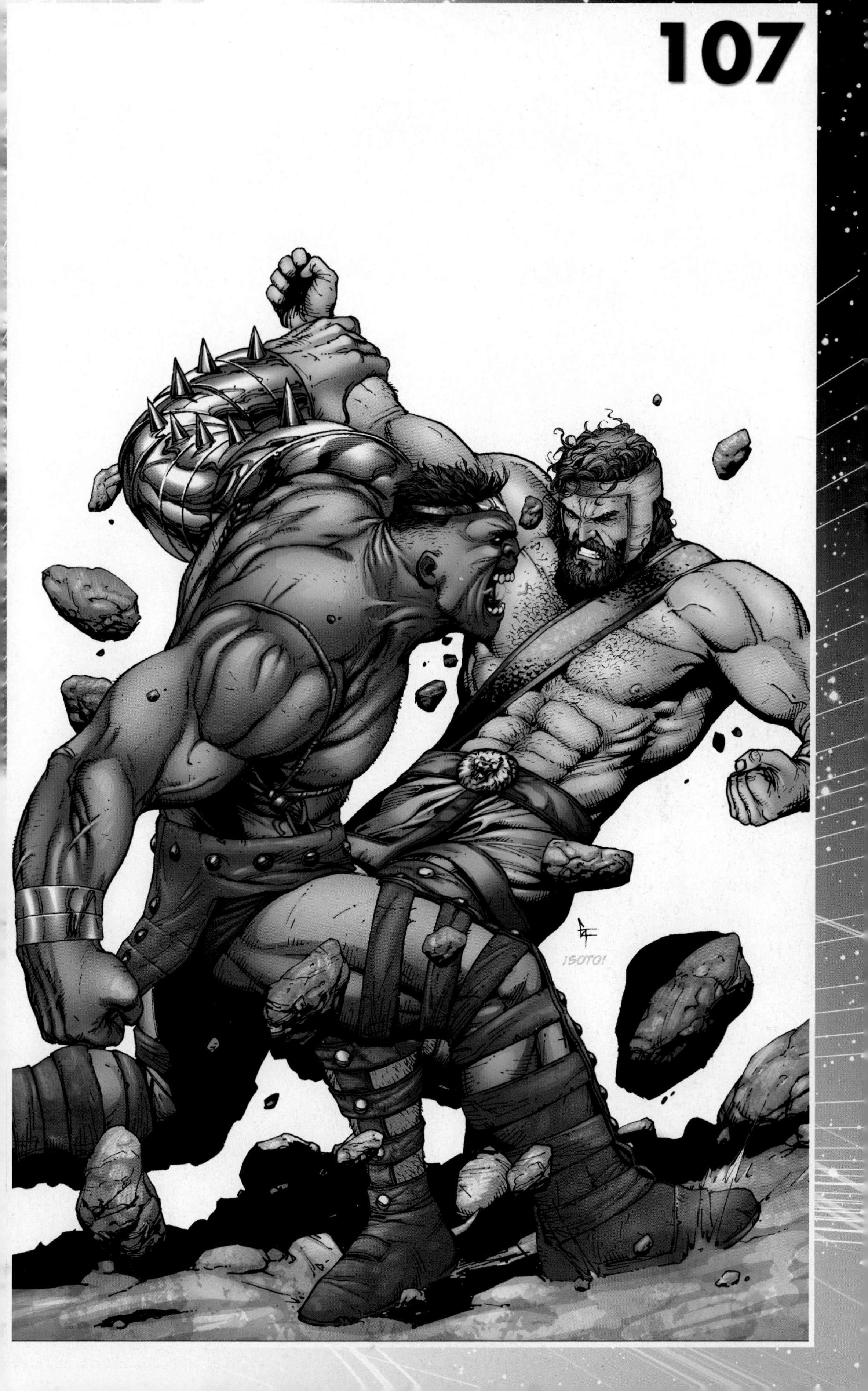
¡SOTO!

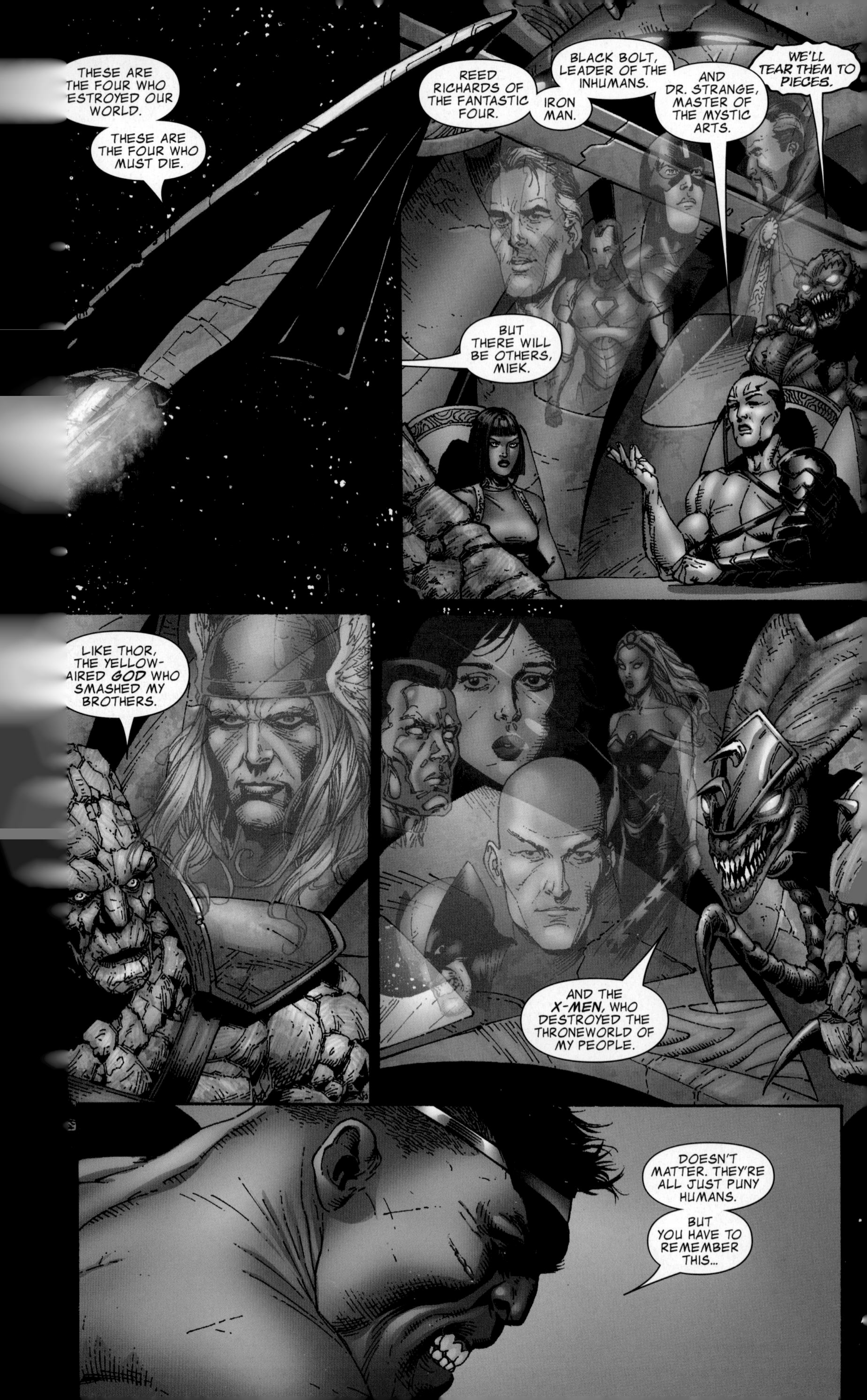
THESE ARE THE FOUR WHO ESTROYED OUR WORLD.
THESE ARE THE FOUR WHO MUST DIE.
REED RICHARDS OF THE FANTASTIC FOUR.
IRON MAN.
BLACK BOLT, LEADER OF THE INHUMANS.
AND DR. STRANGE, MASTER OF THE MYSTIC ARTS.
WE'LL TEAR THEM TO PIECES.
BUT THERE WILL BE OTHERS, MIEK.
LIKE THOR, THE YELLOW-AIRED GOD WHO SMASHED MY BROTHERS.
AND THE X-MEN, WHO DESTROYED THE THRONEWORLD OF MY PEOPLE.
DOESN'T MATTER. THEY'RE ALL JUST PUNY HUMANS.
BUT YOU HAVE TO REMEMBER THIS...

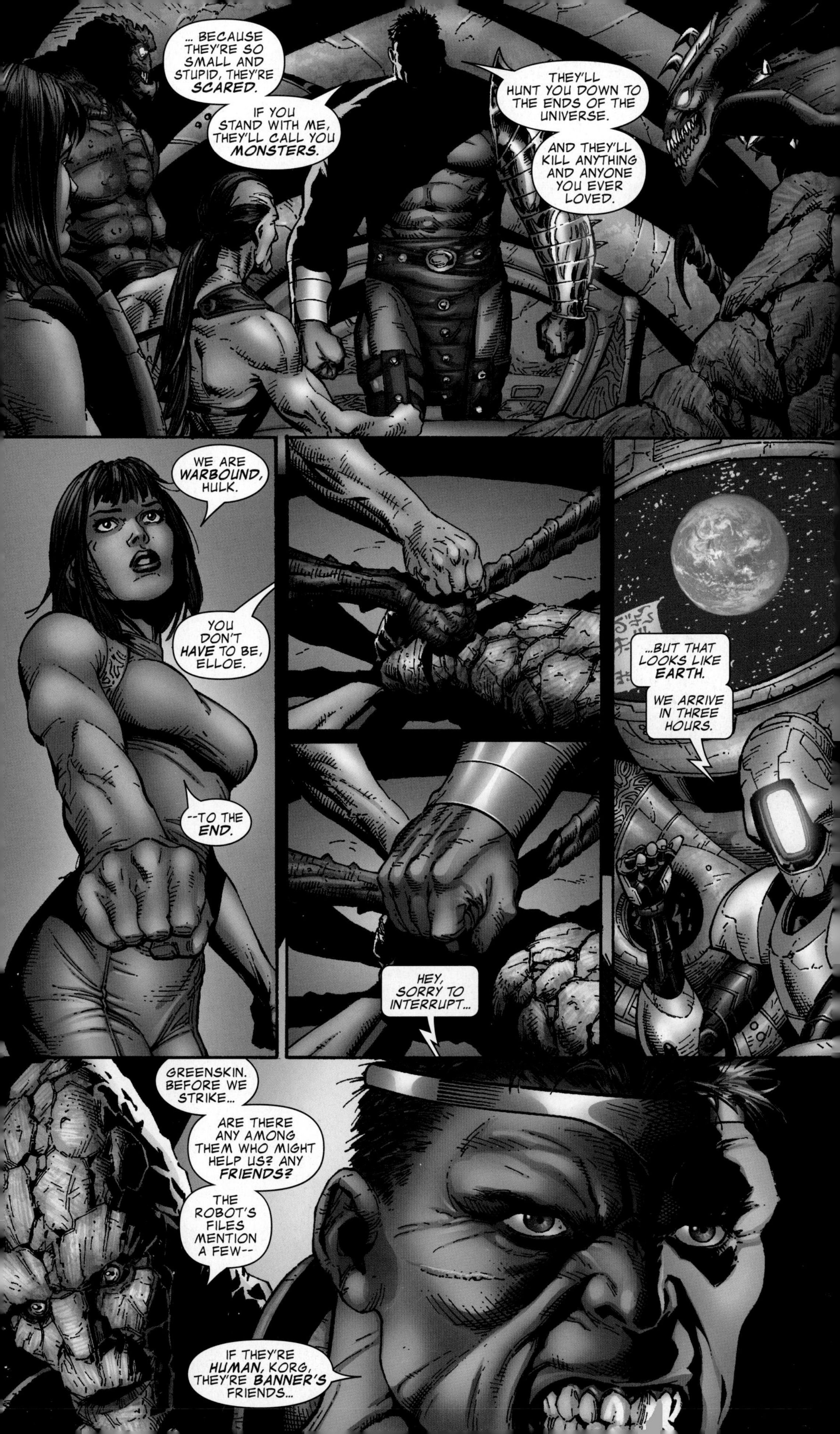
... BECAUSE THEY'RE SO SMALL AND STUPID, THEY'RE SCARED.
IF YOU STAND WITH ME, THEY'LL CALL YOU MONSTERS.
THEY'LL HUNT YOU DOWN TO THE ENDS OF THE UNIVERSE.
AND THEY'LL KILL ANYTHING AND ANYONE YOU EVER LOVED.
WE ARE WARBOUND, HULK.
YOU DON'T HAVE TO BE, ELLOE.
--TO THE END.
HEY, SORRY TO INTERRUPT...
...BUT THAT LOOKS LIKE EARTH.
WE ARRIVE IN THREE HOURS.
GREENSKIN. BEFORE WE STRIKE...
ARE THERE ANY AMONG THEM WHO MIGHT HELP US? ANY FRIENDS?
THE ROBOT'S FILES MENTION A FEW--
IF THEY'RE HUMAN, KORG, THEY'RE BANNER'S FRIENDS...

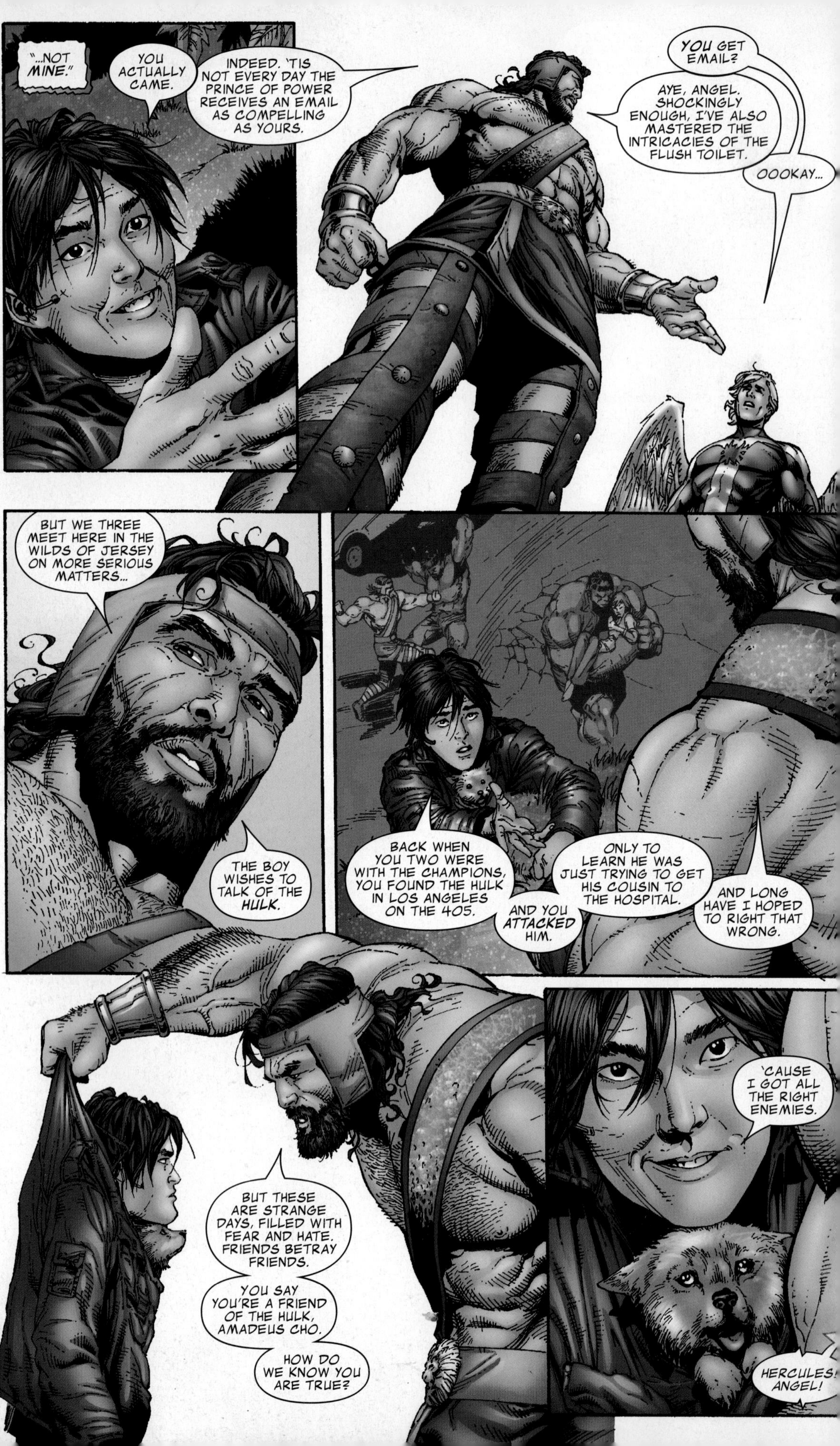
"...NOT *MINE*."
YOU ACTUALLY CAME.
INDEED. 'TIS NOT EVERY DAY THE PRINCE OF POWER RECEIVES AN EMAIL AS COMPELLING AS YOURS.
YOU GET EMAIL?
AYE, ANGEL. SHOCKINGLY ENOUGH, I'VE ALSO MASTERED THE INTRICACIES OF THE FLUSH TOILET.
OOOKAY...
BUT WE THREE MEET HERE IN THE WILDS OF JERSEY ON MORE SERIOUS MATTERS...
THE BOY WISHES TO TALK OF THE *HULK*.
BACK WHEN YOU TWO WERE WITH THE CHAMPIONS, YOU FOUND THE HULK IN LOS ANGELES ON THE 405.
AND YOU *ATTACKED* HIM.
ONLY TO LEARN HE WAS JUST TRYING TO GET HIS COUSIN TO THE HOSPITAL.
AND LONG HAVE I HOPED TO RIGHT THAT WRONG.
BUT THESE ARE STRANGE DAYS, FILLED WITH FEAR AND HATE. FRIENDS BETRAY FRIENDS.
YOU SAY YOU'RE A FRIEND OF THE HULK, AMADEUS CHO.
HOW DO WE KNOW YOU ARE TRUE?
'CAUSE I GOT ALL THE RIGHT ENEMIES.
HERCULES! ANGEL!

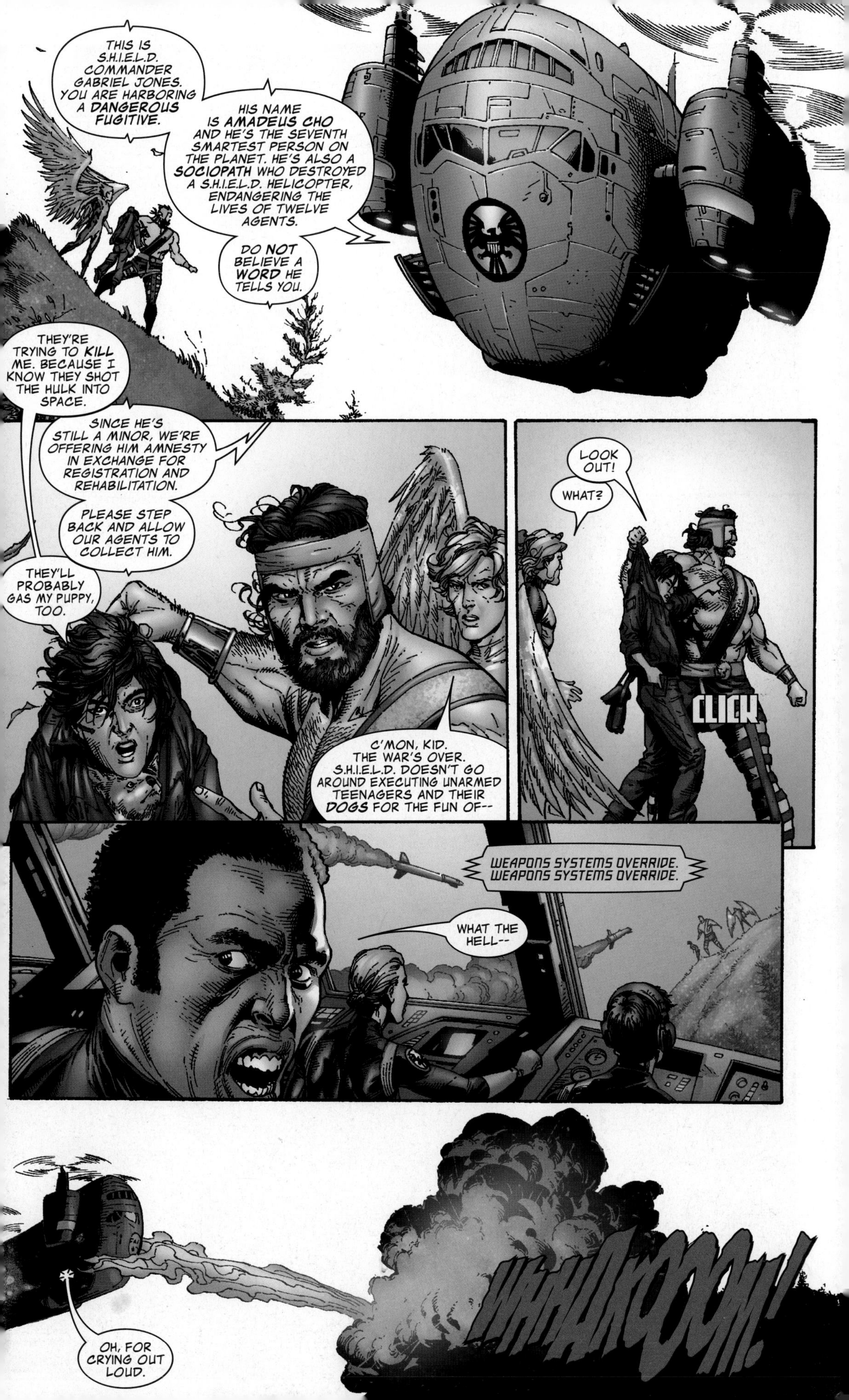
THIS IS S.H.I.E.L.D. COMMANDER GABRIEL JONES. YOU ARE HARBORING A DANGEROUS FUGITIVE.
HIS NAME IS AMADEUS CHO AND HE'S THE SEVENTH SMARTEST PERSON ON THE PLANET. HE'S ALSO A SOCIOPATH WHO DESTROYED A S.H.I.E.L.D. HELICOPTER, ENDANGERING THE LIVES OF TWELVE AGENTS.
DO NOT BELIEVE A WORD HE TELLS YOU.
THEY'RE TRYING TO KILL ME. BECAUSE I KNOW THEY SHOT THE HULK INTO SPACE.
SINCE HE'S STILL A MINOR, WE'RE OFFERING HIM AMNESTY IN EXCHANGE FOR REGISTRATION AND REHABILITATION.
PLEASE STEP BACK AND ALLOW OUR AGENTS TO COLLECT HIM.
THEY'LL PROBABLY GAS MY PUPPY, TOO.
C'MON, KID. THE WAR'S OVER. S.H.I.E.L.D. DOESN'T GO AROUND EXECUTING UNARMED TEENAGERS AND THEIR DOGS FOR THE FUN OF--
LOOK OUT!
WHAT?
CLICK
WEAPONS SYSTEMS OVERRIDE. WEAPONS SYSTEMS OVERRIDE.
WHAT THE HELL--
WHHAKOOOM!
OH, FOR CRYING OUT LOUD.

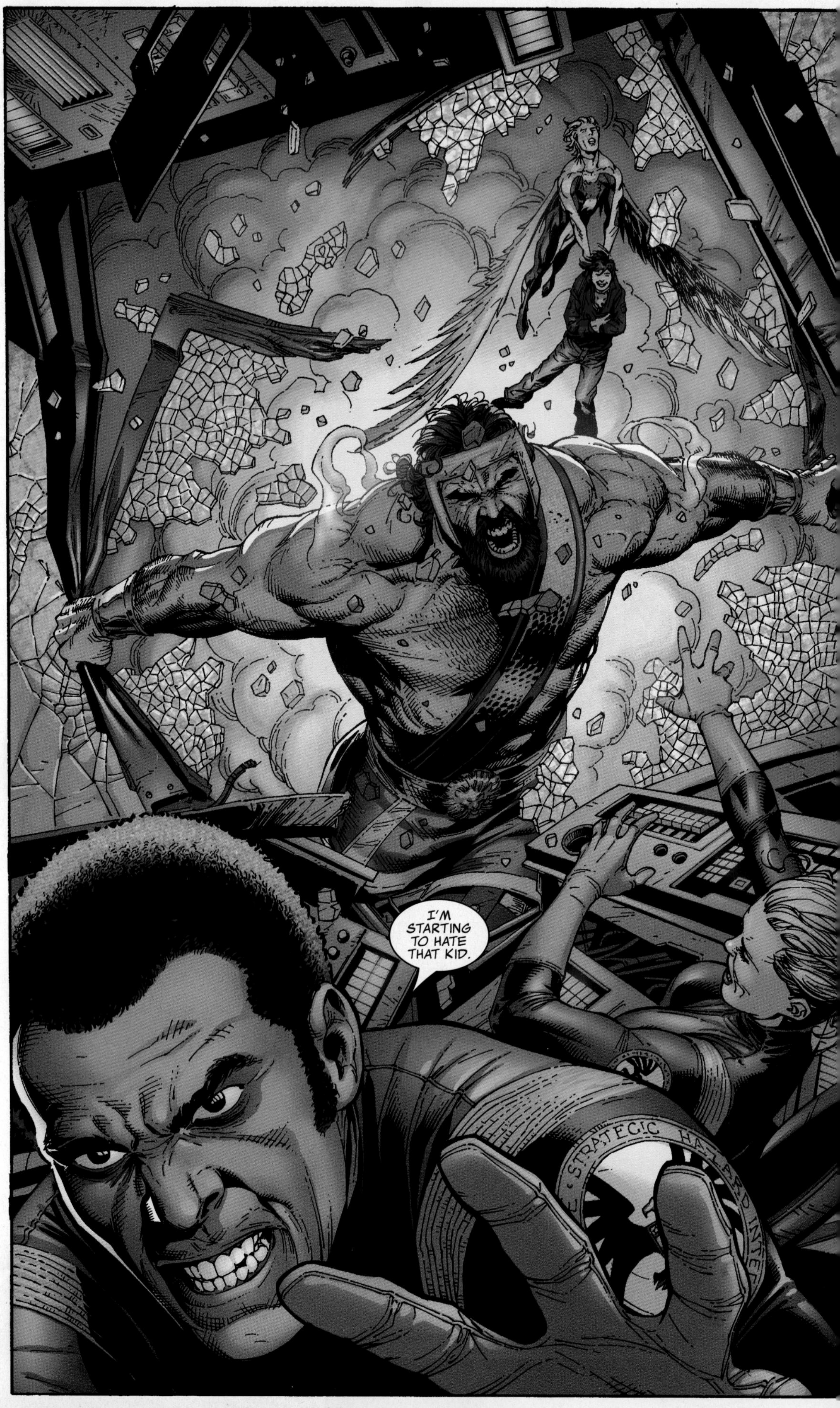
I'M STARTING TO HATE THAT KID.

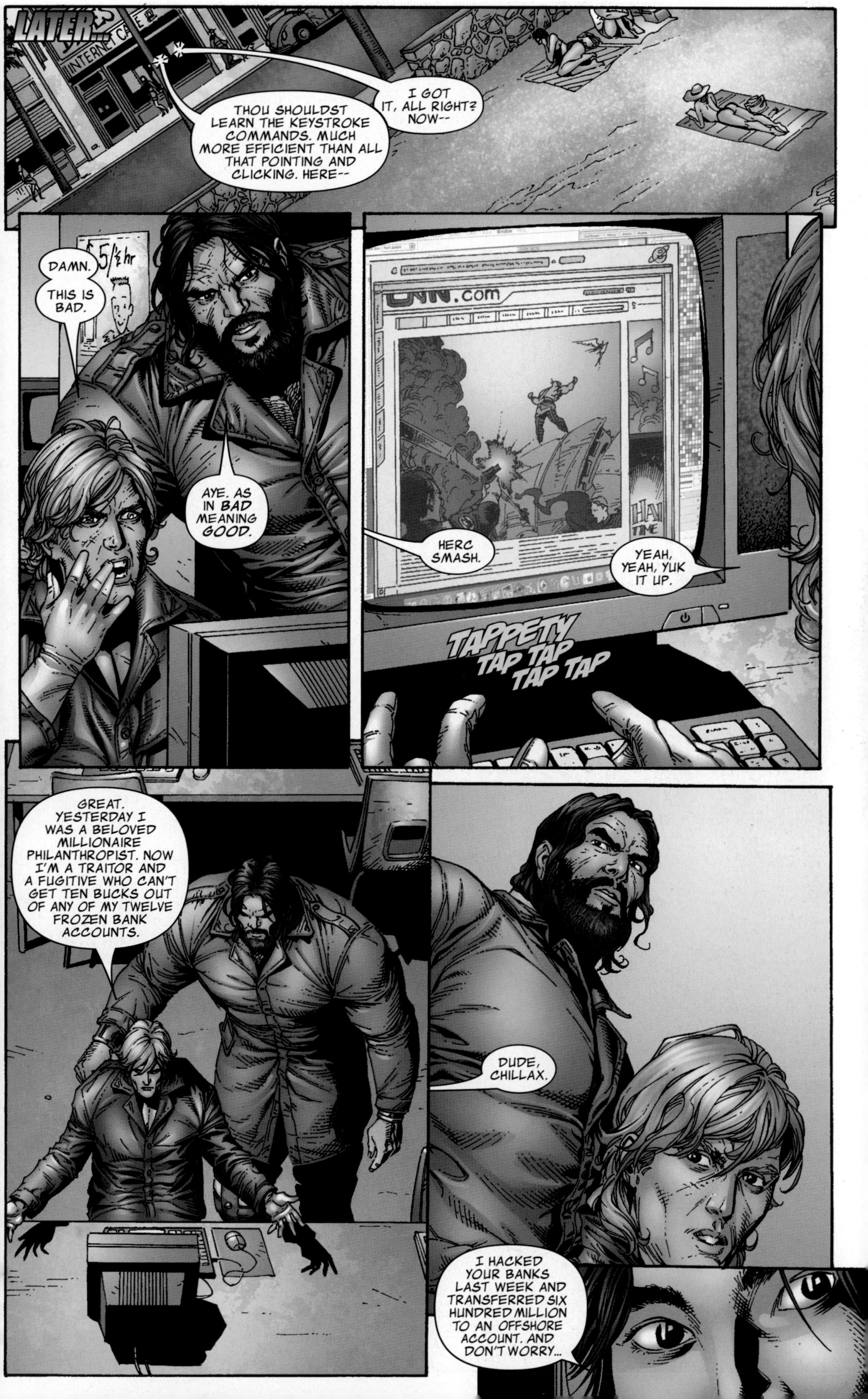

LATER...
INTERNET CAFE
THOU SHOULDST LEARN THE KEYSTROKE COMMANDS. MUCH MORE EFFICIENT THAN ALL THAT POINTING AND CLICKING. HERE--
I GOT IT, ALL RIGHT? NOW--
$5/½ hr
DAMN.
THIS IS BAD.
AYE. AS IN BAD MEANING GOOD.
.com
HERC SMASH.
YEAH, YEAH, YUK IT UP.
TAPPETY TAP TAP TAP TAP
GREAT. YESTERDAY I WAS A BELOVED MILLIONAIRE PHILANTHROPIST. NOW I'M A TRAITOR AND A FUGITIVE WHO CAN'T GET TEN BUCKS OUT OF ANY OF MY TWELVE FROZEN BANK ACCOUNTS.
DUDE, CHILLAX.
I HACKED YOUR BANKS LAST WEEK AND TRANSFERRED SIX HUNDRED MILLION TO AN OFFSHORE ACCOUNT. AND DON'T WORRY...

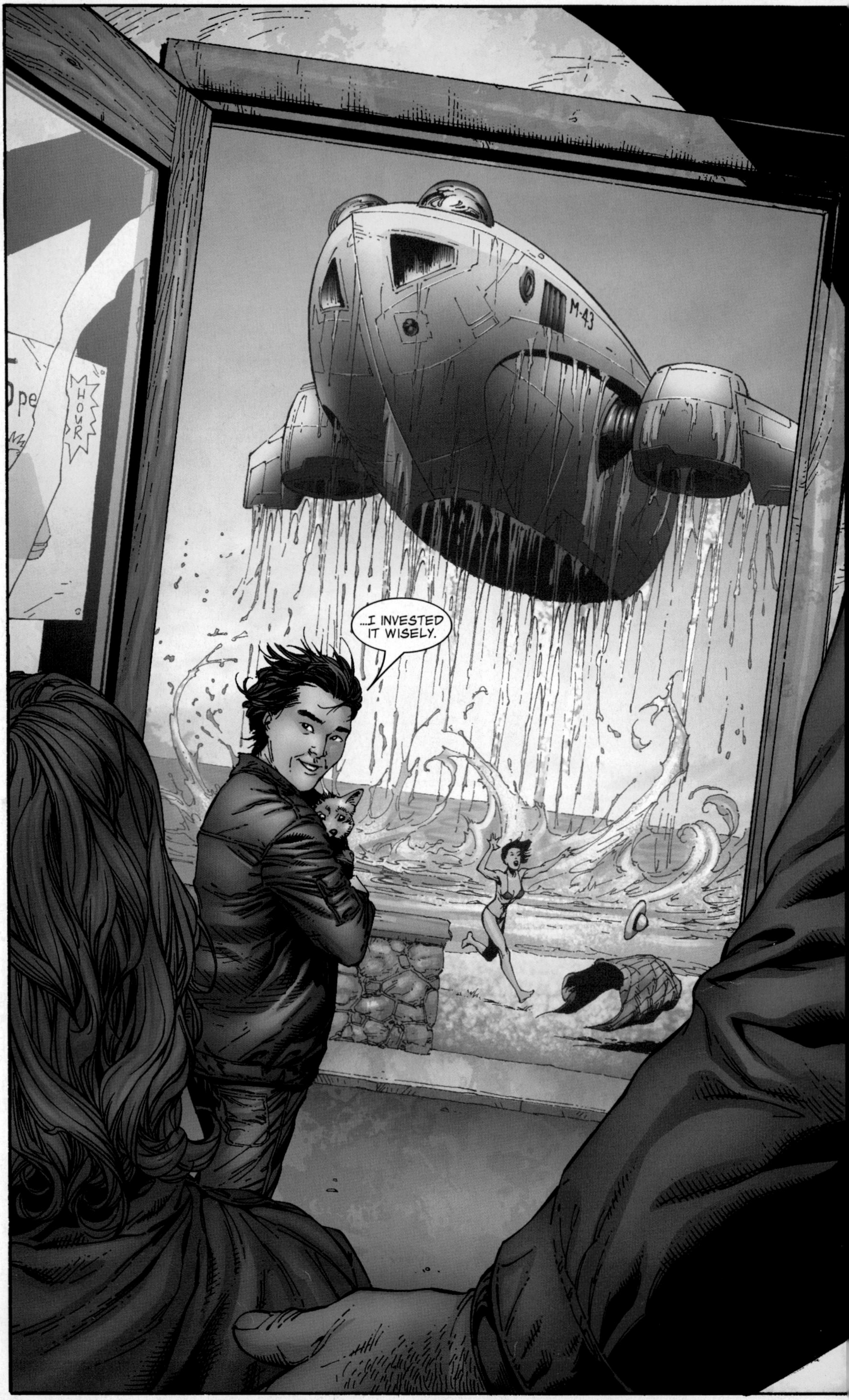
...I INVESTED IT WISELY.
M-43

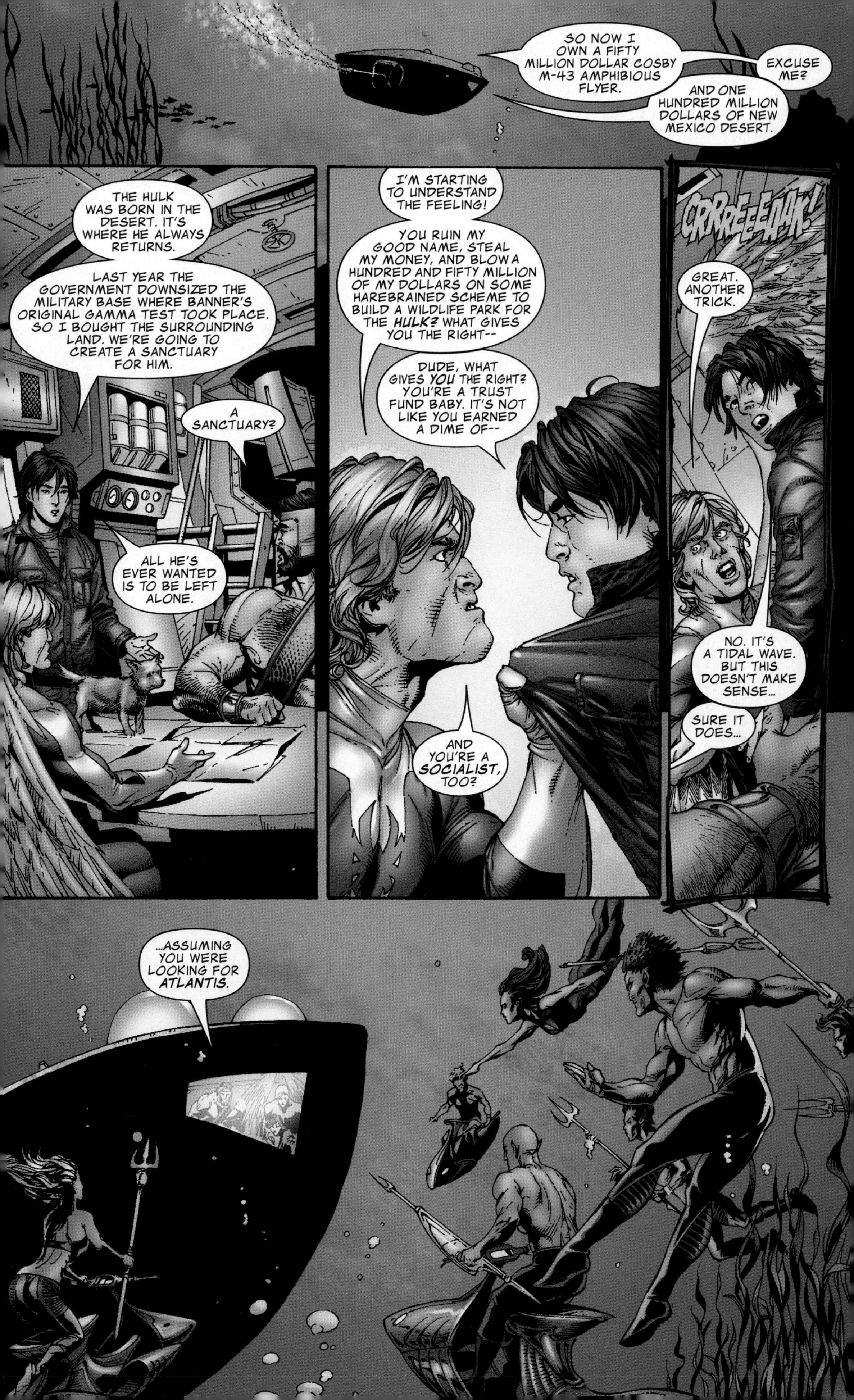

SO NOW I OWN A FIFTY MILLION DOLLAR COSBY M-43 AMPHIBIOUS FLYER.
EXCUSE ME?
AND ONE HUNDRED MILLION DOLLARS OF NEW MEXICO DESERT.
THE HULK WAS BORN IN THE DESERT. IT'S WHERE HE ALWAYS RETURNS.
LAST YEAR THE GOVERNMENT DOWNSIZED THE MILITARY BASE WHERE BANNER'S ORIGINAL GAMMA TEST TOOK PLACE. SO I BOUGHT THE SURROUNDING LAND. WE'RE GOING TO CREATE A SANCTUARY FOR HIM.
A SANCTUARY?
ALL HE'S EVER WANTED IS TO BE LEFT ALONE.
I'M STARTING TO UNDERSTAND THE FEELING!
YOU RUIN MY GOOD NAME, STEAL MY MONEY, AND BLOW A HUNDRED AND FIFTY MILLION OF MY DOLLARS ON SOME HAREBRAINED SCHEME TO BUILD A WILDLIFE PARK FOR THE HULK? WHAT GIVES YOU THE RIGHT--
DUDE, WHAT GIVES YOU THE RIGHT? YOU'RE A TRUST FUND BABY. IT'S NOT LIKE YOU EARNED A DIME OF--
AND YOU'RE A SOCIALIST, TOO?
CRRREEEAAK!
GREAT. ANOTHER TRICK.
NO. IT'S A TIDAL WAVE. BUT THIS DOESN'T MAKE SENSE...
SURE IT DOES...
...ASSUMING YOU WERE LOOKING FOR ATLANTIS.

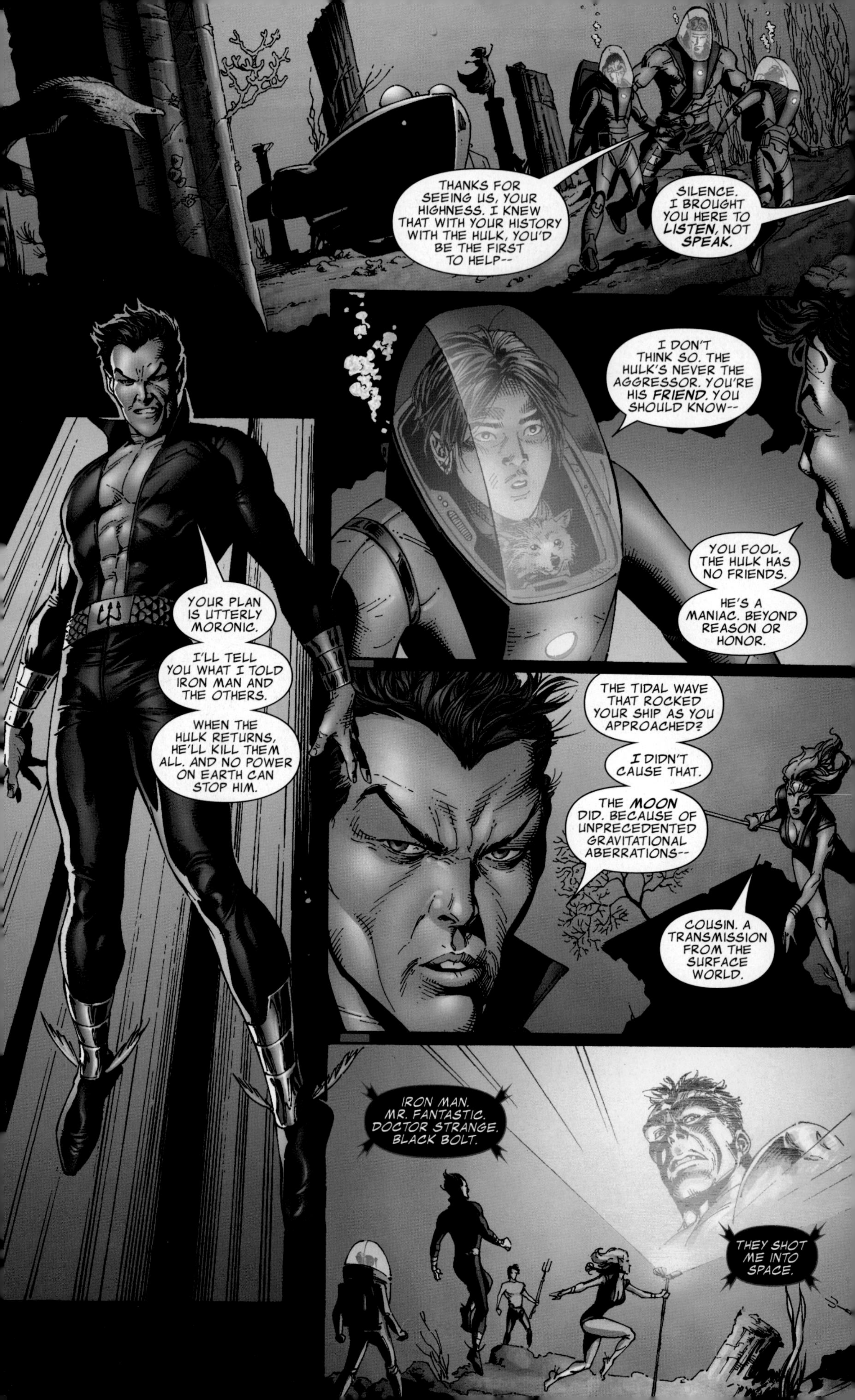
THANKS FOR SEEING US, YOUR HIGHNESS. I KNEW THAT WITH YOUR HISTORY WITH THE HULK, YOU'D BE THE FIRST TO HELP--
SILENCE. I BROUGHT YOU HERE TO LISTEN, NOT SPEAK.
I DON'T THINK SO. THE HULK'S NEVER THE AGGRESSOR. YOU'RE HIS FRIEND. YOU SHOULD KNOW--
YOU FOOL. THE HULK HAS NO FRIENDS.
HE'S A MANIAC. BEYOND REASON OR HONOR.
YOUR PLAN IS UTTERLY MORONIC.
I'LL TELL YOU WHAT I TOLD IRON MAN AND THE OTHERS.
WHEN THE HULK RETURNS, HE'LL KILL THEM ALL. AND NO POWER ON EARTH CAN STOP HIM.
THE TIDAL WAVE THAT ROCKED YOUR SHIP AS YOU APPROACHED?
I DIDN'T CAUSE THAT.
THE MOON DID. BECAUSE OF UNPRECEDENTED GRAVITATIONAL ABERRATIONS--
COUSIN. A TRANSMISSION FROM THE SURFACE WORLD.
IRON MAN. MR. FANTASTIC. DOCTOR STRANGE. BLACK BOLT.
THEY SHOT ME INTO SPACE.

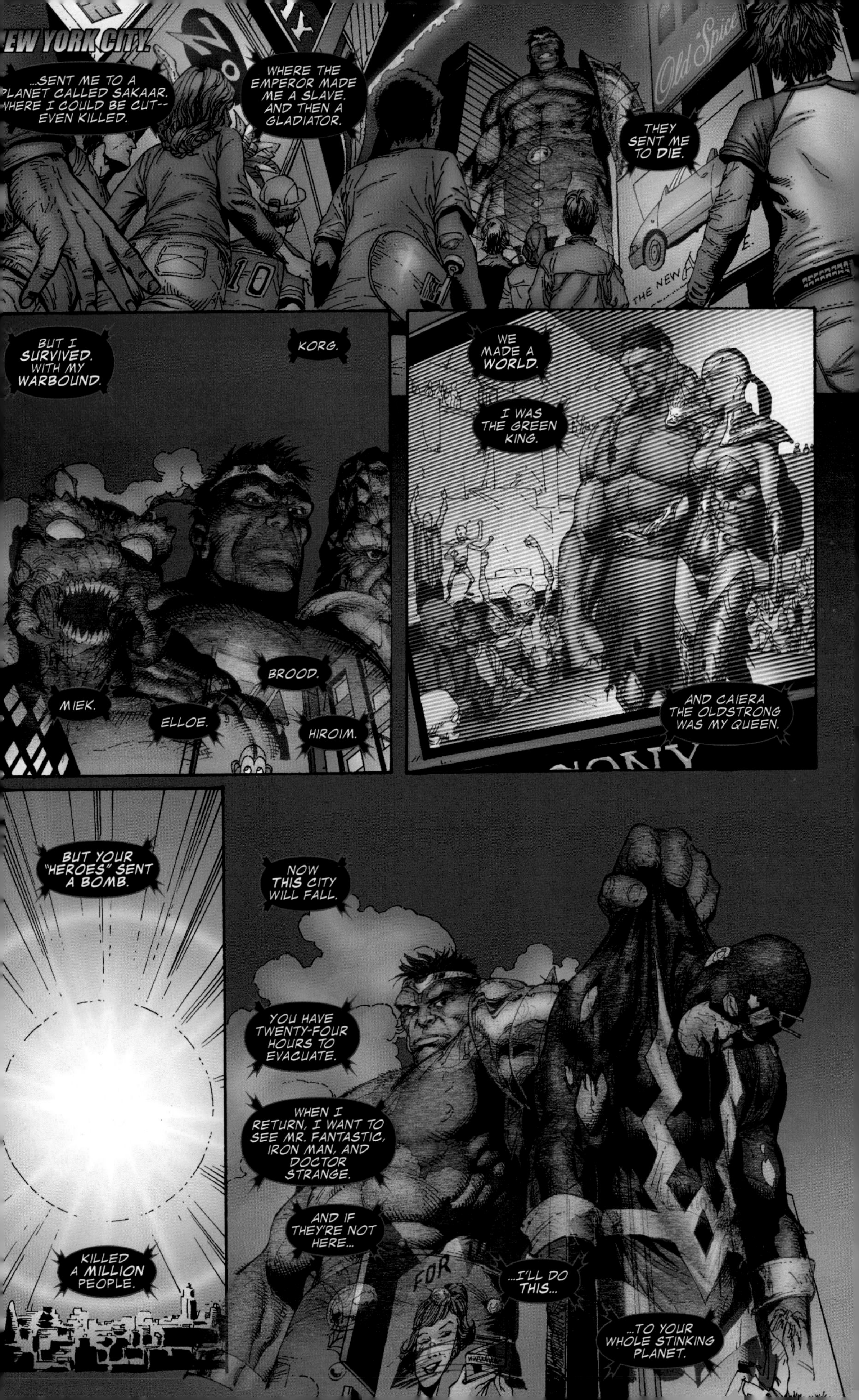
EW YORK CITY.
...SENT ME TO A PLANET CALLED SAKAAR. WHERE I COULD BE CUT-- EVEN KILLED.
WHERE THE EMPEROR MADE ME A SLAVE. AND THEN A GLADIATOR.
THEY SENT ME TO DIE.
Old Spice
THE NEW
BUT I SURVIVED. WITH MY WARBOUND.
KORG.
BROOD.
MIEK.
ELLOE.
HIROIM.
WE MADE A WORLD.
I WAS THE GREEN KING.
AND CAIERA THE OLDSTRONG WAS MY QUEEN.
SONY
BUT YOUR "HEROES" SENT A BOMB.
KILLED A MILLION PEOPLE.
NOW THIS CITY WILL FALL.
YOU HAVE TWENTY-FOUR HOURS TO EVACUATE.
WHEN I RETURN, I WANT TO SEE MR. FANTASTIC, IRON MAN, AND DOCTOR STRANGE.
AND IF THEY'RE NOT HERE...
...I'LL DO THIS...
...TO YOUR WHOLE STINKING PLANET.

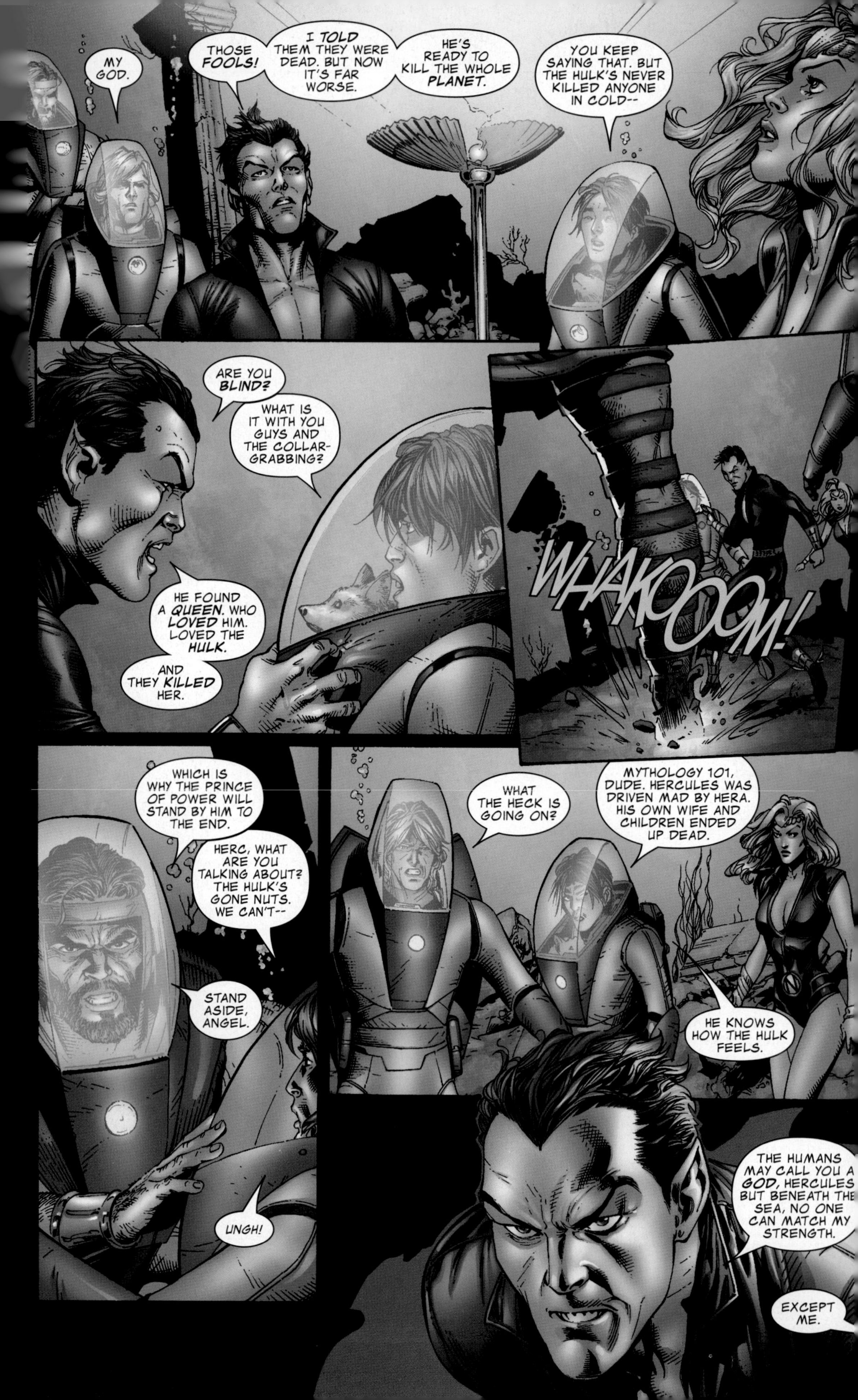
MY GOD.
THOSE FOOLS!
I TOLD THEM THEY WERE DEAD. BUT NOW IT'S FAR WORSE.
HE'S READY TO KILL THE WHOLE PLANET.
YOU KEEP SAYING THAT. BUT THE HULK'S NEVER KILLED ANYONE IN COLD--
ARE YOU BLIND?
WHAT IS IT WITH YOU GUYS AND THE COLLAR-GRABBING?
HE FOUND A QUEEN. WHO LOVED HIM. LOVED THE HULK.
AND THEY KILLED HER.
WHAKOOOM!
WHICH IS WHY THE PRINCE OF POWER WILL STAND BY HIM TO THE END.
HERC, WHAT ARE YOU TALKING ABOUT? THE HULK'S GONE NUTS. WE CAN'T--
STAND ASIDE, ANGEL.
UNGH!
WHAT THE HECK IS GOING ON?
MYTHOLOGY 101, DUDE. HERCULES WAS DRIVEN MAD BY HERA. HIS OWN WIFE AND CHILDREN ENDED UP DEAD.
HE KNOWS HOW THE HULK FEELS.
THE HUMANS MAY CALL YOU A GOD, HERCULES BUT BENEATH THE SEA, NO ONE CAN MATCH MY STRENGTH.
EXCEPT ME.

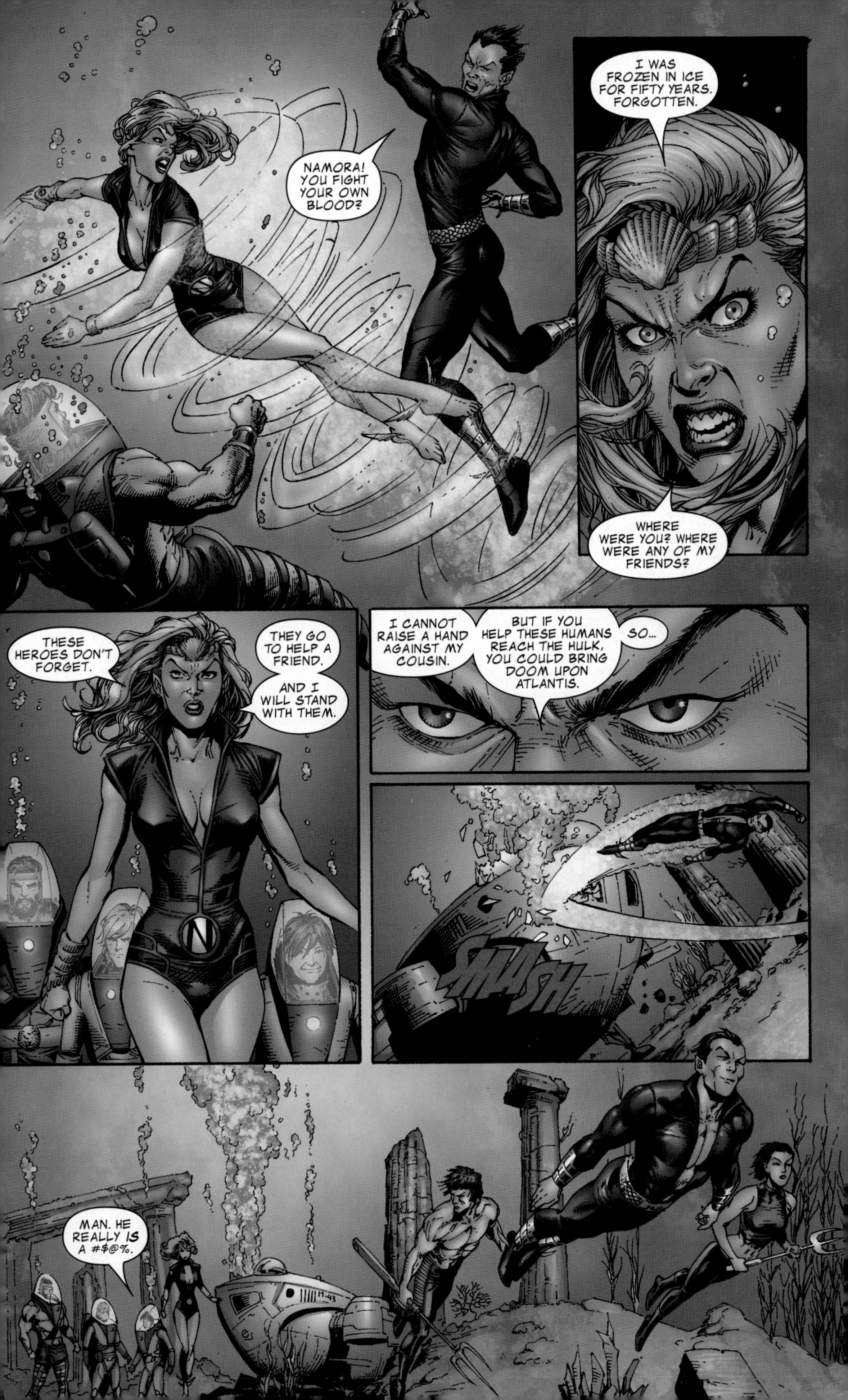
NAMORA! YOU FIGHT YOUR OWN BLOOD?
I WAS FROZEN IN ICE FOR FIFTY YEARS. FORGOTTEN.
WHERE WERE YOU? WHERE WERE ANY OF MY FRIENDS?
THESE HEROES DON'T FORGET.
THEY GO TO HELP A FRIEND.
AND I WILL STAND WITH THEM.
I CANNOT RAISE A HAND AGAINST MY COUSIN.
BUT IF YOU HELP THESE HUMANS REACH THE HULK, YOU COULD BRING DOOM UPON ATLANTIS.
SO...
SMASH
MAN. HE REALLY IS A #$@%.

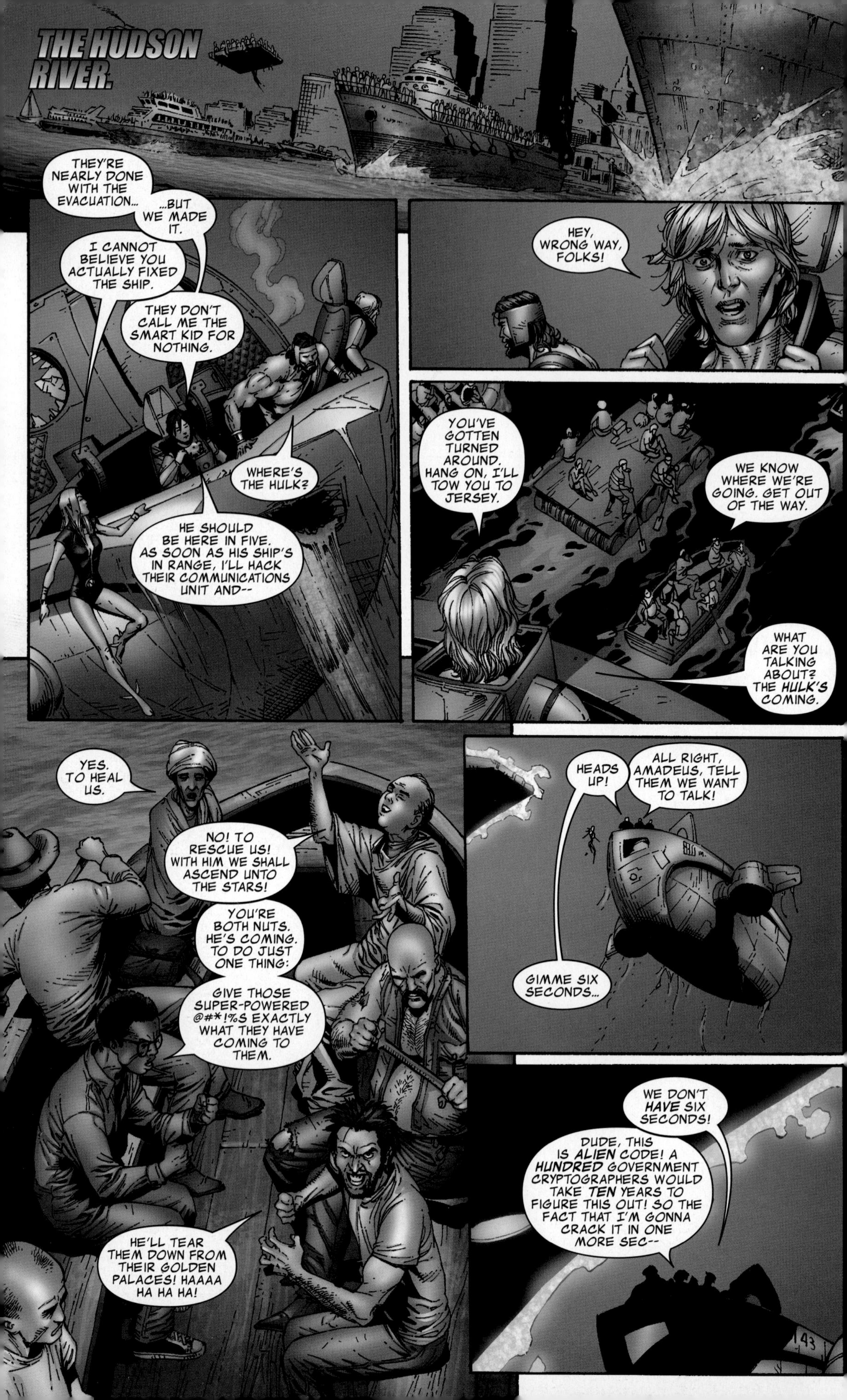
THE HUDSON RIVER.
THEY'RE NEARLY DONE WITH THE EVACUATION...
...BUT WE MADE IT.
I CANNOT BELIEVE YOU ACTUALLY FIXED THE SHIP.
THEY DON'T CALL ME THE SMART KID FOR NOTHING.
WHERE'S THE HULK?
HE SHOULD BE HERE IN FIVE. AS SOON AS HIS SHIP'S IN RANGE, I'LL HACK THEIR COMMUNICATIONS UNIT AND--
HEY, WRONG WAY, FOLKS!
YOU'VE GOTTEN TURNED AROUND. HANG ON, I'LL TOW YOU TO JERSEY.
WE KNOW WHERE WE'RE GOING. GET OUT OF THE WAY.
WHAT ARE YOU TALKING ABOUT? THE HULK'S COMING.
YES. TO HEAL US.
NO! TO RESCUE US! WITH HIM WE SHALL ASCEND UNTO THE STARS!
YOU'RE BOTH NUTS. HE'S COMING. TO DO JUST ONE THING:
GIVE THOSE SUPER-POWERED @#*!%S EXACTLY WHAT THEY HAVE COMING TO THEM.
HE'LL TEAR THEM DOWN FROM THEIR GOLDEN PALACES! HAAAA HA HA HA!
HEADS UP!
ALL RIGHT, AMADEUS, TELL THEM WE WANT TO TALK!
GIMME SIX SECONDS...
WE DON'T HAVE SIX SECONDS!
DUDE, THIS IS ALIEN CODE! A HUNDRED GOVERNMENT CRYPTOGRAPHERS WOULD TAKE TEN YEARS TO FIGURE THIS OUT! SO THE FACT THAT I'M GONNA CRACK IT IN ONE MORE SEC--

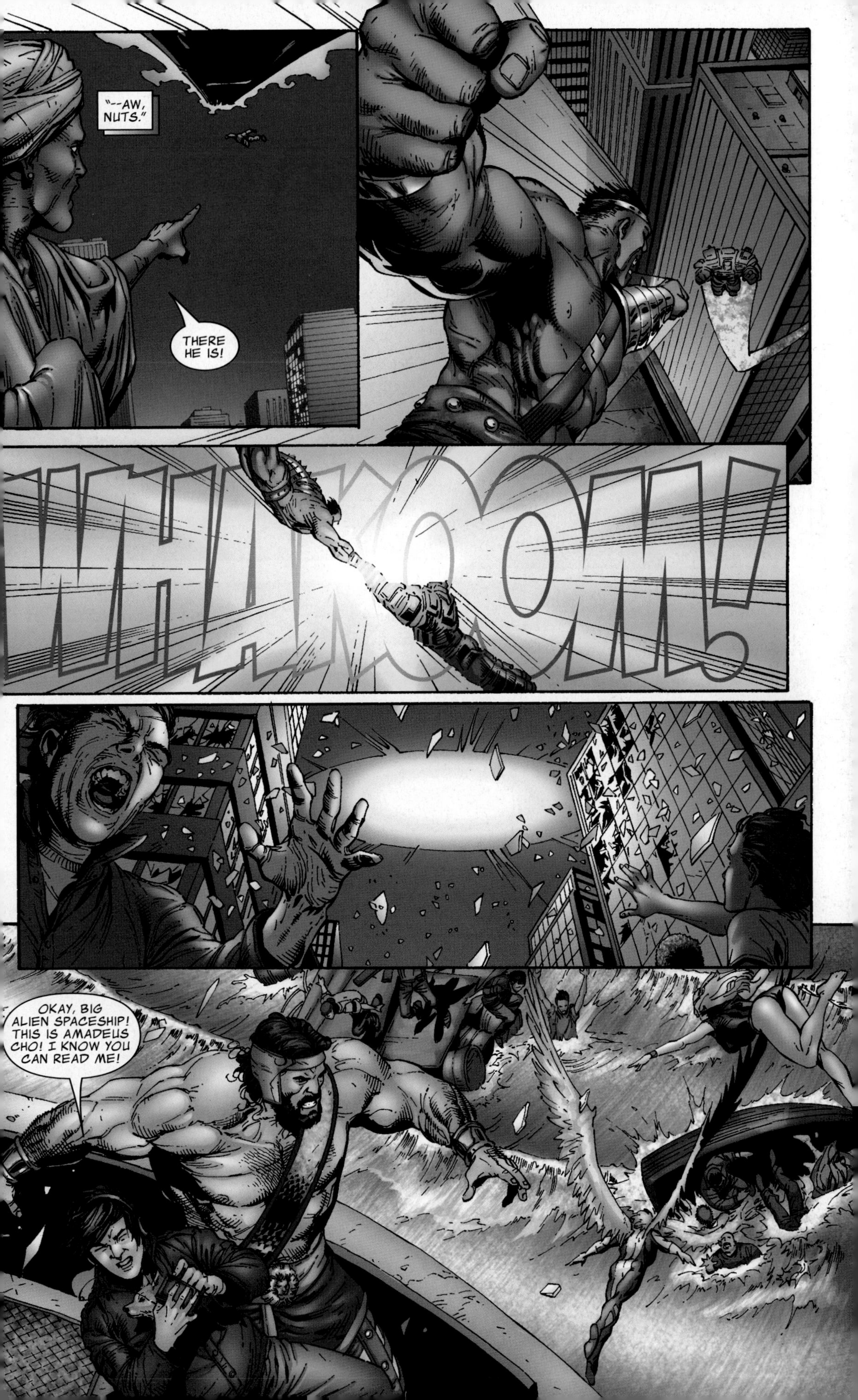
"--AW, NUTS."
THERE HE IS!
WHKOOM!
OKAY, BIG ALIEN SPACESHIP! THIS IS AMADEUS CHO! I KNOW YOU CAN READ ME!

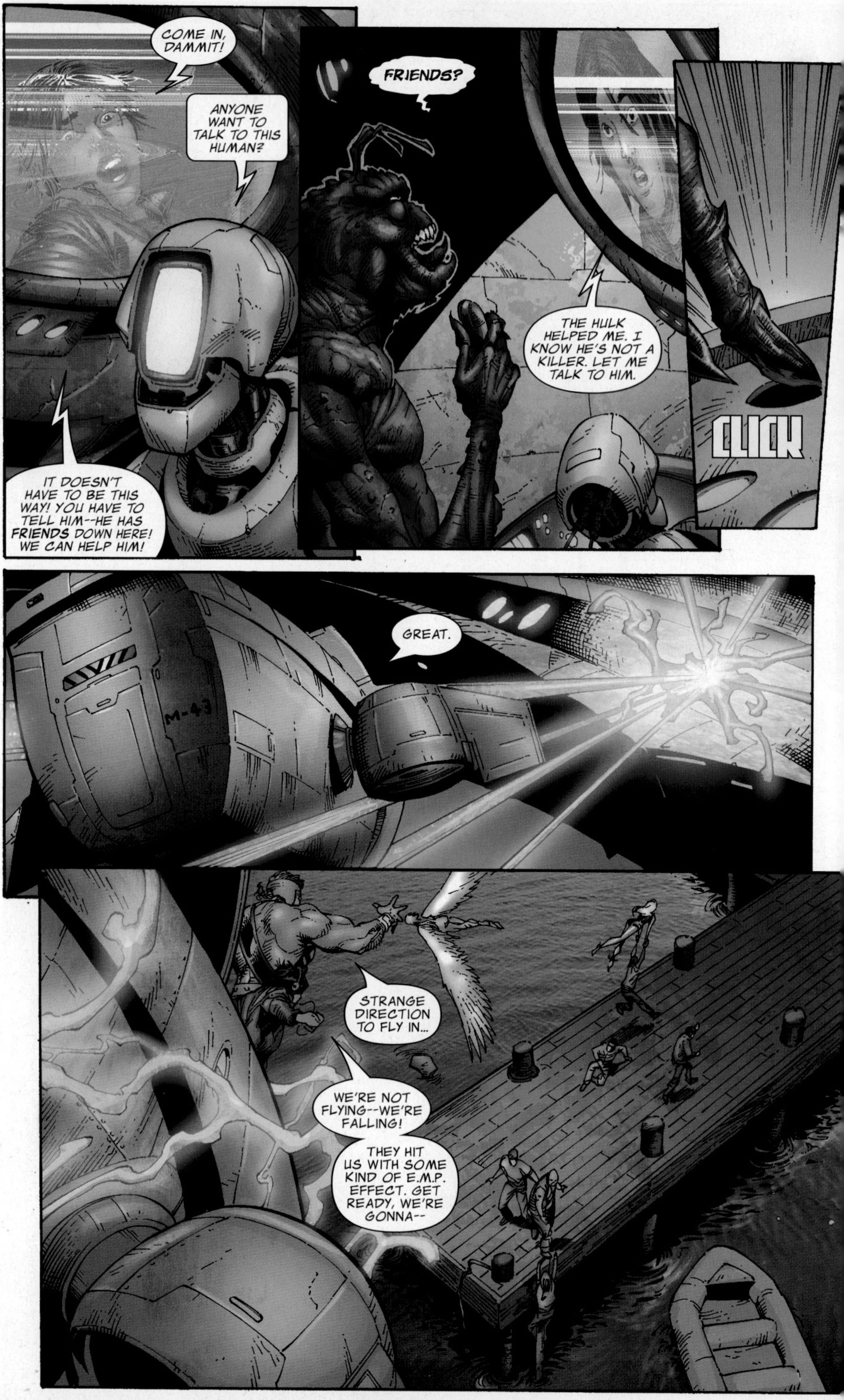
COME IN, DAMMIT!
ANYONE WANT TO TALK TO THIS HUMAN?
IT DOESN'T HAVE TO BE THIS WAY! YOU HAVE TO TELL HIM--HE HAS FRIENDS DOWN HERE! WE CAN HELP HIM!
FRIENDS?
THE HULK HELPED ME. I KNOW HE'S NOT A KILLER. LET ME TALK TO HIM.
CLICK
GREAT.
M-43
STRANGE DIRECTION TO FLY IN...
WE'RE NOT FLYING--WE'RE FALLING!
THEY HIT US WITH SOME KIND OF E.M.P. EFFECT. GET READY, WE'RE GONNA--

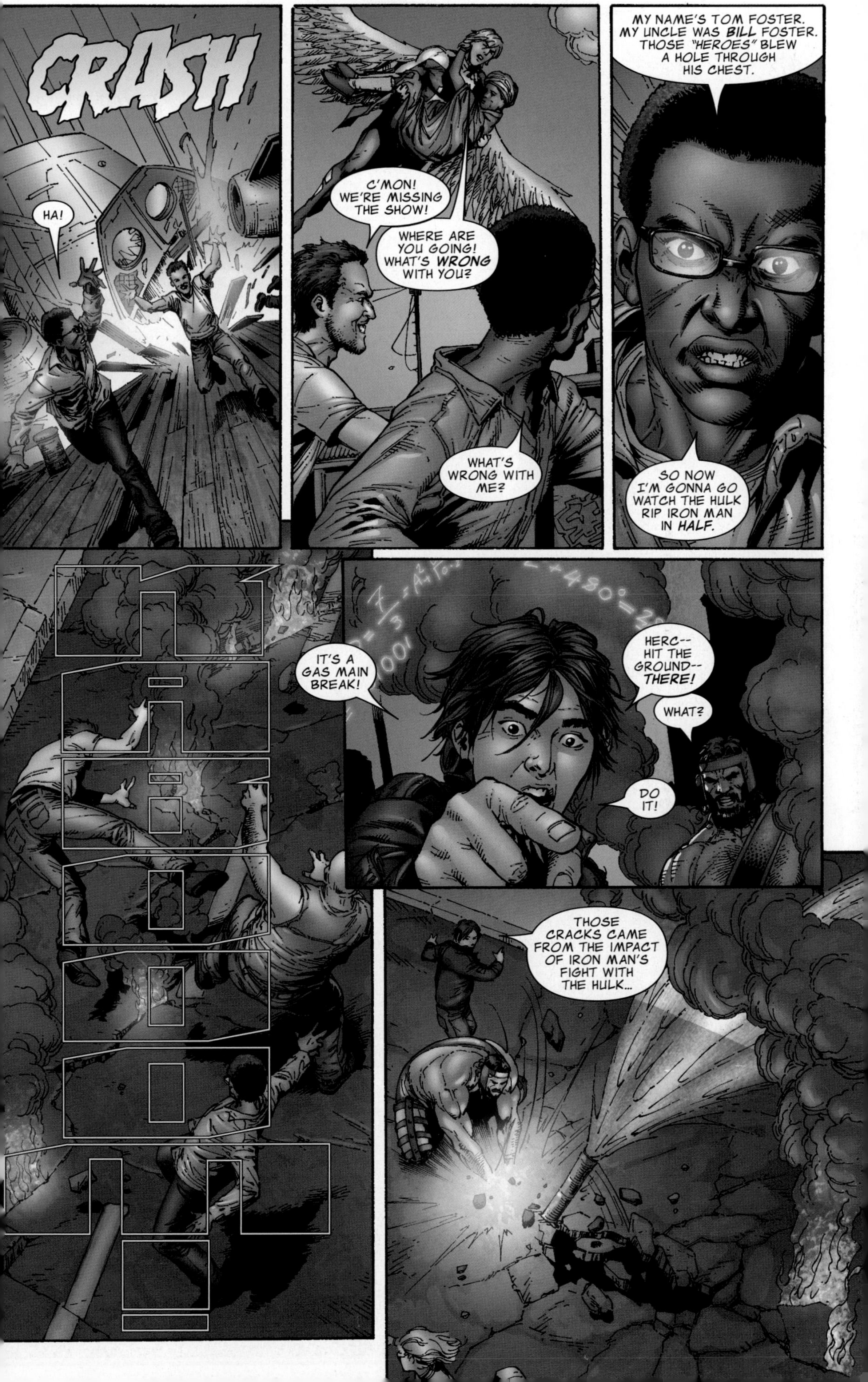
CRASH
HA!
C'MON! WE'RE MISSING THE SHOW!
WHERE ARE YOU GOING! WHAT'S WRONG WITH YOU?
WHAT'S WRONG WITH ME?
MY NAME'S TOM FOSTER. MY UNCLE WAS BILL FOSTER. THOSE "HEROES" BLEW A HOLE THROUGH HIS CHEST.
SO NOW I'M GONNA GO WATCH THE HULK RIP IRON MAN IN HALF.
IT'S A GAS MAIN BREAK!
HERC-- HIT THE GROUND-- THERE!
WHAT?
DO IT!
THOSE CRACKS CAME FROM THE IMPACT OF IRON MAN'S FIGHT WITH THE HULK...

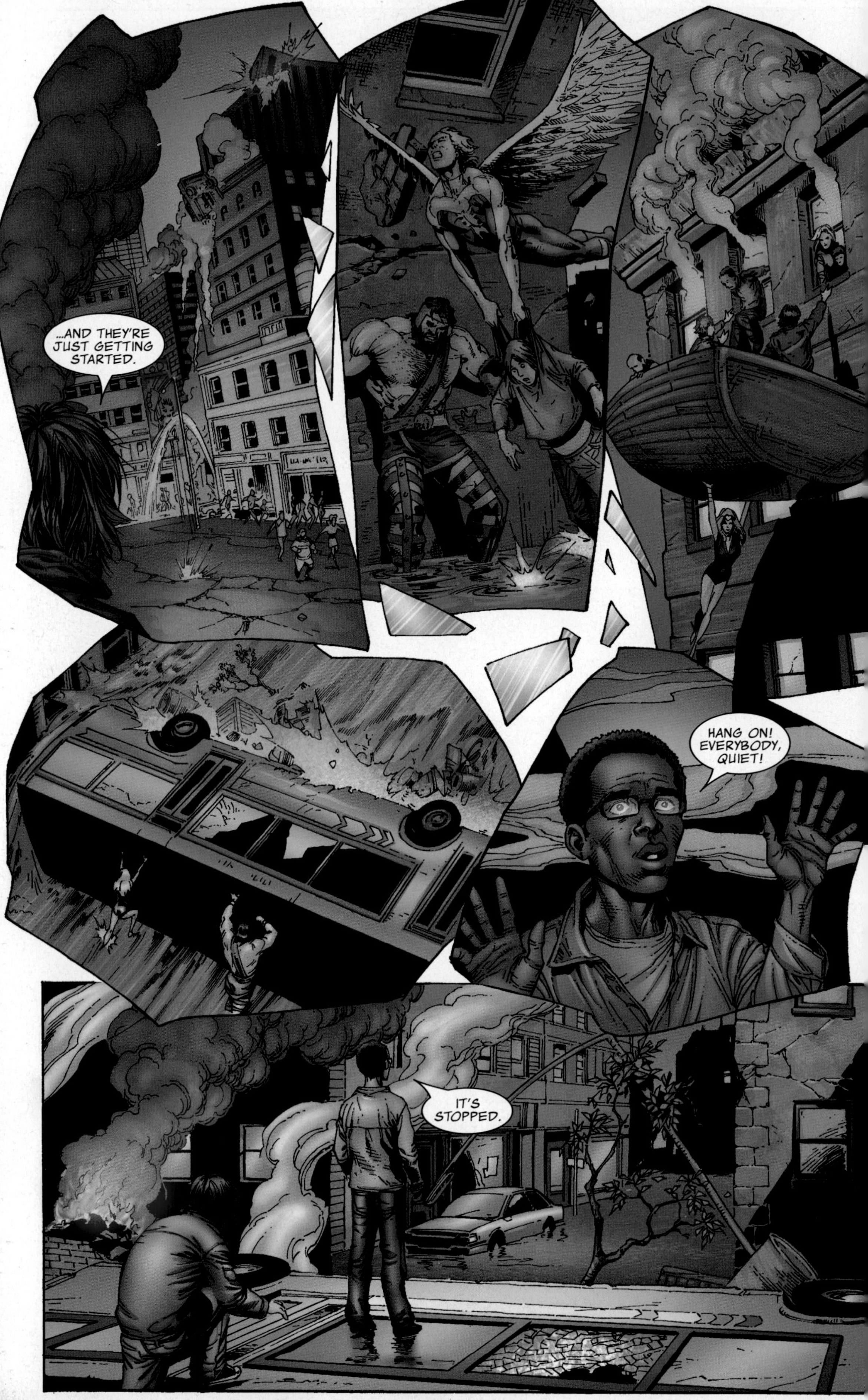
...AND THEY'RE JUST GETTING STARTED.
HANG ON! EVERYBODY, QUIET!
IT'S STOPPED.

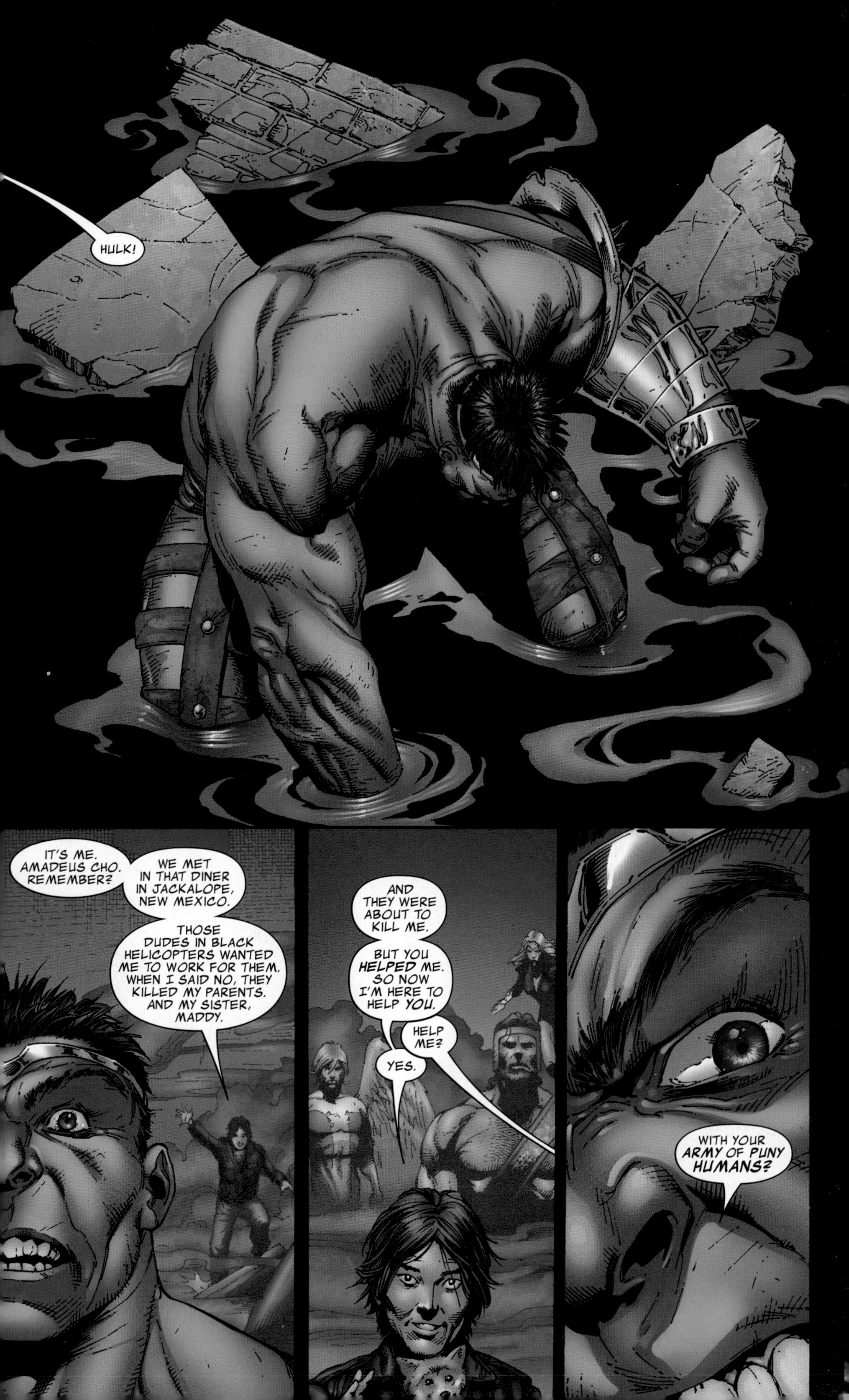
HULK!
IT'S ME. AMADEUS CHO. REMEMBER?
WE MET IN THAT DINER IN JACKALOPE, NEW MEXICO.
THOSE DUDES IN BLACK HELICOPTERS WANTED ME TO WORK FOR THEM. WHEN I SAID NO, THEY KILLED MY PARENTS. AND MY SISTER, MADDY.
AND THEY WERE ABOUT TO KILL ME.
BUT YOU HELPED ME. SO NOW I'M HERE TO HELP YOU.
HELP ME?
YES.
WITH YOUR ARMY OF PUNY HUMANS?

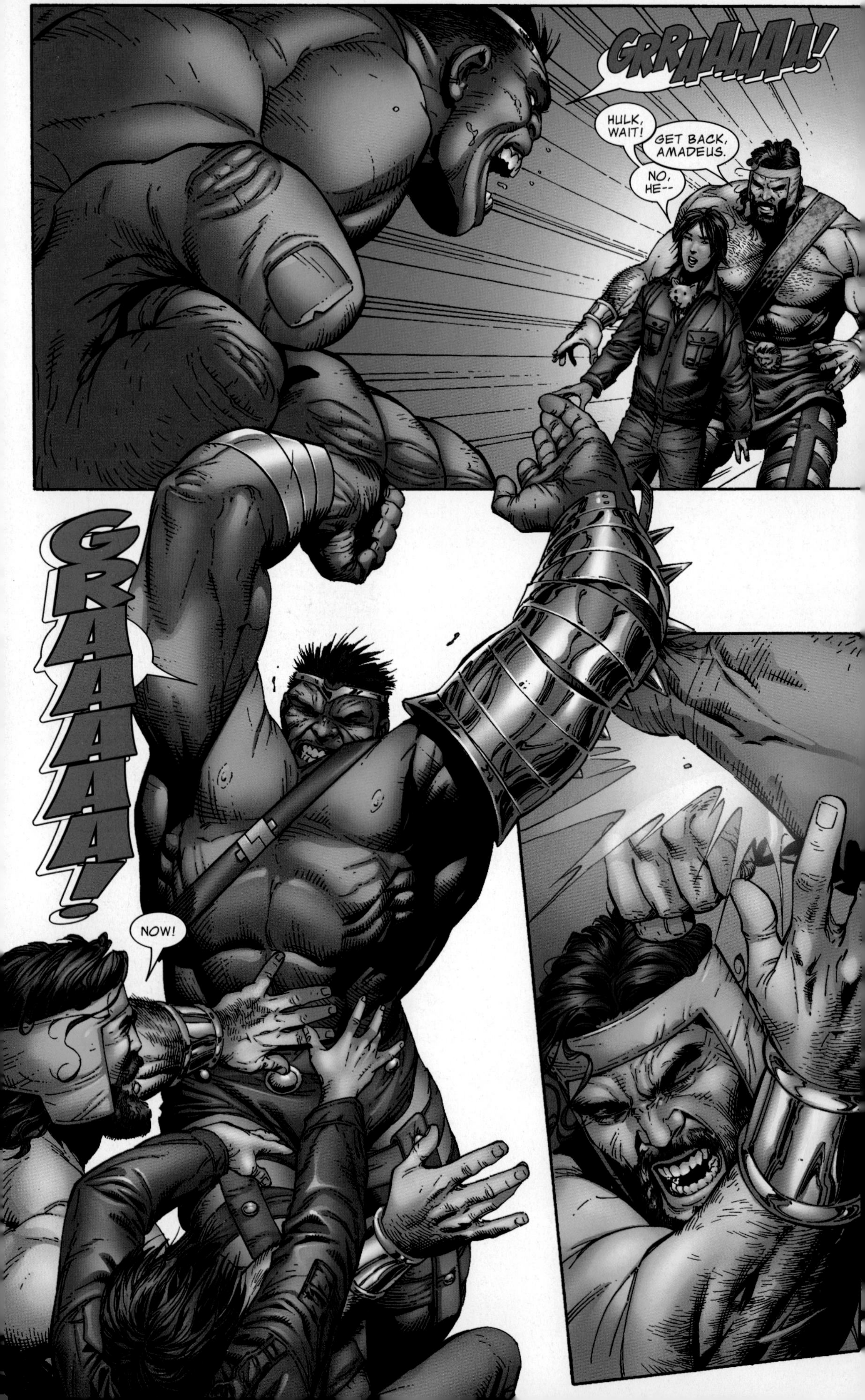
GRRAAAAA!
HULK, WAIT!
GET BACK, AMADEUS.
NO, HE--
GRAAAAAA!
NOW!

BRAKKKOOOOOOOOOOOOOOOOOOOOM

RRRRAAA!

VOOSH

ALL RIGHT, HERC! NOW, WHILE THE DUST--

GRAAAAA!

WHAKOOOM!

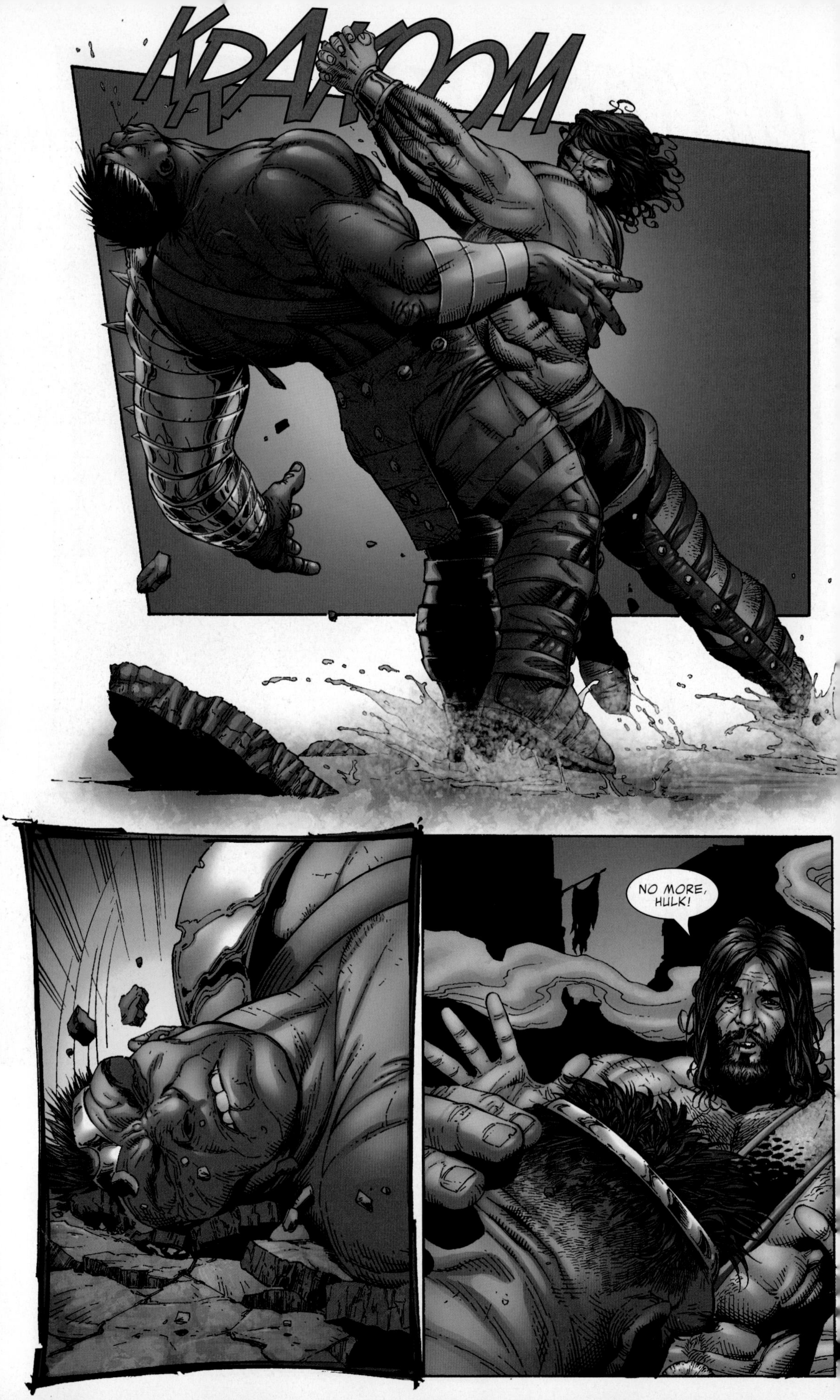
KRAKOOM
NO MORE, HULK!

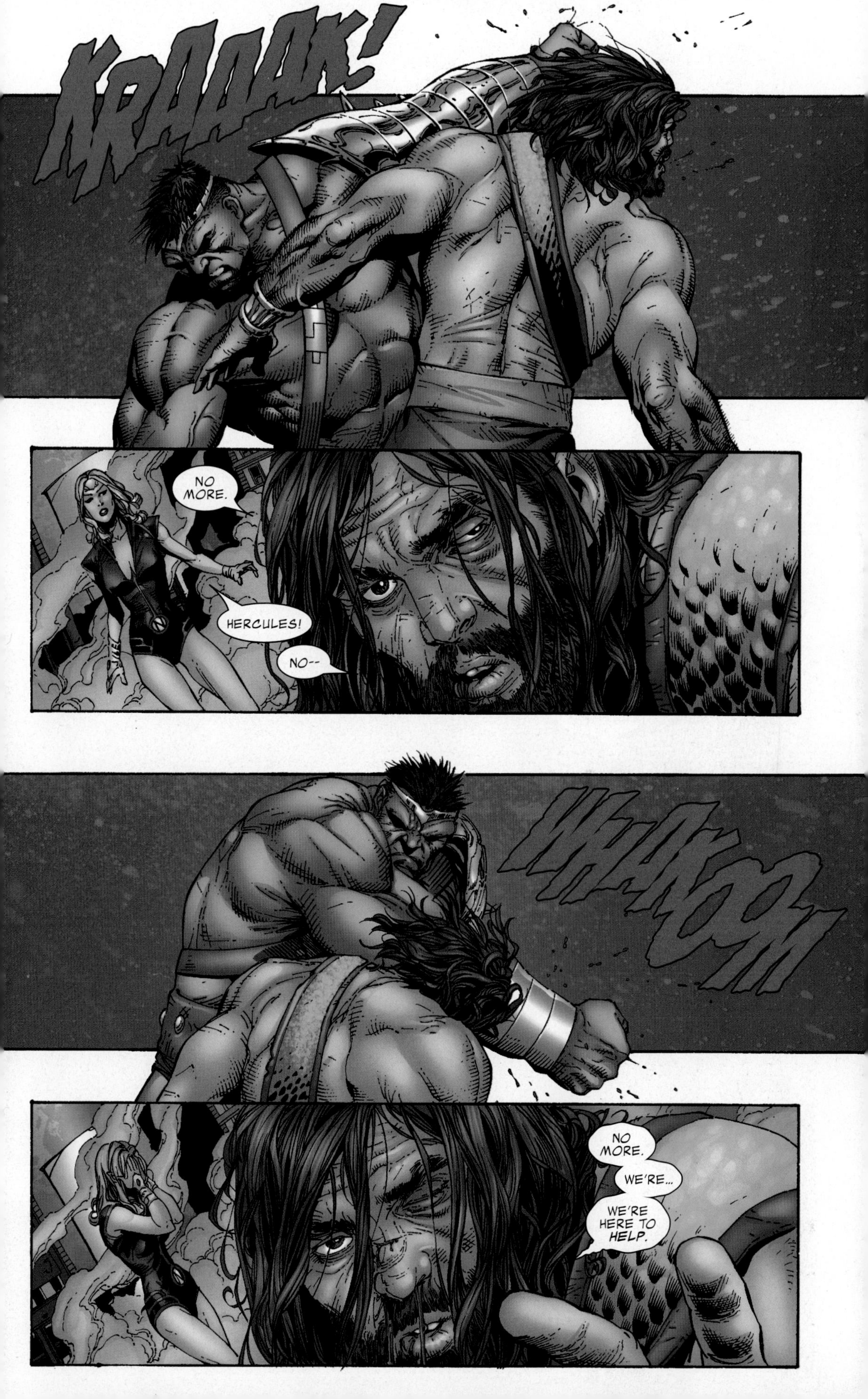
KRAAAK!
NO MORE.
HERCULES!
NO--
WHHOOM
NO MORE.
WE'RE...
WE'RE HERE TO HELP.

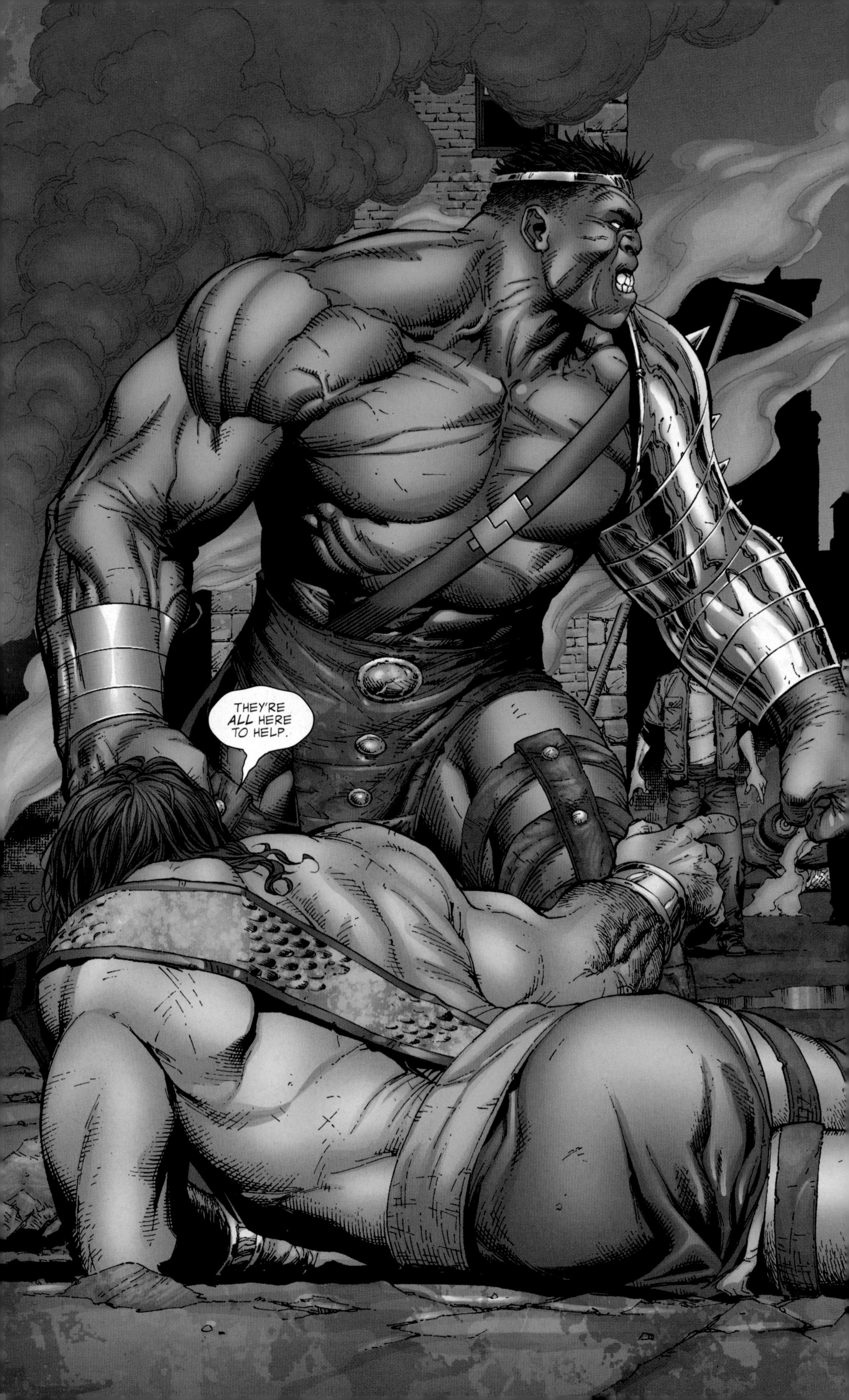
THEY'RE ALL HERE TO HELP.

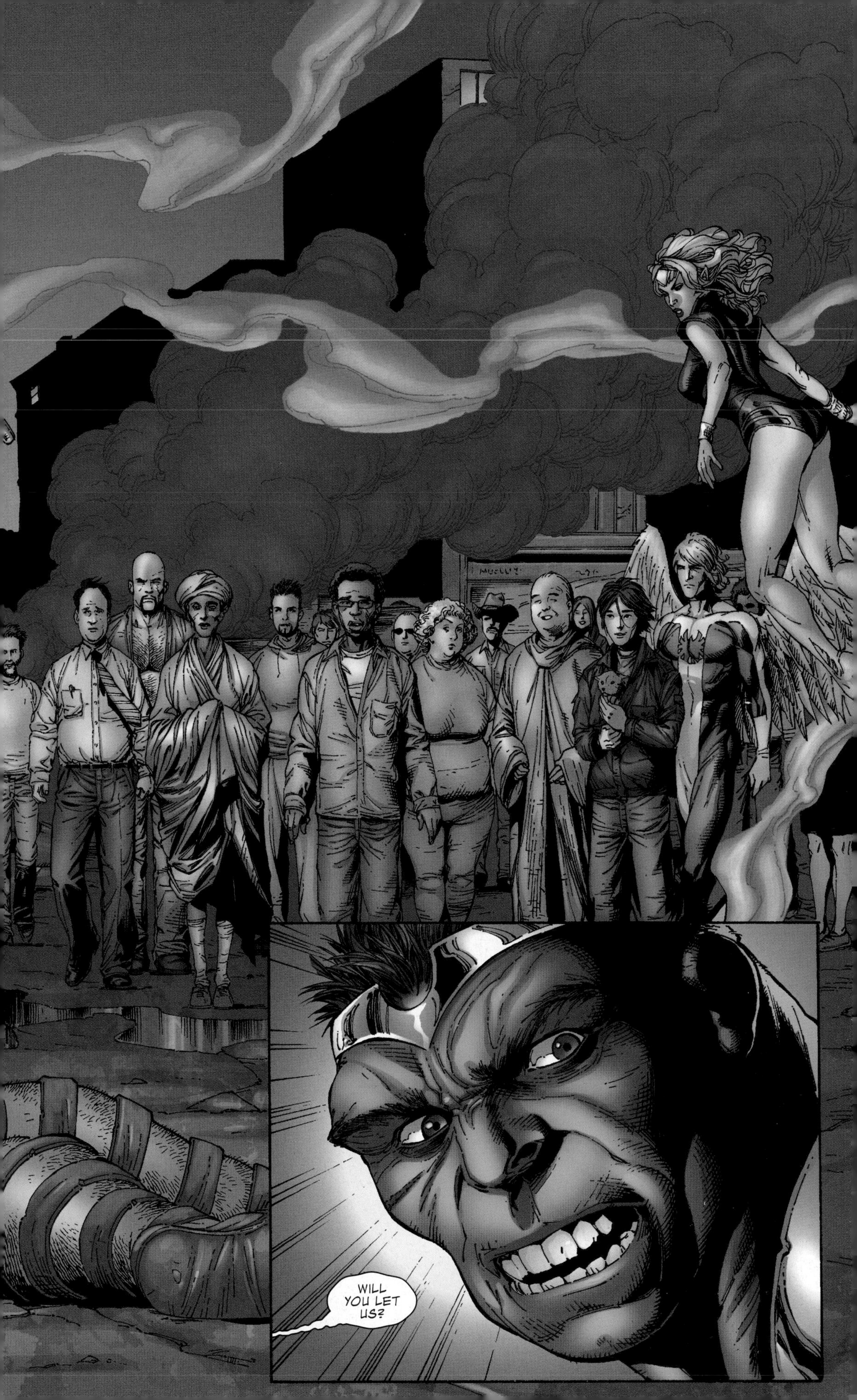
WILL YOU LET US?

108

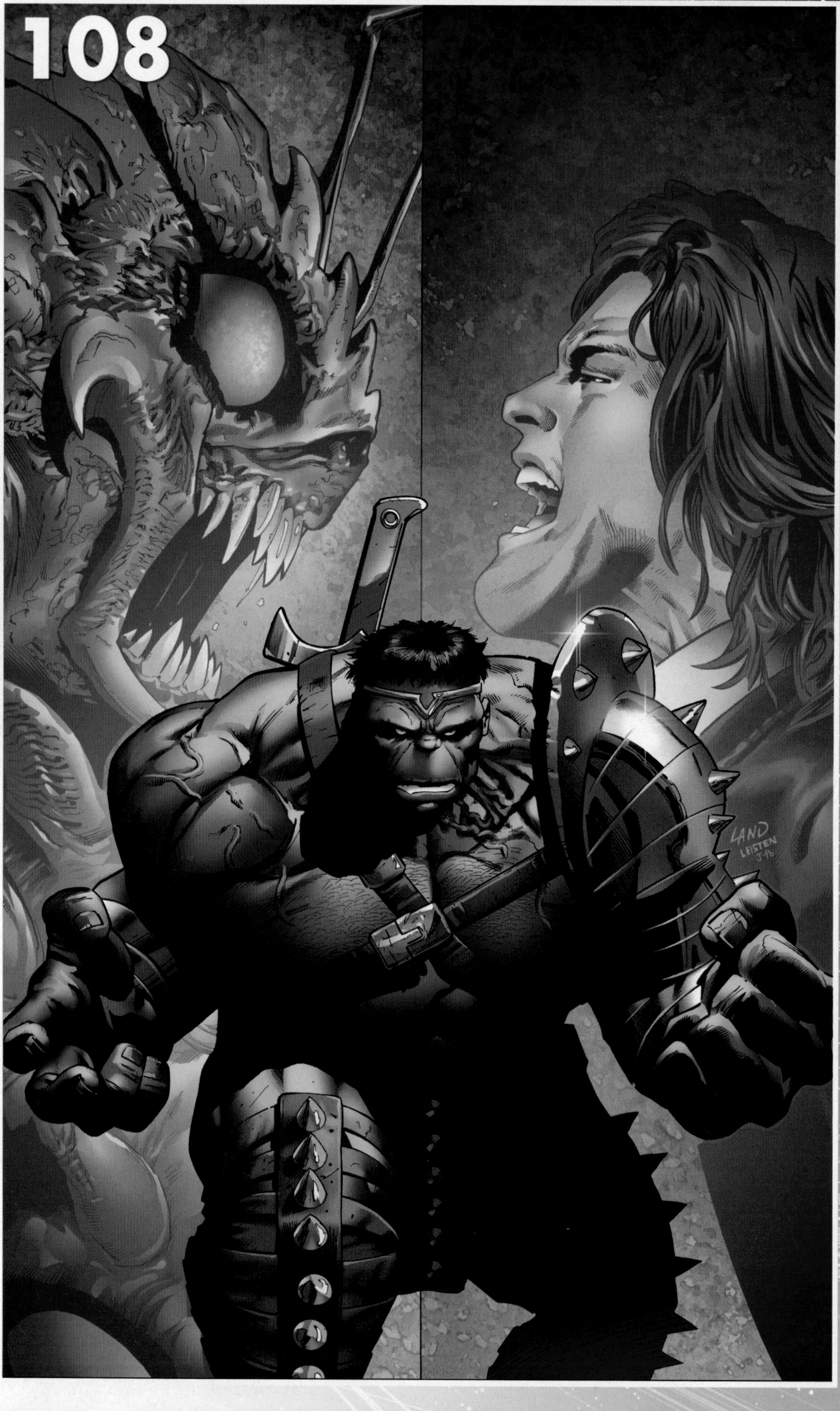

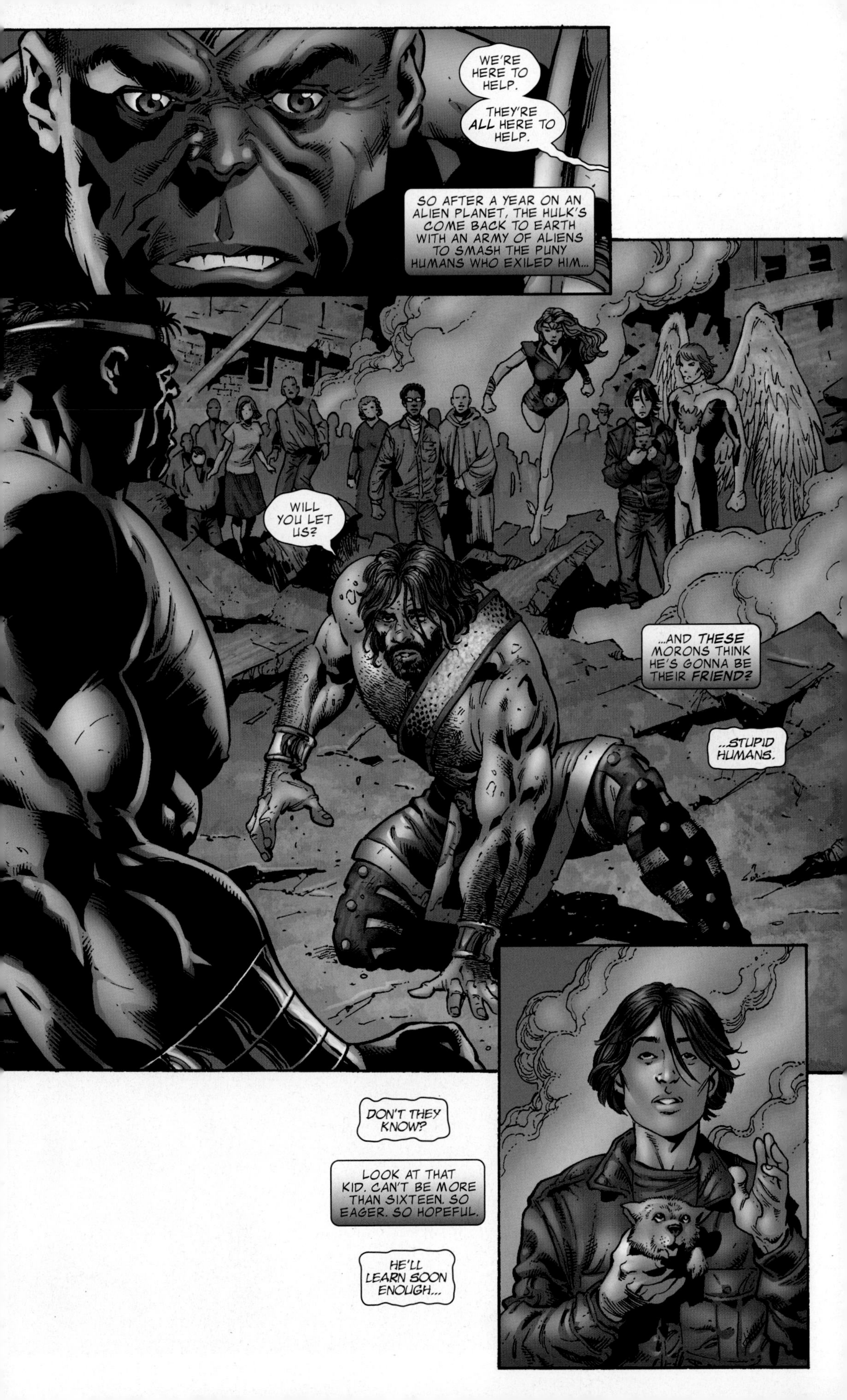
WE'RE HERE TO HELP.
THEY'RE ALL HERE TO HELP.
SO AFTER A YEAR ON AN ALIEN PLANET, THE HULK'S COME BACK TO EARTH WITH AN ARMY OF ALIENS TO SMASH THE PUNY HUMANS WHO EXILED HIM...
WILL YOU LET US?
...AND THESE MORONS THINK HE'S GONNA BE THEIR FRIEND?
...STUPID HUMANS.
DON'T THEY KNOW?
LOOK AT THAT KID. CAN'T BE MORE THAN SIXTEEN. SO EAGER. SO HOPEFUL.
HE'LL LEARN SOON ENOUGH...

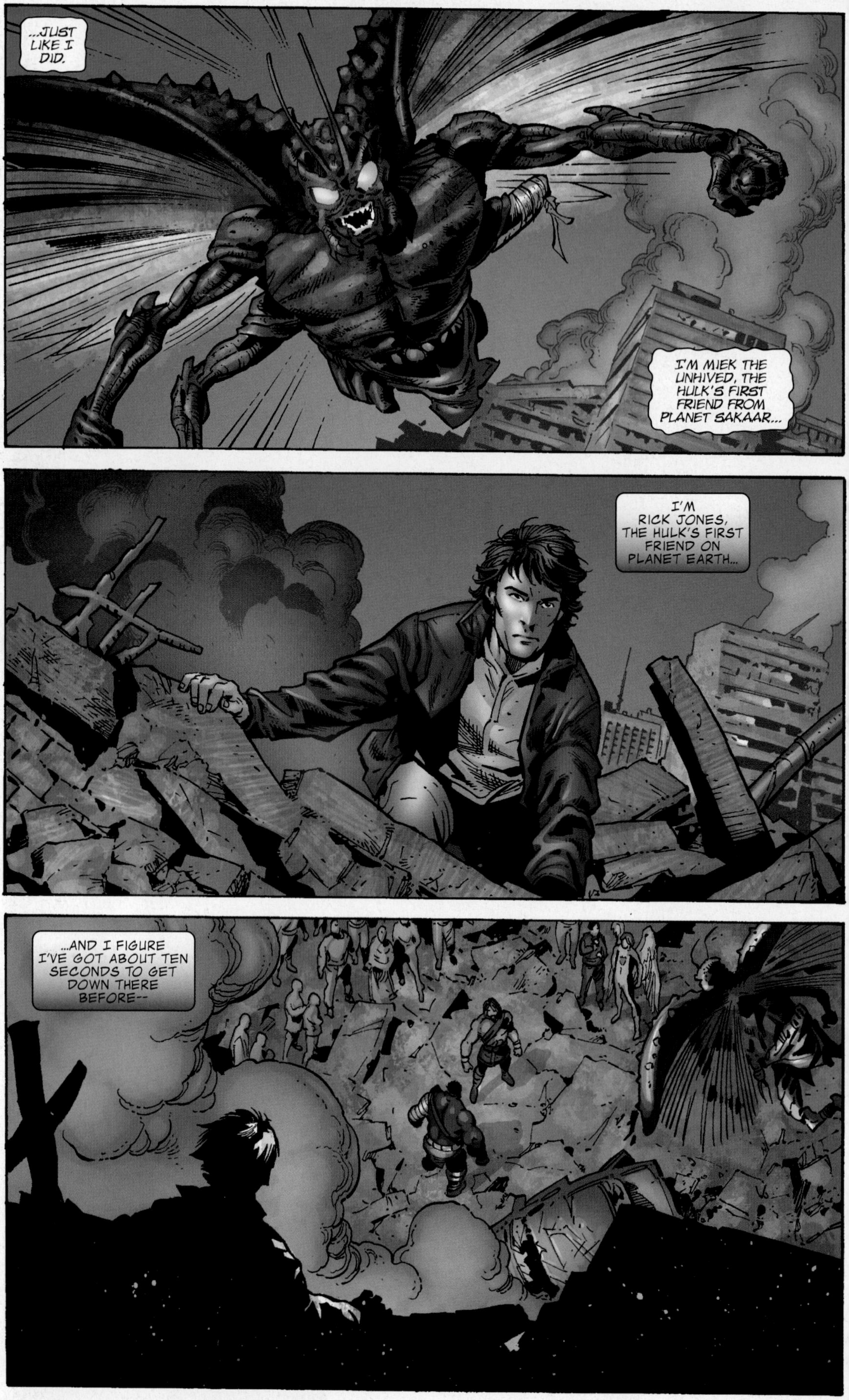
...JUST LIKE I DID.
I'M MIEK THE UNHIVED, THE HULK'S FIRST FRIEND FROM PLANET SAKAAR...
I'M RICK JONES, THE HULK'S FIRST FRIEND ON PLANET EARTH...
...AND I FIGURE I'VE GOT ABOUT TEN SECONDS TO GET DOWN THERE BEFORE--

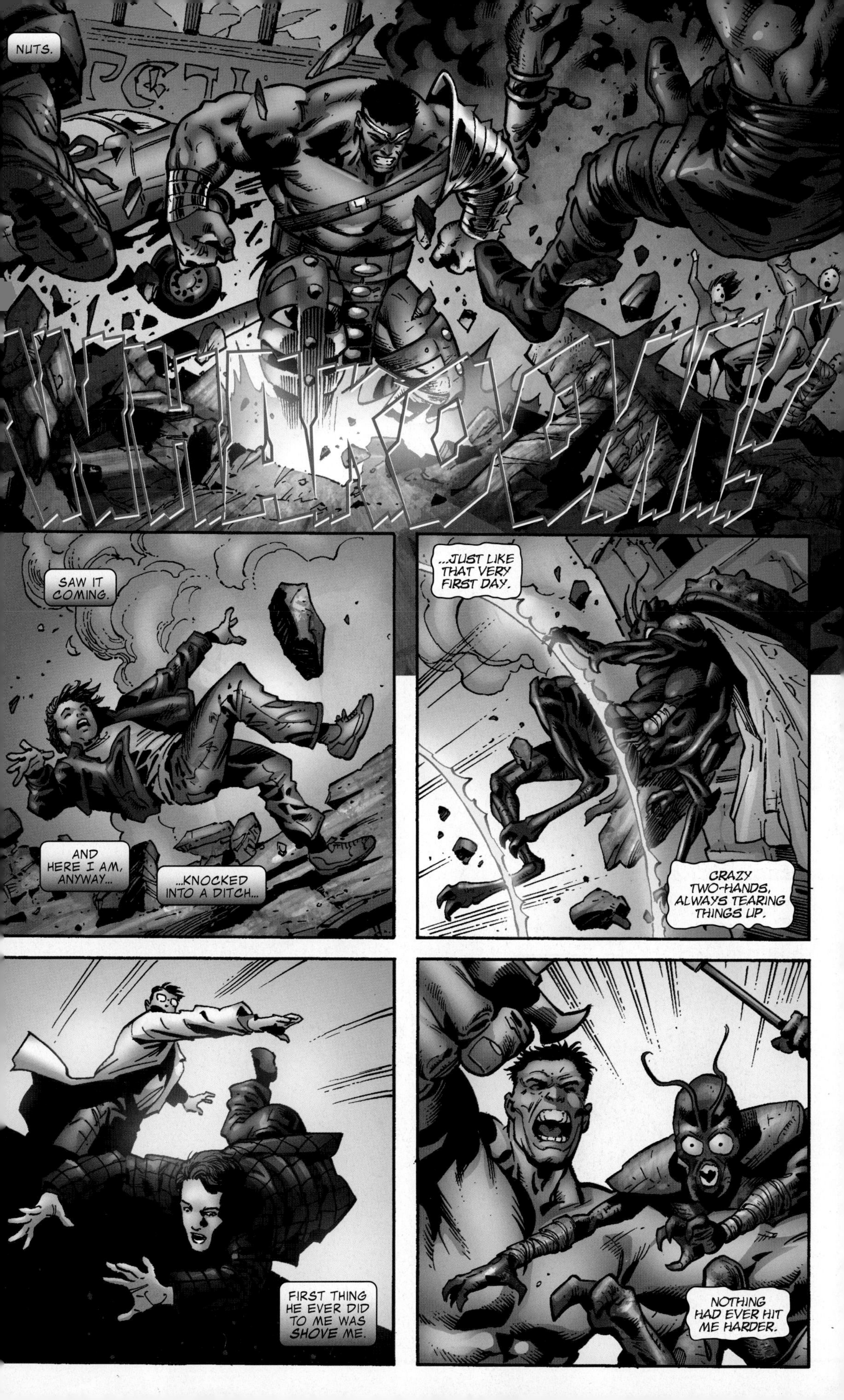
NUTS.
SAW IT COMING.
AND HERE I AM, ANYWAY...
...KNOCKED INTO A DITCH...
...JUST LIKE THAT VERY FIRST DAY.
CRAZY TWO-HANDS, ALWAYS TEARING THINGS UP.
FIRST THING HE EVER DID TO ME WAS *SHOVE* ME.
NOTHING HAD EVER HIT ME HARDER.

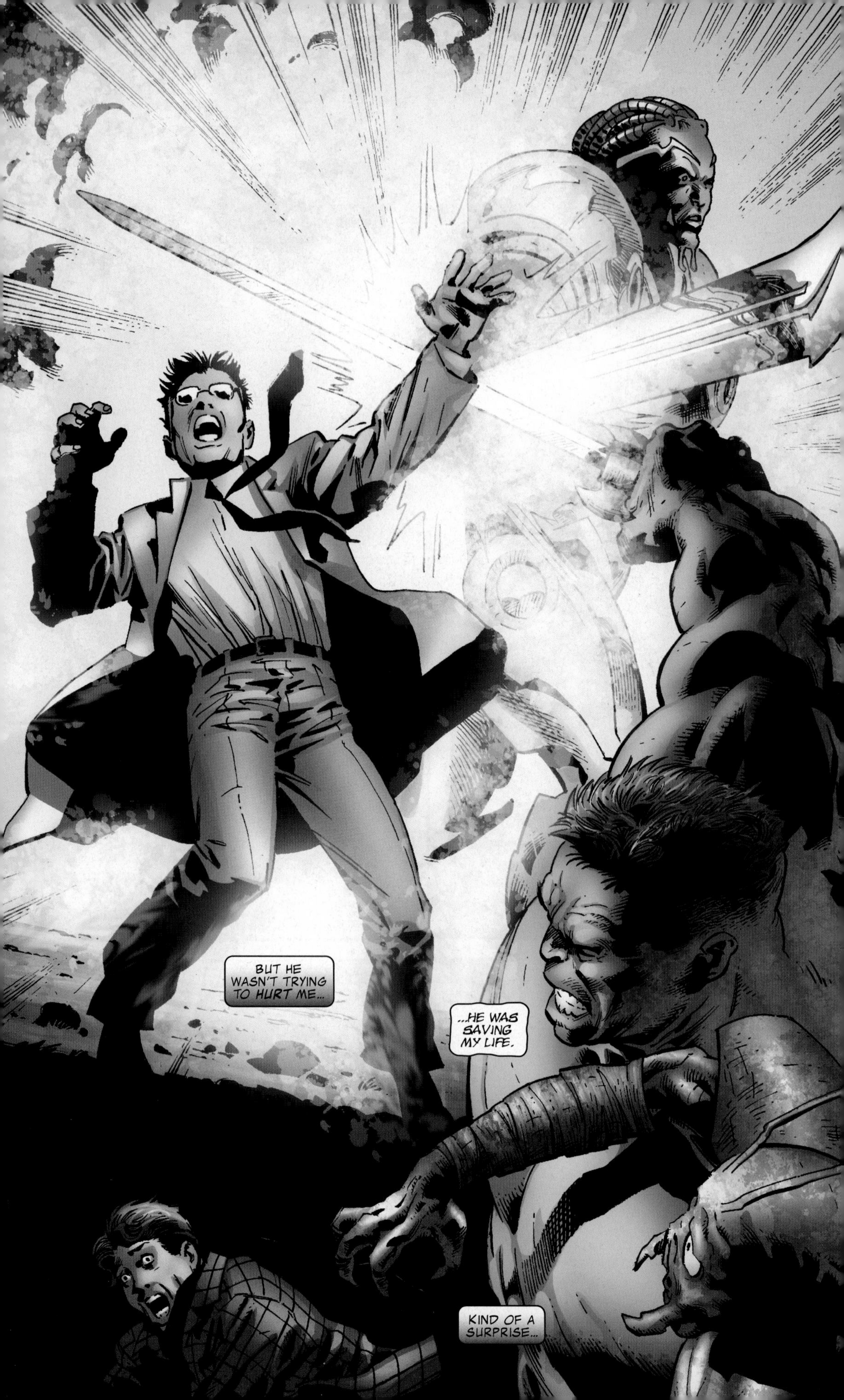
BUT HE WASN'T TRYING TO HURT ME...
...HE WAS SAVING MY LIFE.
KIND OF A SURPRISE...

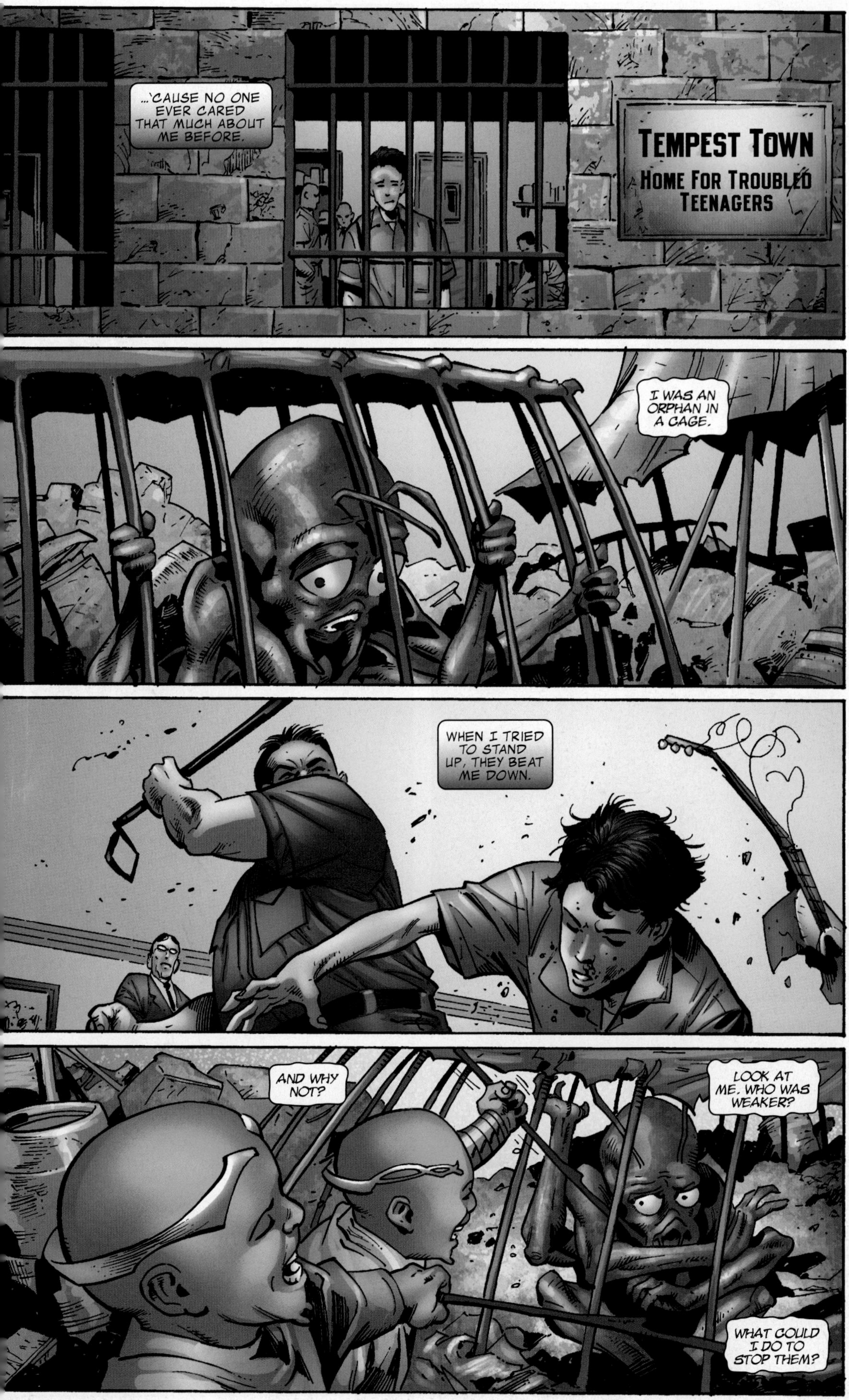
...'CAUSE NO ONE EVER CARED THAT MUCH ABOUT ME BEFORE.
TEMPEST TOWN
HOME FOR TROUBLED TEENAGERS
I WAS AN ORPHAN IN A CAGE.
WHEN I TRIED TO STAND UP, THEY BEAT ME DOWN.
AND WHY NOT?
LOOK AT ME. WHO WAS WEAKER?
WHAT COULD I DO TO STOP THEM?

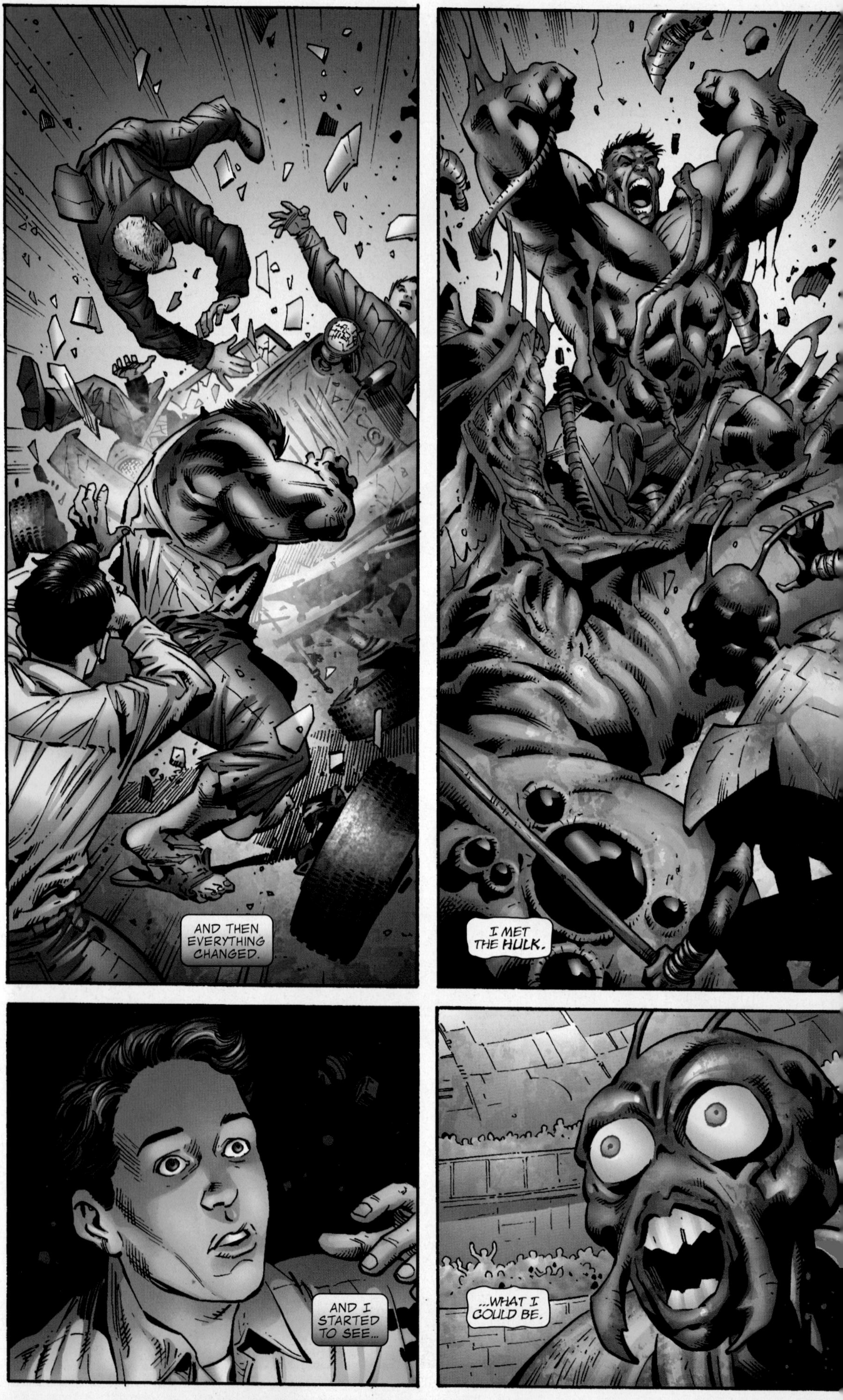
AND THEN EVERYTHING CHANGED.
I MET THE HULK.
AND I STARTED TO SEE...
...WHAT I COULD BE.

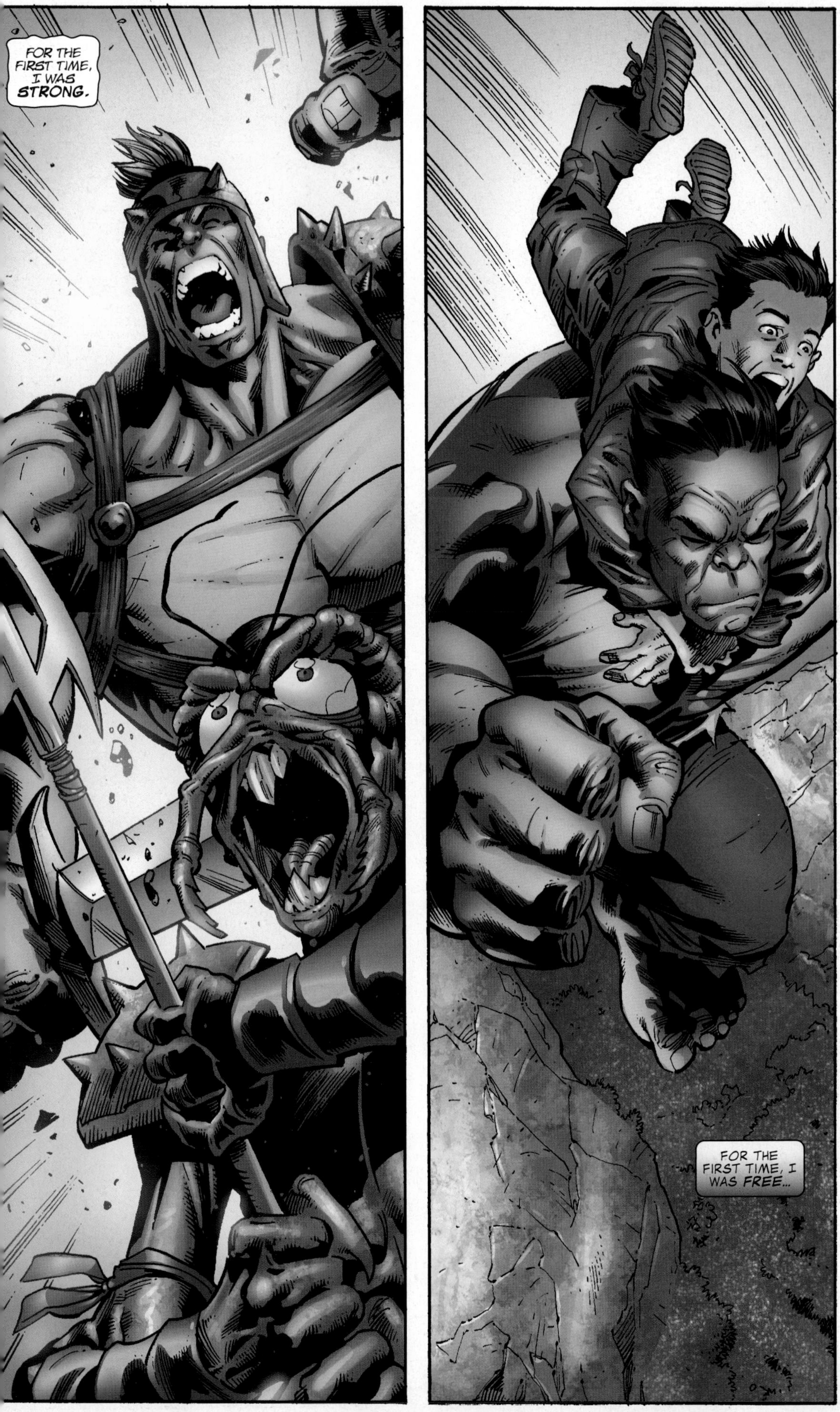
FOR THE FIRST TIME, I WAS STRONG.
FOR THE FIRST TIME, I WAS FREE...

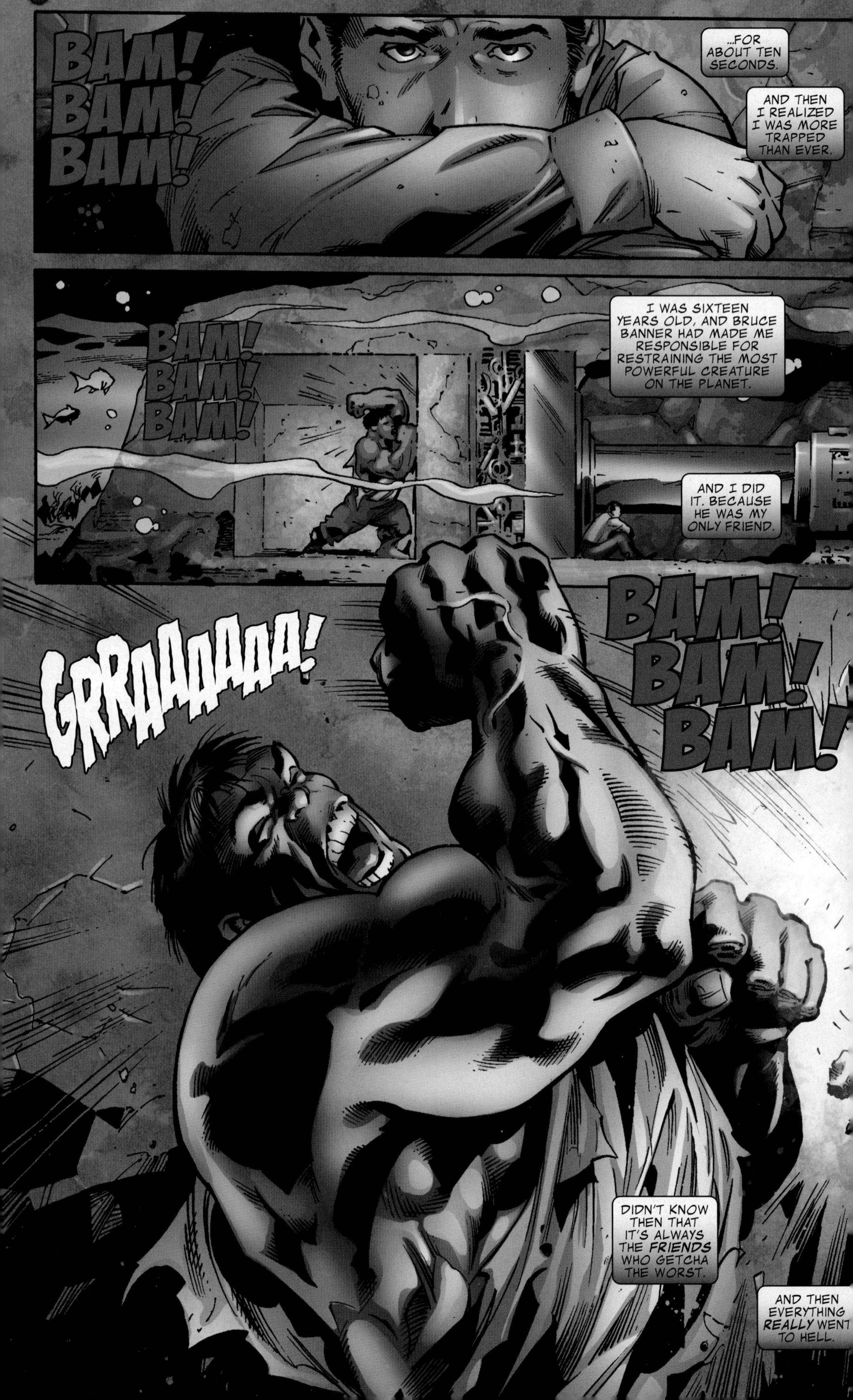
BAM! BAM! BAM!
...FOR ABOUT TEN SECONDS.
AND THEN I REALIZED I WAS MORE TRAPPED THAN EVER.
BAM! BAM! BAM!
I WAS SIXTEEN YEARS OLD, AND BRUCE BANNER HAD MADE ME RESPONSIBLE FOR RESTRAINING THE MOST POWERFUL CREATURE ON THE PLANET.
AND I DID IT. BECAUSE HE WAS MY ONLY FRIEND.
GRRAAAAAA!
BAM! BAM! BAM!
DIDN'T KNOW THEN THAT IT'S ALWAYS THE *FRIENDS* WHO GETCHA THE WORST.
AND THEN EVERYTHING *REALLY* WENT TO HELL.

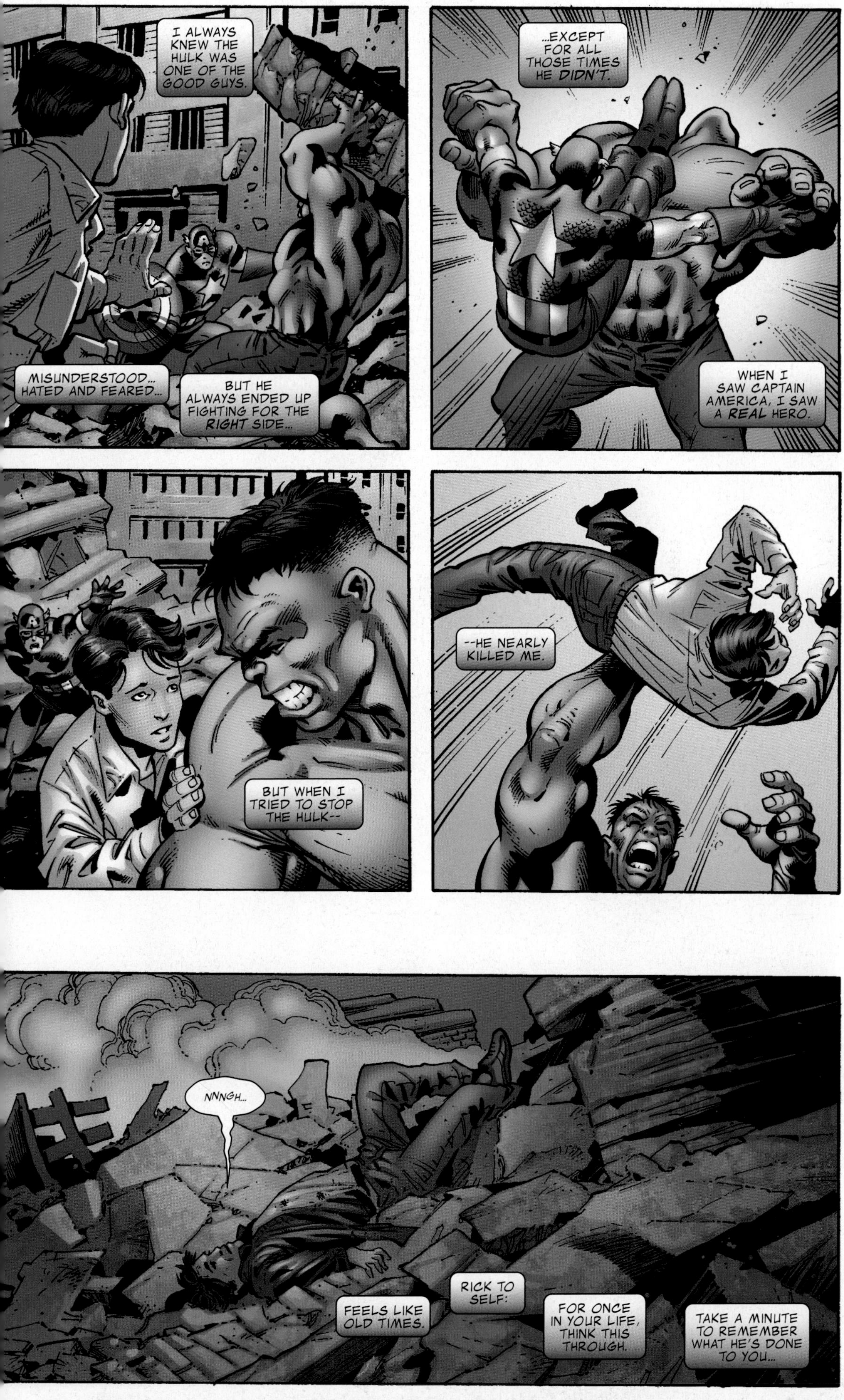
I ALWAYS KNEW THE HULK WAS ONE OF THE GOOD GUYS.
MISUNDERSTOOD... HATED AND FEARED...
BUT HE ALWAYS ENDED UP FIGHTING FOR THE RIGHT SIDE...
...EXCEPT FOR ALL THOSE TIMES HE DIDN'T.
WHEN I SAW CAPTAIN AMERICA, I SAW A REAL HERO.
BUT WHEN I TRIED TO STOP THE HULK--
--HE NEARLY KILLED ME.
NNNGH...
FEELS LIKE OLD TIMES.
RICK TO SELF:
FOR ONCE IN YOUR LIFE, THINK THIS THROUGH.
TAKE A MINUTE TO REMEMBER WHAT HE'S DONE TO YOU...

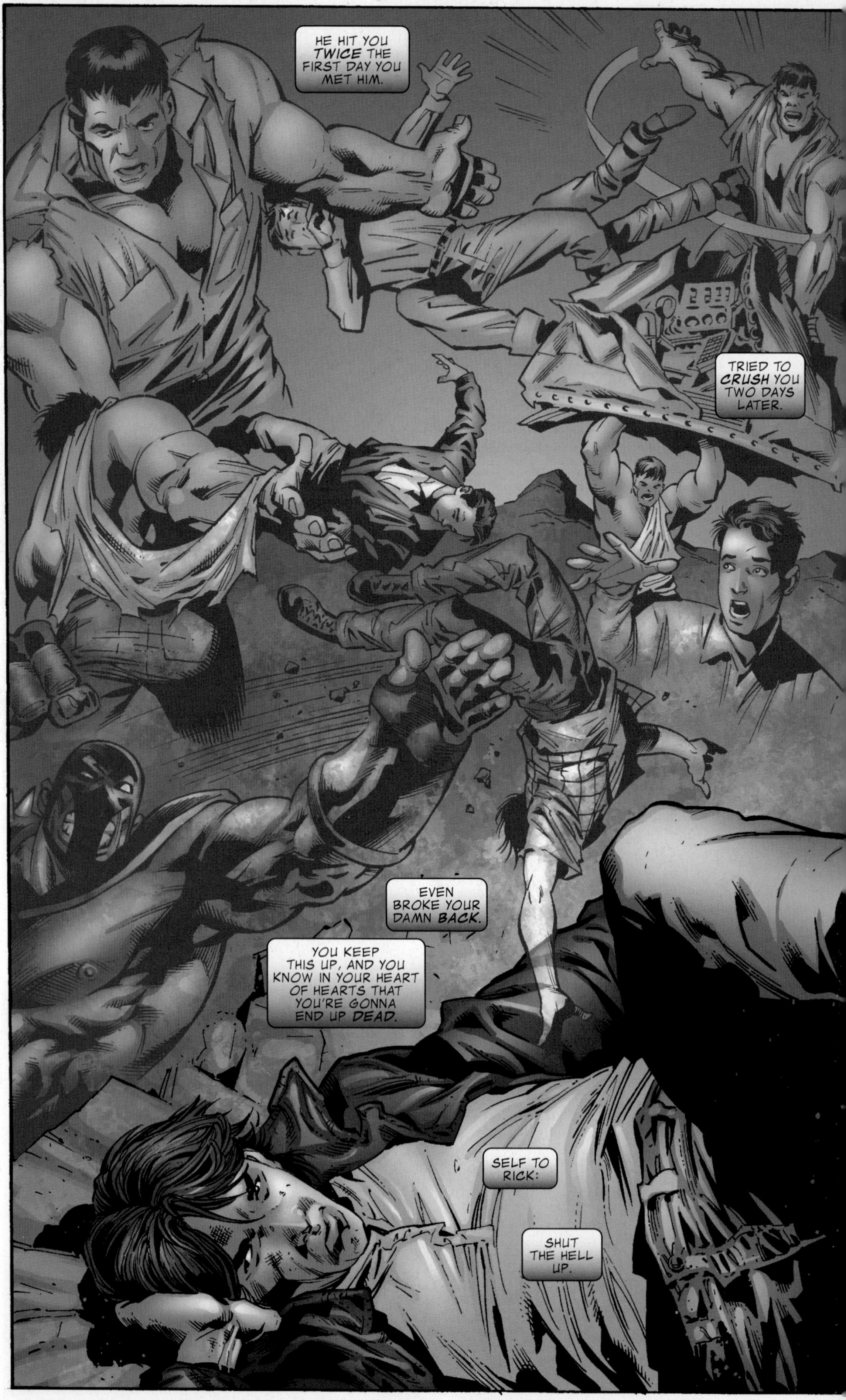
HE HIT YOU TWICE THE FIRST DAY YOU MET HIM.
TRIED TO CRUSH YOU TWO DAYS LATER.
EVEN BROKE YOUR DAMN BACK.
YOU KEEP THIS UP, AND YOU KNOW IN YOUR HEART OF HEARTS THAT YOU'RE GONNA END UP DEAD.
SELF TO RICK:
SHUT THE HELL UP.

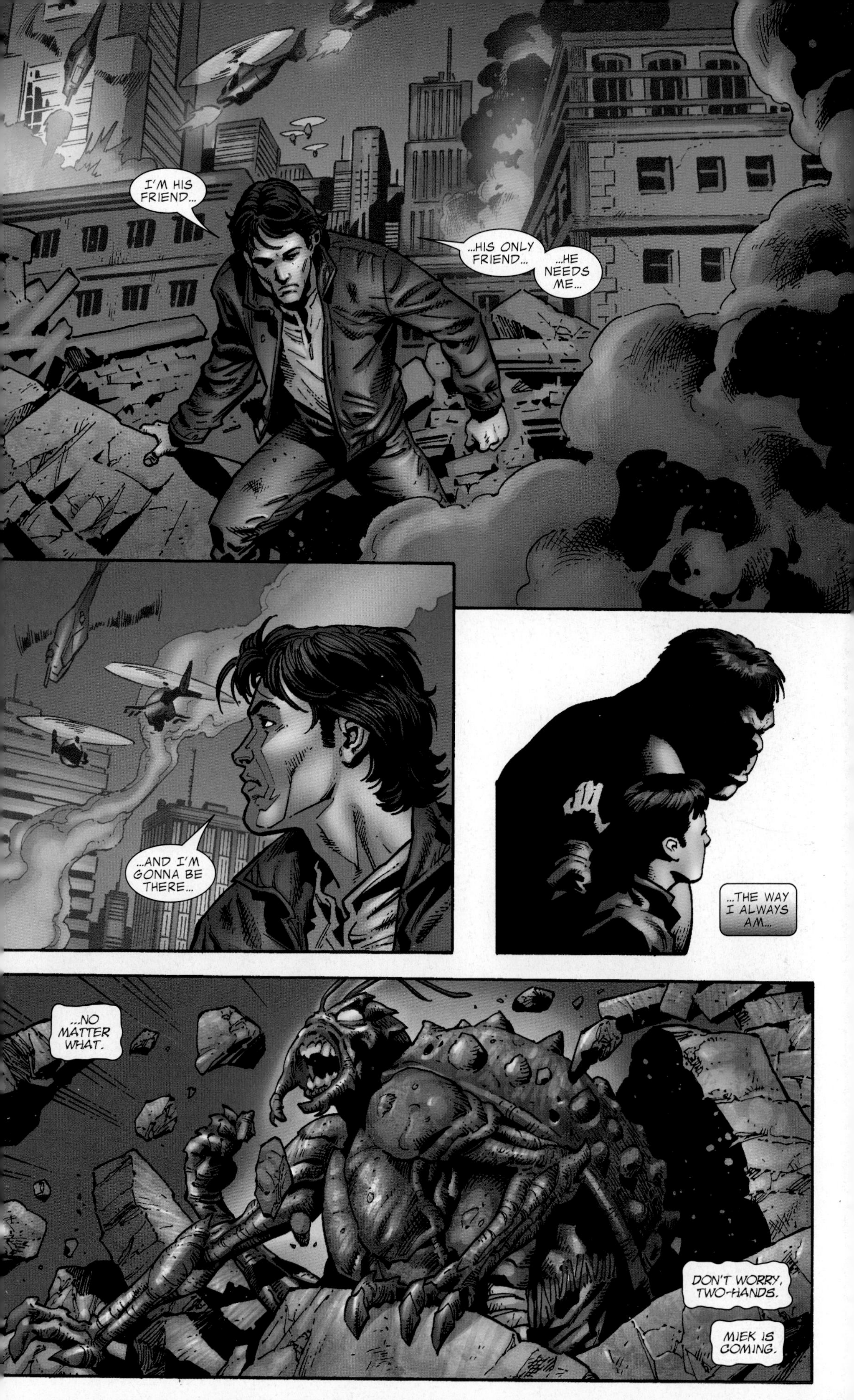
I'M HIS FRIEND...
...HIS ONLY FRIEND...
...HE NEEDS ME...
...AND I'M GONNA BE THERE...
...THE WAY I ALWAYS AM...
...NO MATTER WHAT.
DON'T WORRY, TWO-HANDS.
MIEK IS COMING.

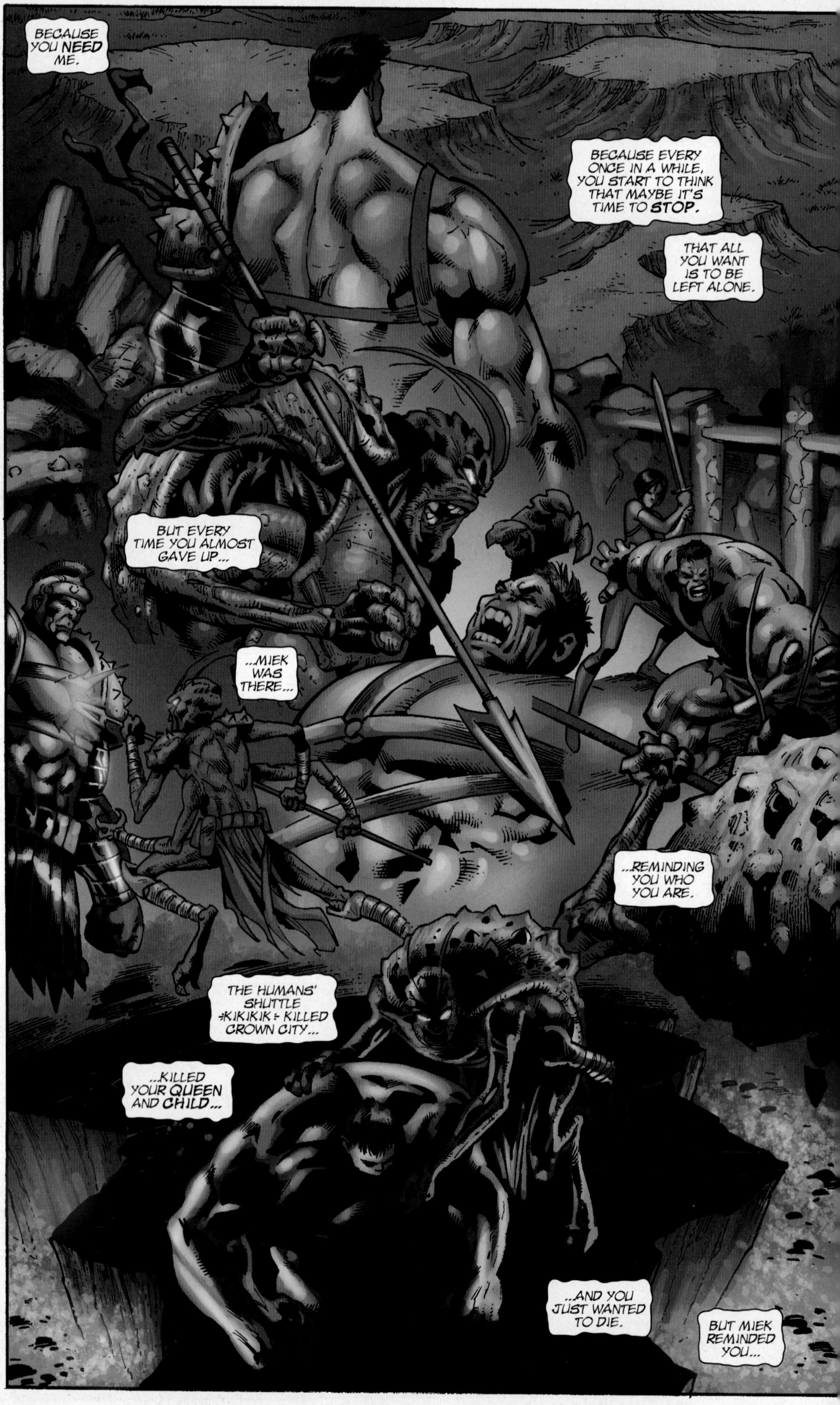
BECAUSE YOU NEED ME.
BECAUSE EVERY ONCE IN A WHILE, YOU START TO THINK THAT MAYBE IT'S TIME TO STOP.
THAT ALL YOU WANT IS TO BE LEFT ALONE.
BUT EVERY TIME YOU ALMOST GAVE UP...
...MIEK WAS THERE...
...REMINDING YOU WHO YOU ARE.
THE HUMANS' SHUTTLE ÷KIKIKIK÷ KILLED CROWN CITY...
...KILLED YOUR QUEEN AND CHILD...
...AND YOU JUST WANTED TO DIE.
BUT MIEK REMINDED YOU...

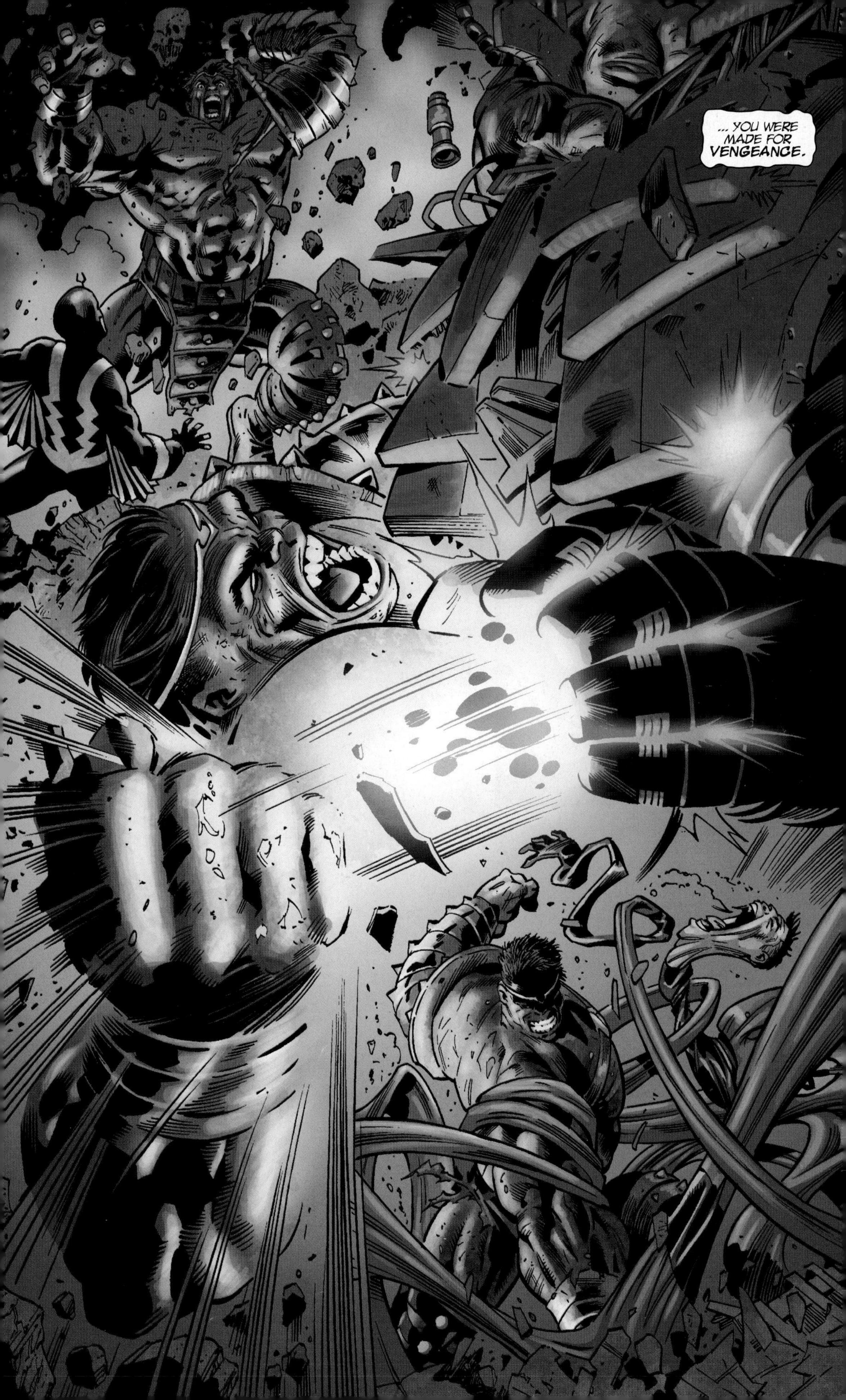
... YOU WERE MADE FOR VENGEANCE.

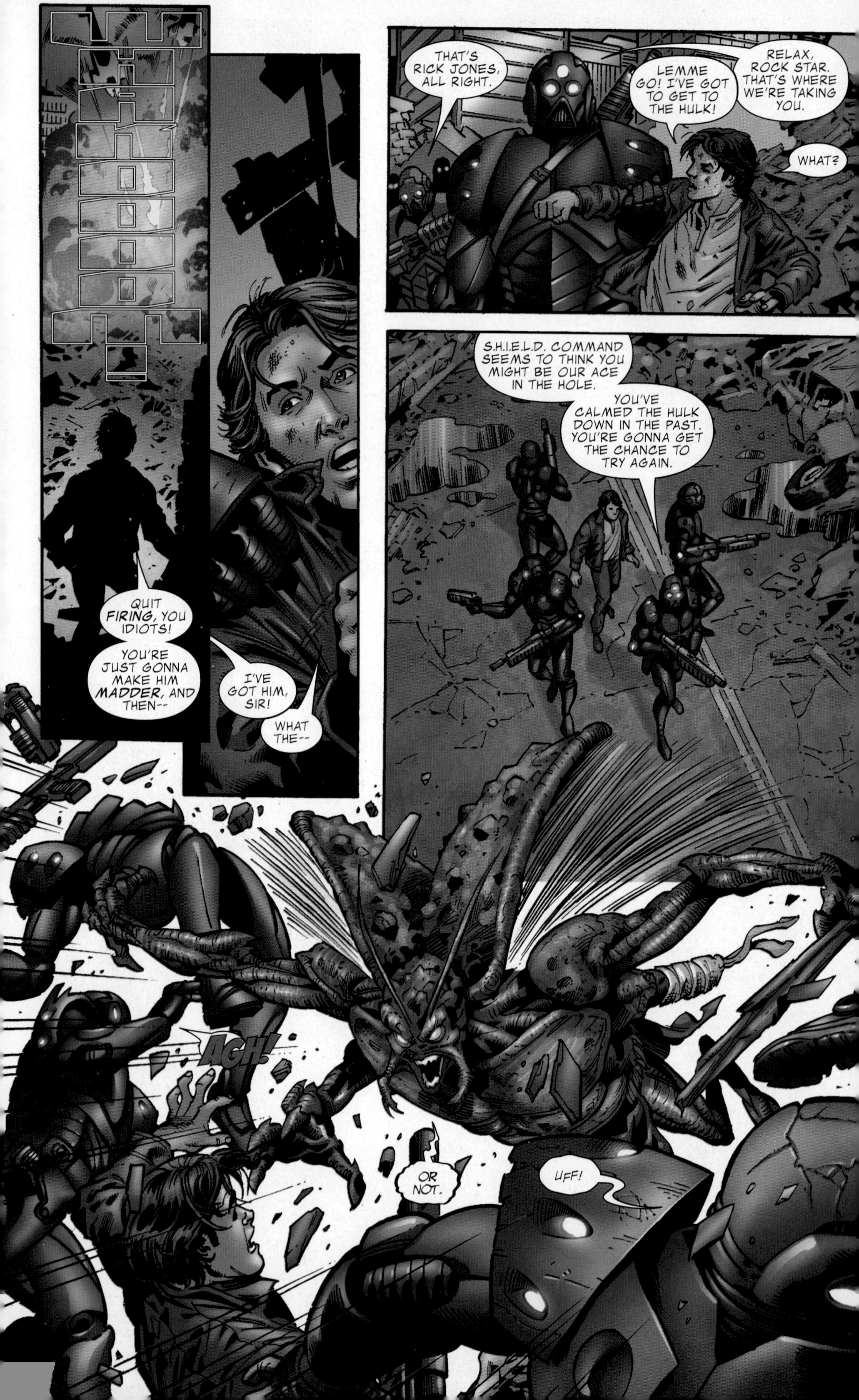
QUIT FIRING, YOU IDIOTS!
YOU'RE JUST GONNA MAKE HIM MADDER, AND THEN--
I'VE GOT HIM, SIR!
WHAT THE--
THAT'S RICK JONES, ALL RIGHT.
LEMME GO! I'VE GOT TO GET TO THE HULK!
RELAX, ROCK STAR. THAT'S WHERE WE'RE TAKING YOU.
WHAT?
S.H.I.E.L.D. COMMAND SEEMS TO THINK YOU MIGHT BE OUR ACE IN THE HOLE.
YOU'VE CALMED THE HULK DOWN IN THE PAST. YOU'RE GONNA GET THE CHANCE TO TRY AGAIN.
AGH!
OR NOT.
UFF!

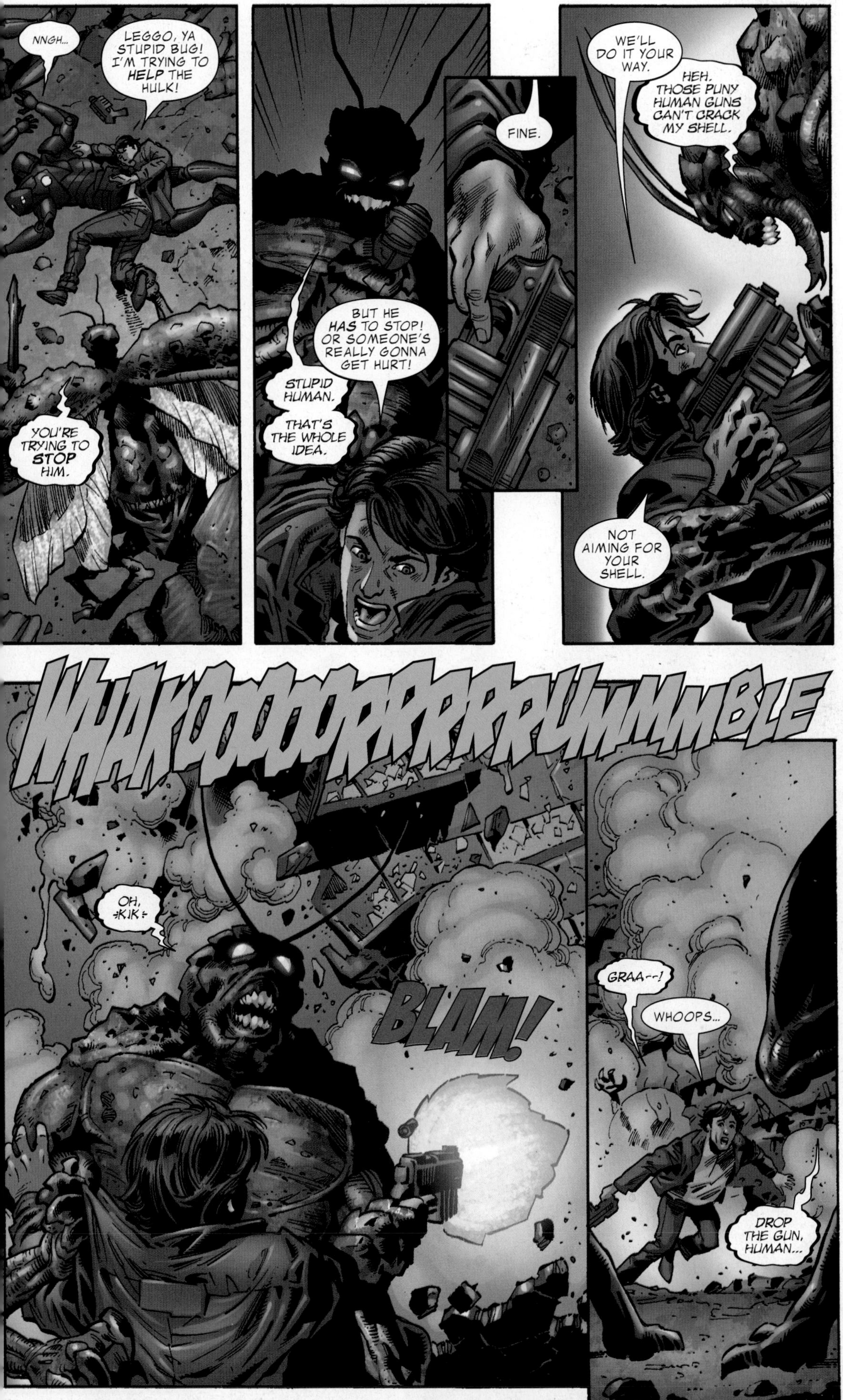
NNGH...
LEGGO, YA STUPID BUG! I'M TRYING TO HELP THE HULK!
YOU'RE TRYING TO STOP HIM.
BUT HE HAS TO STOP! OR SOMEONE'S REALLY GONNA GET HURT!
STUPID HUMAN.
THAT'S THE WHOLE IDEA.
FINE.
WE'LL DO IT YOUR WAY.
HEH. THOSE PUNY HUMAN GUNS CAN'T CRACK MY SHELL.
NOT AIMING FOR YOUR SHELL.
WHAKOOOOORRRRRUMMMMBLE
OH, KIK
BLAM!
GRAA--!
WHOOPS...
DROP THE GUN, HUMAN...

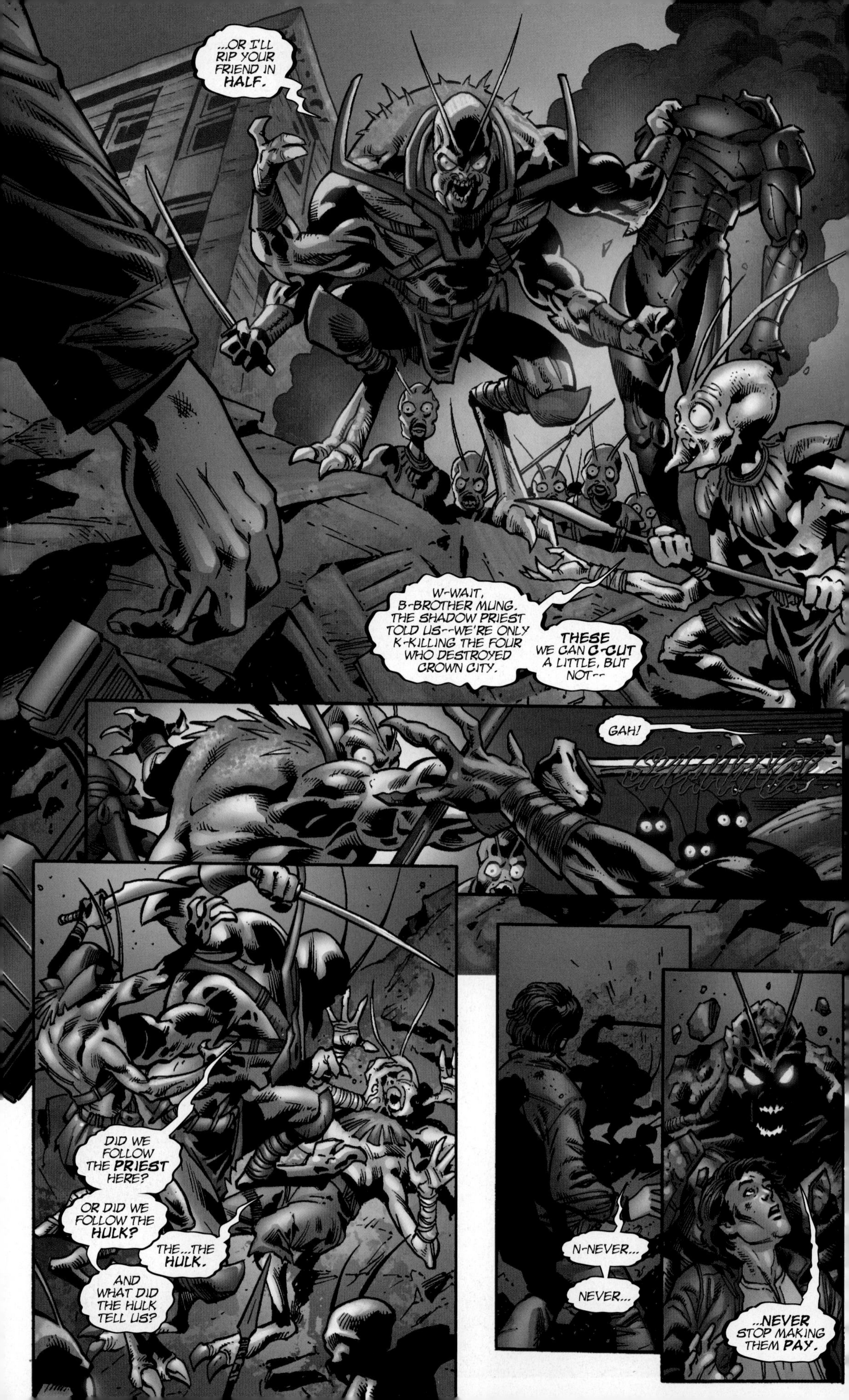
...OR I'LL RIP YOUR FRIEND IN HALF.
W-WAIT, B-BROTHER MUNG. THE SHADOW PRIEST TOLD US--WE'RE ONLY K-KILLING THE FOUR WHO DESTROYED CROWN CITY.
THESE WE CAN C-CUT A LITTLE, BUT NOT--
GAH!
DID WE FOLLOW THE PRIEST HERE?
OR DID WE FOLLOW THE HULK?
THE...THE HULK.
AND WHAT DID THE HULK TELL US?
N-NEVER...
NEVER...
...NEVER STOP MAKING THEM PAY.

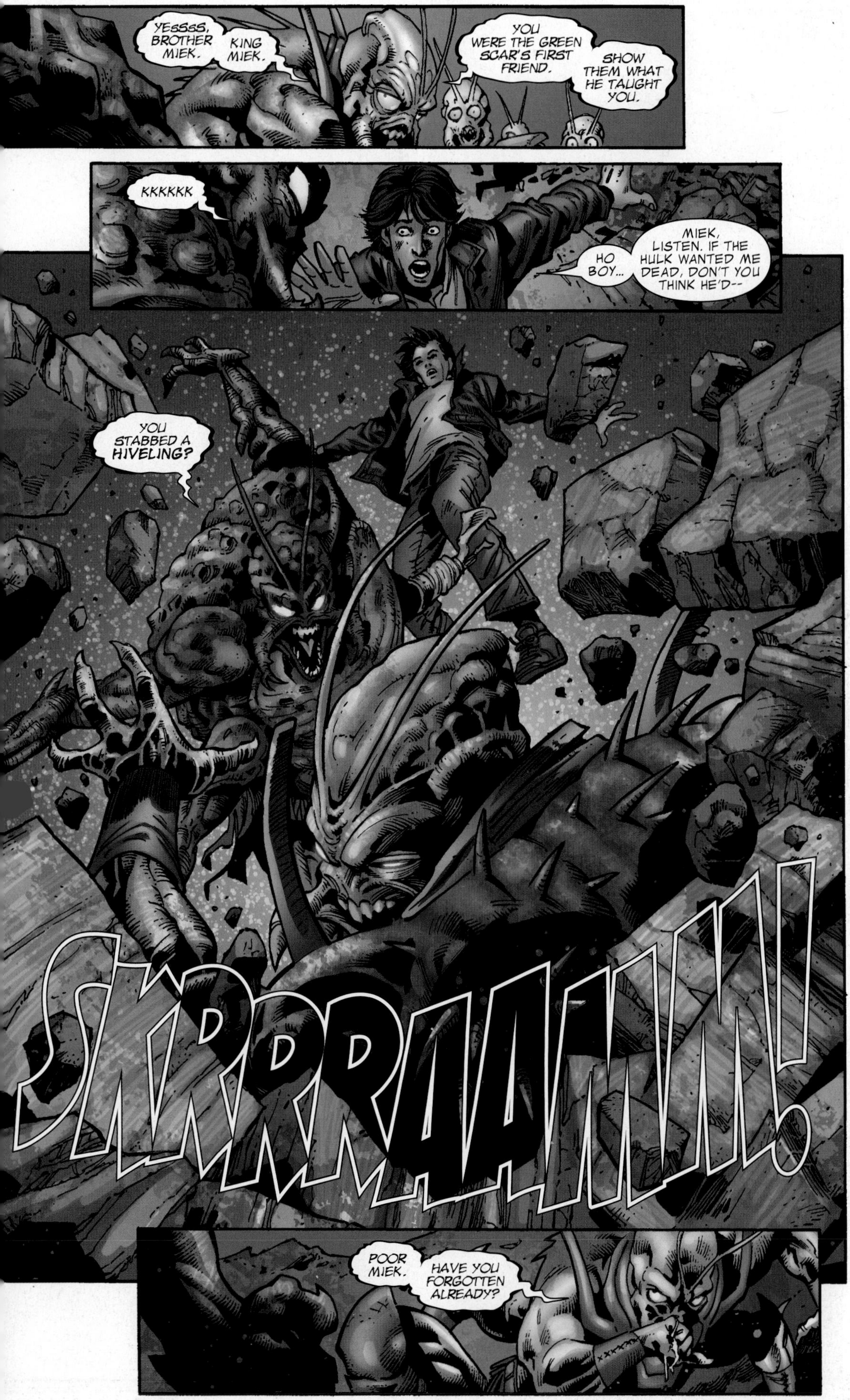
YESSSS, BROTHER MIEK.
KING MIEK.
YOU WERE THE GREEN SCAR'S FIRST FRIEND.
SHOW THEM WHAT HE TAUGHT YOU.
KKKKKK
HO BOY...
MIEK, LISTEN. IF THE HULK WANTED ME DEAD, DON'T YOU THINK HE'D--
YOU STABBED A HIVELING?
SKRRRAAAMM!
POOR MIEK.
HAVE YOU FORGOTTEN ALREADY?

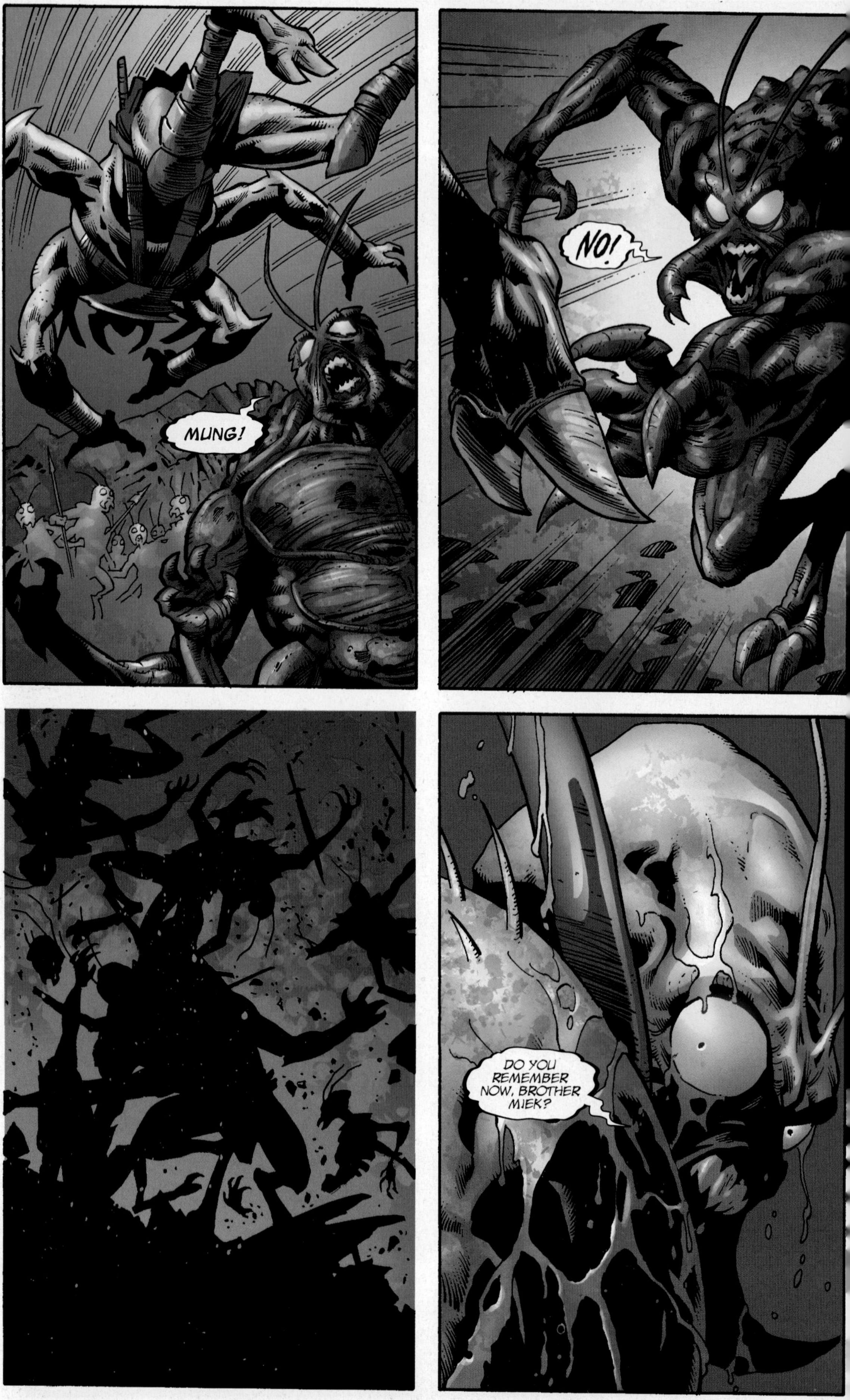
MUNG!
NO!
DO YOU REMEMBER NOW, BROTHER MIEK?

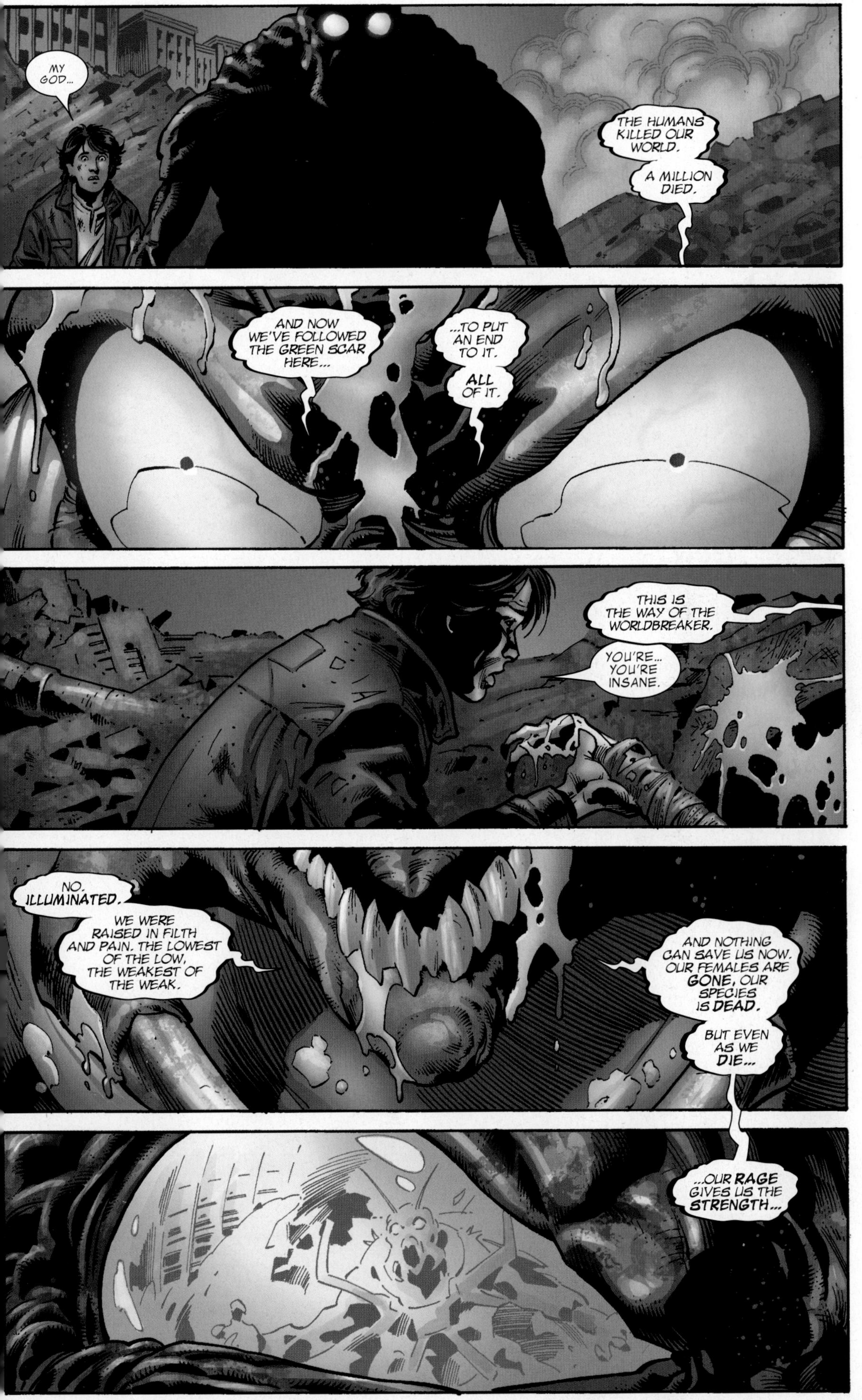
MY GOD...
THE HUMANS KILLED OUR WORLD.
A MILLION DIED.
AND NOW WE'VE FOLLOWED THE GREEN SCAR HERE...
...TO PUT AN END TO IT.
ALL OF IT.
THIS IS THE WAY OF THE WORLDBREAKER.
YOU'RE... YOU'RE INSANE.
NO. ILLUMINATED.
WE WERE RAISED IN FILTH AND PAIN. THE LOWEST OF THE LOW, THE WEAKEST OF THE WEAK.
AND NOTHING CAN SAVE US NOW. OUR FEMALES ARE GONE, OUR SPECIES IS DEAD.
BUT EVEN AS WE DIE...
...OUR RAGE GIVES US THE STRENGTH...

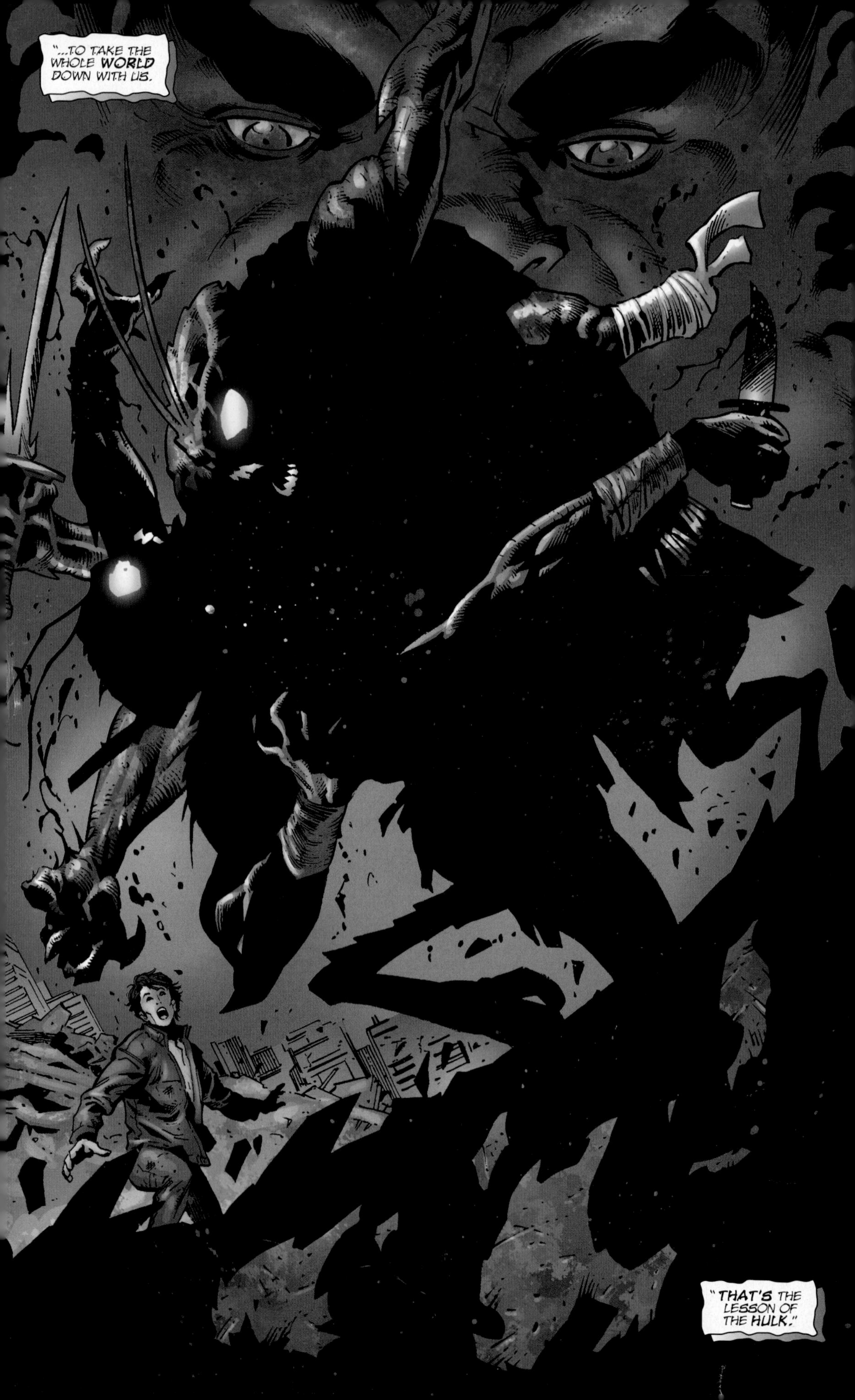
"...TO TAKE THE WHOLE WORLD DOWN WITH US.
"THAT'S THE LESSON OF THE HULK."

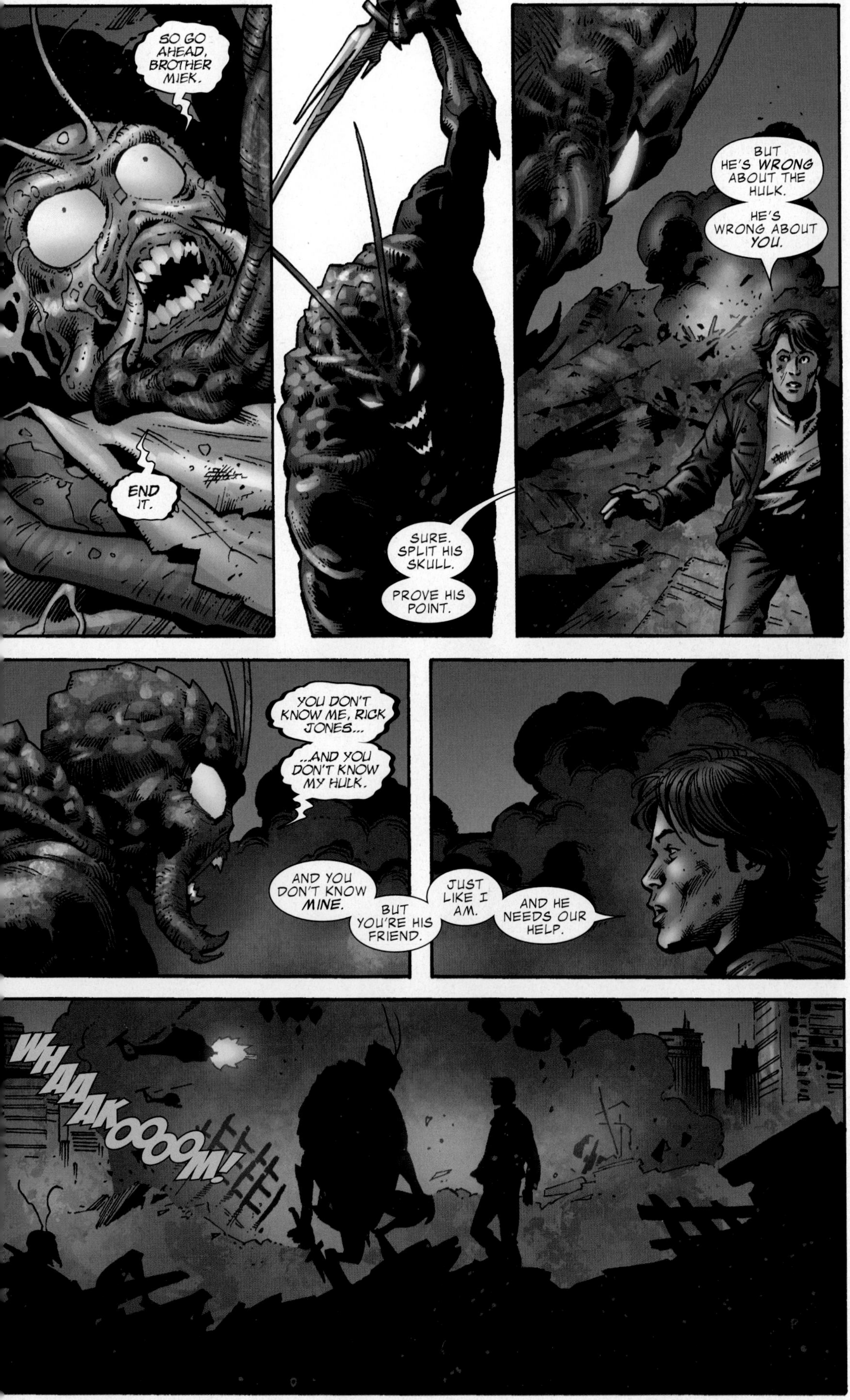
SO GO AHEAD, BROTHER MIEK.
END IT.
SURE. SPLIT HIS SKULL.
PROVE HIS POINT.
BUT HE'S WRONG ABOUT THE HULK.
HE'S WRONG ABOUT YOU.
YOU DON'T KNOW ME, RICK JONES...
...AND YOU DON'T KNOW MY HULK.
AND YOU DON'T KNOW MINE.
BUT YOU'RE HIS FRIEND.
JUST LIKE I AM.
AND HE NEEDS OUR HELP.
WHAAAKOOOOM!

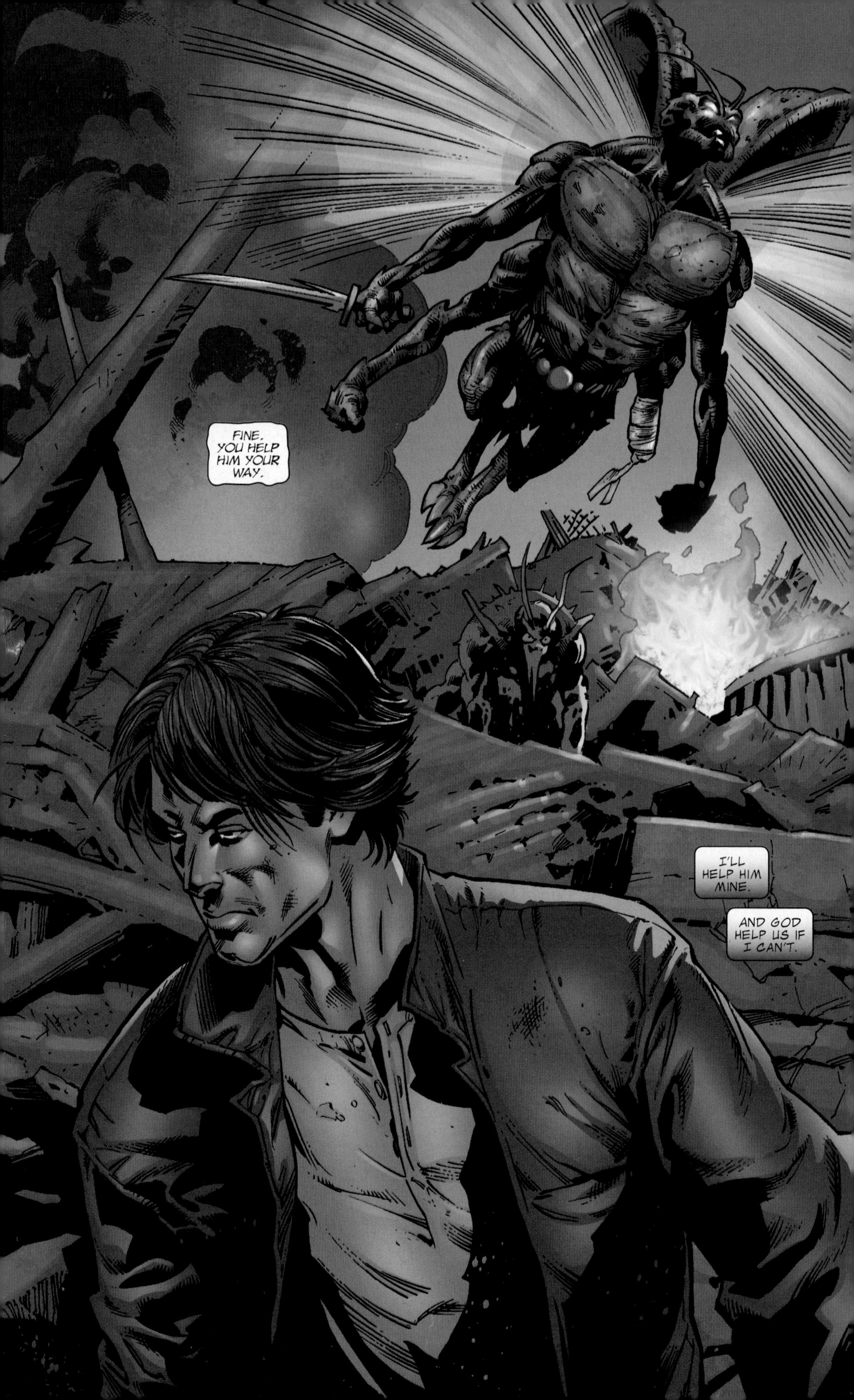
FINE. YOU HELP HIM YOUR WAY.
I'LL HELP HIM MINE.
AND GOD HELP US IF I CAN'T.

109

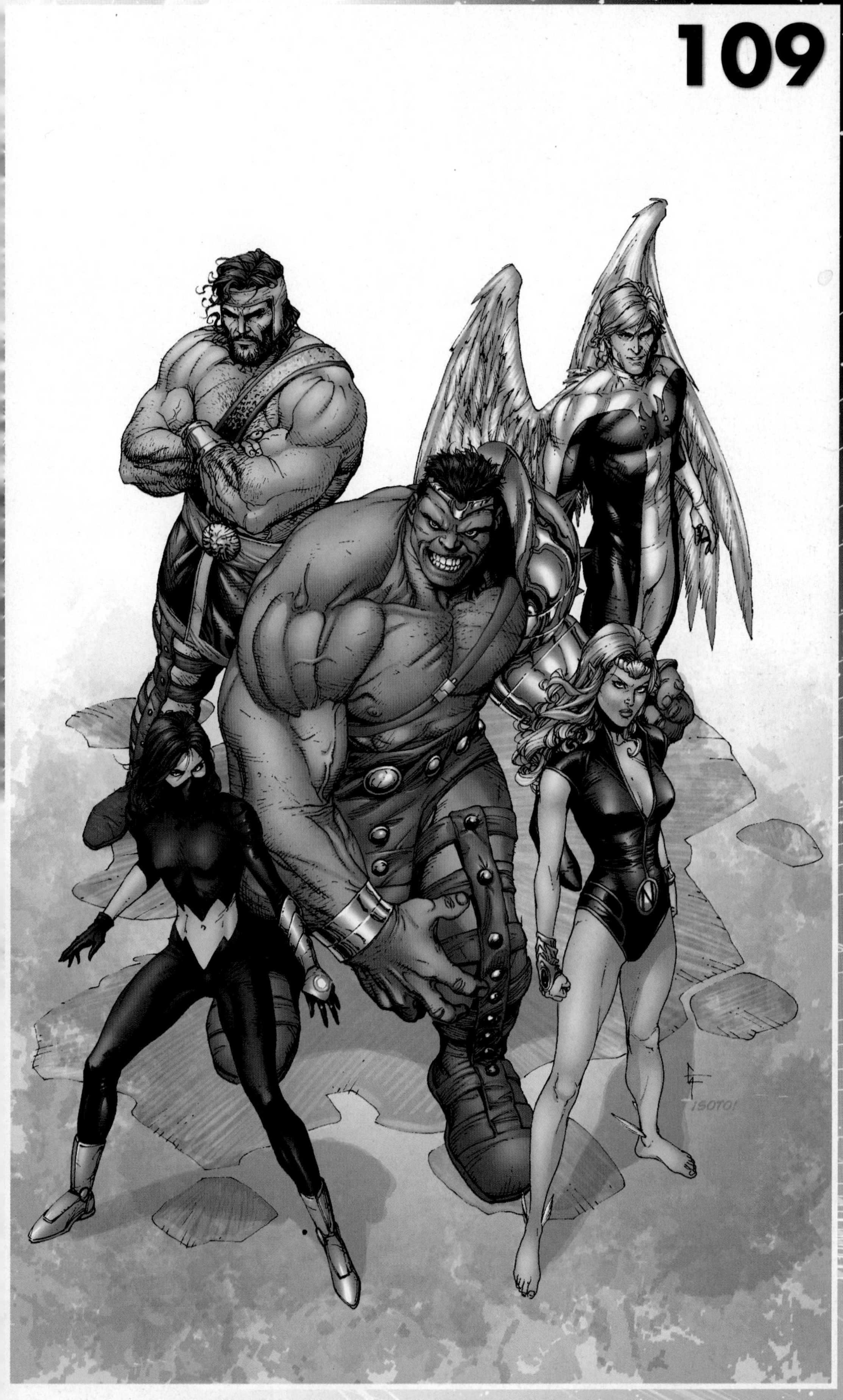
¡SOTO!

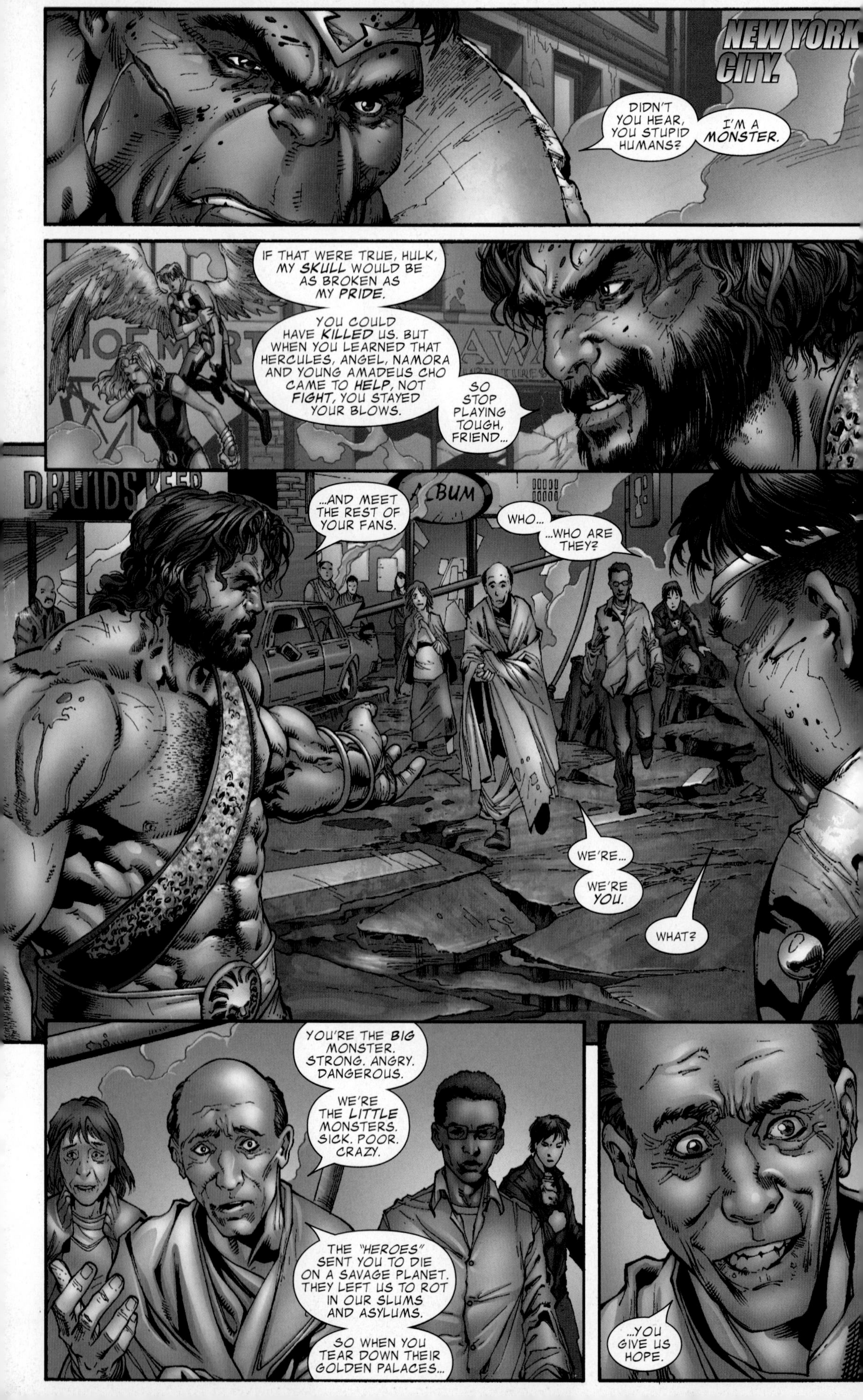
NEW YORK CITY.
DIDN'T YOU HEAR, YOU STUPID HUMANS?
I'M A MONSTER.
IF THAT WERE TRUE, HULK, MY SKULL WOULD BE AS BROKEN AS MY PRIDE.
YOU COULD HAVE KILLED US. BUT WHEN YOU LEARNED THAT HERCULES, ANGEL, NAMORA AND YOUNG AMADEUS CHO CAME TO HELP, NOT FIGHT, YOU STAYED YOUR BLOWS.
SO STOP PLAYING TOUGH, FRIEND...
...AND MEET THE REST OF YOUR FANS.
WHO...
...WHO ARE THEY?
WE'RE...
WE'RE YOU.
WHAT?
YOU'RE THE BIG MONSTER. STRONG. ANGRY. DANGEROUS.
WE'RE THE LITTLE MONSTERS. SICK. POOR. CRAZY.
THE "HEROES" SENT YOU TO DIE ON A SAVAGE PLANET. THEY LEFT US TO ROT IN OUR SLUMS AND ASYLUMS.
SO WHEN YOU TEAR DOWN THEIR GOLDEN PALACES...
...YOU GIVE US HOPE.

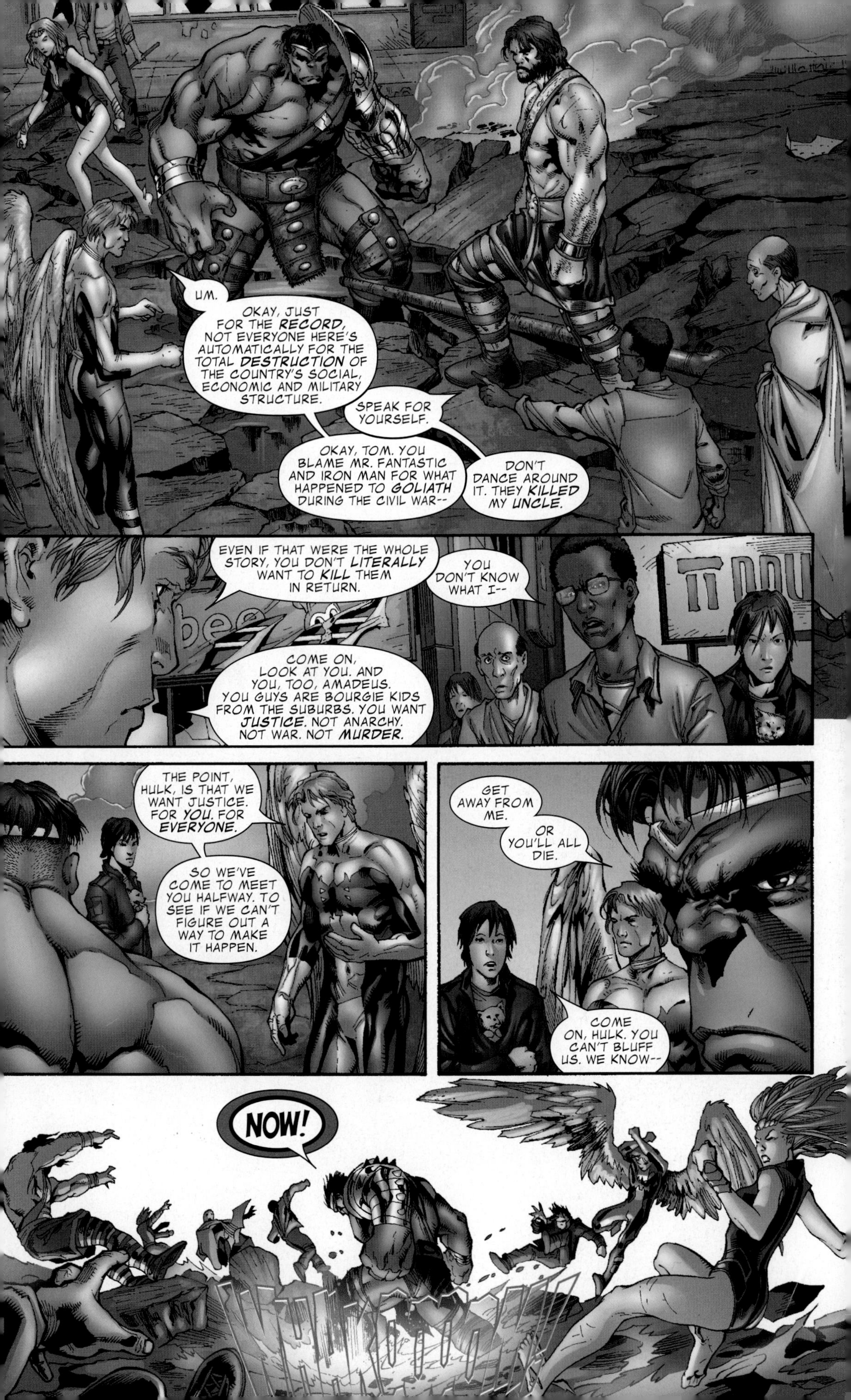

UM.
OKAY, JUST FOR THE RECORD, NOT EVERYONE HERE'S AUTOMATICALLY FOR THE TOTAL DESTRUCTION OF THE COUNTRY'S SOCIAL, ECONOMIC AND MILITARY STRUCTURE.
SPEAK FOR YOURSELF.
OKAY, TOM. YOU BLAME MR. FANTASTIC AND IRON MAN FOR WHAT HAPPENED TO GOLIATH DURING THE CIVIL WAR--
DON'T DANCE AROUND IT. THEY KILLED MY UNCLE.
EVEN IF THAT WERE THE WHOLE STORY, YOU DON'T LITERALLY WANT TO KILL THEM IN RETURN.
YOU DON'T KNOW WHAT I--
COME ON, LOOK AT YOU. AND YOU, TOO, AMADEUS. YOU GUYS ARE BOURGIE KIDS FROM THE SUBURBS. YOU WANT JUSTICE. NOT ANARCHY. NOT WAR. NOT MURDER.
THE POINT, HULK, IS THAT WE WANT JUSTICE. FOR YOU. FOR EVERYONE.
SO WE'VE COME TO MEET YOU HALFWAY. TO SEE IF WE CAN'T FIGURE OUT A WAY TO MAKE IT HAPPEN.
GET AWAY FROM ME.
OR YOU'LL ALL DIE.
COME ON, HULK. YOU CAN'T BLUFF US. WE KNOW--
NOW!

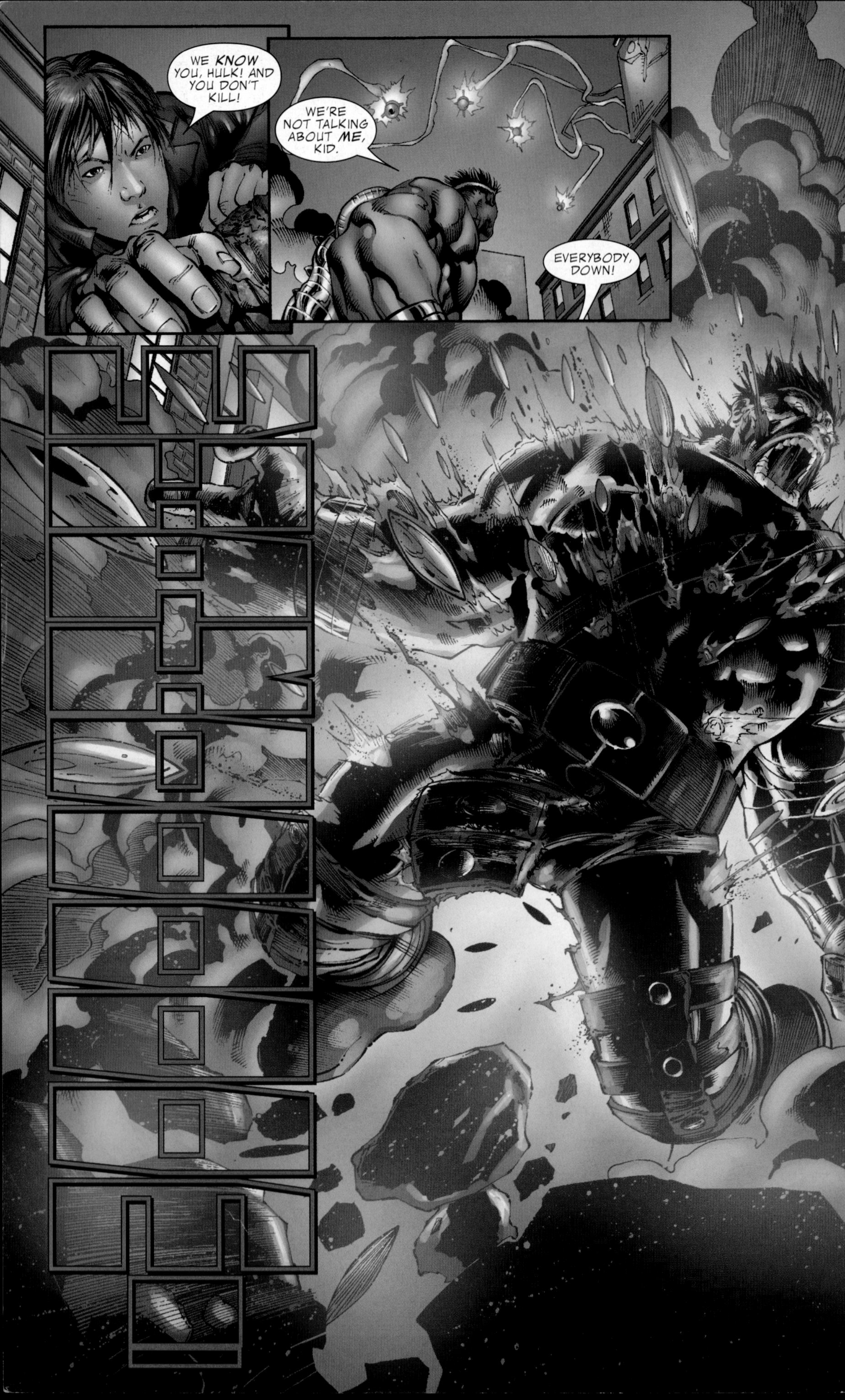
WE KNOW YOU, HULK! AND YOU DON'T KILL!
WE'RE NOT TALKING ABOUT ME, KID.
EVERYBODY, DOWN!

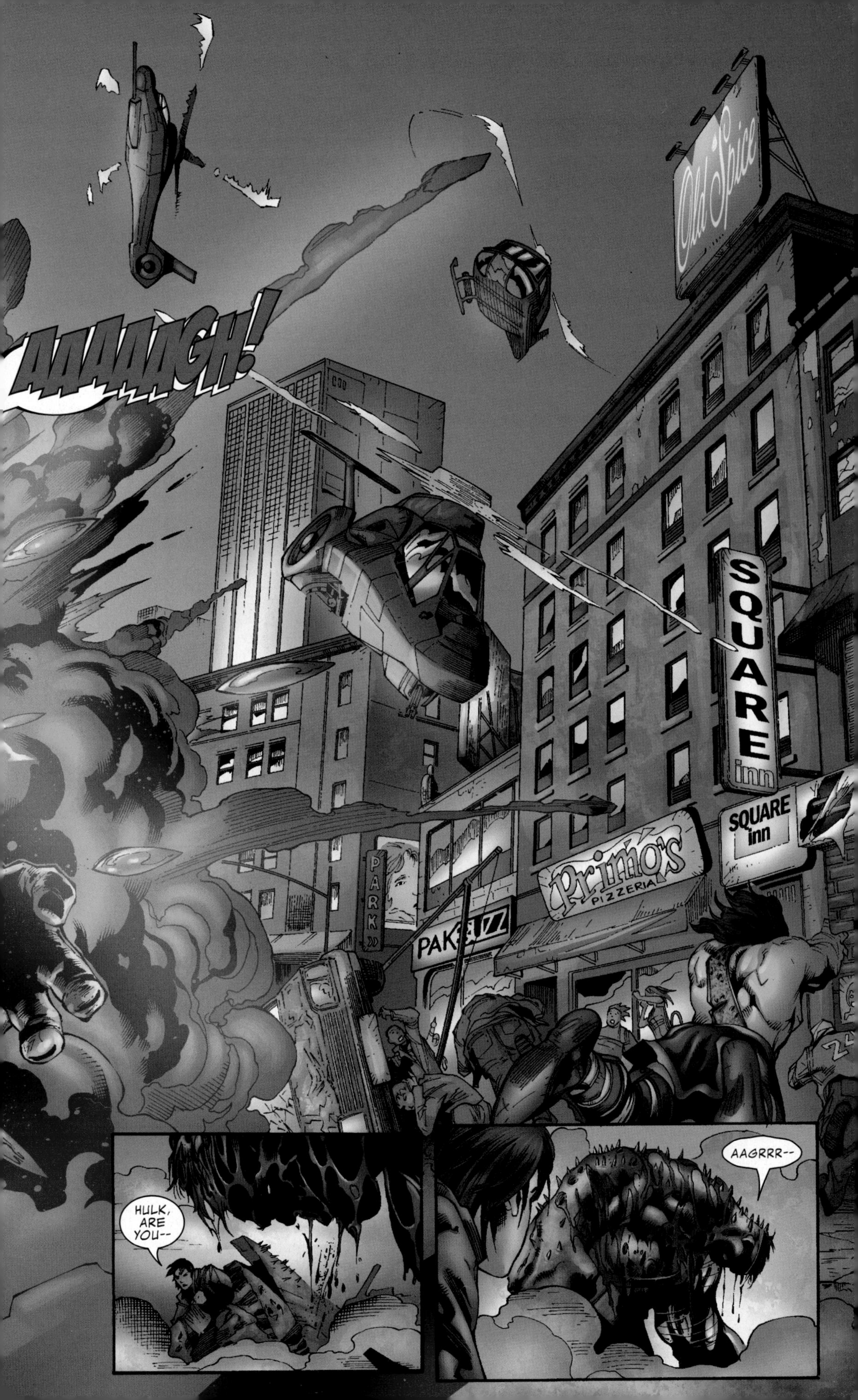
AAAAAGH!
Old Spice
SQUARE inn
SQUARE inn
Primo's PIZZERIA
PARK
HULK, ARE YOU--
AAGRRR--

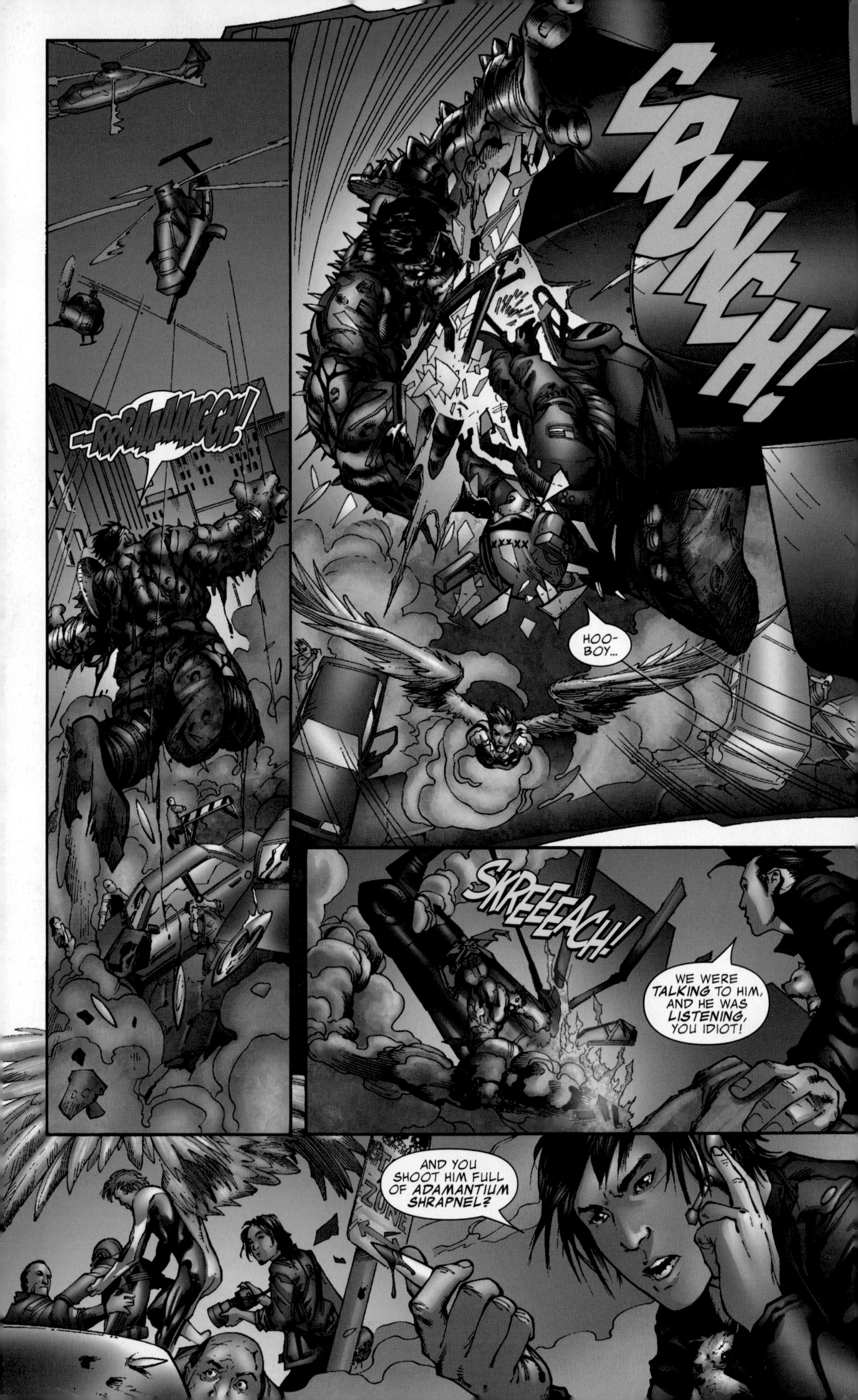
CRUNCH!
RRRAAAAAGGH!
HOO-BOY...
SKREEEEACH!
WE WERE TALKING TO HIM, AND HE WAS LISTENING, YOU IDIOT!
AND YOU SHOOT HIM FULL OF ADAMANTIUM SHRAPNEL?

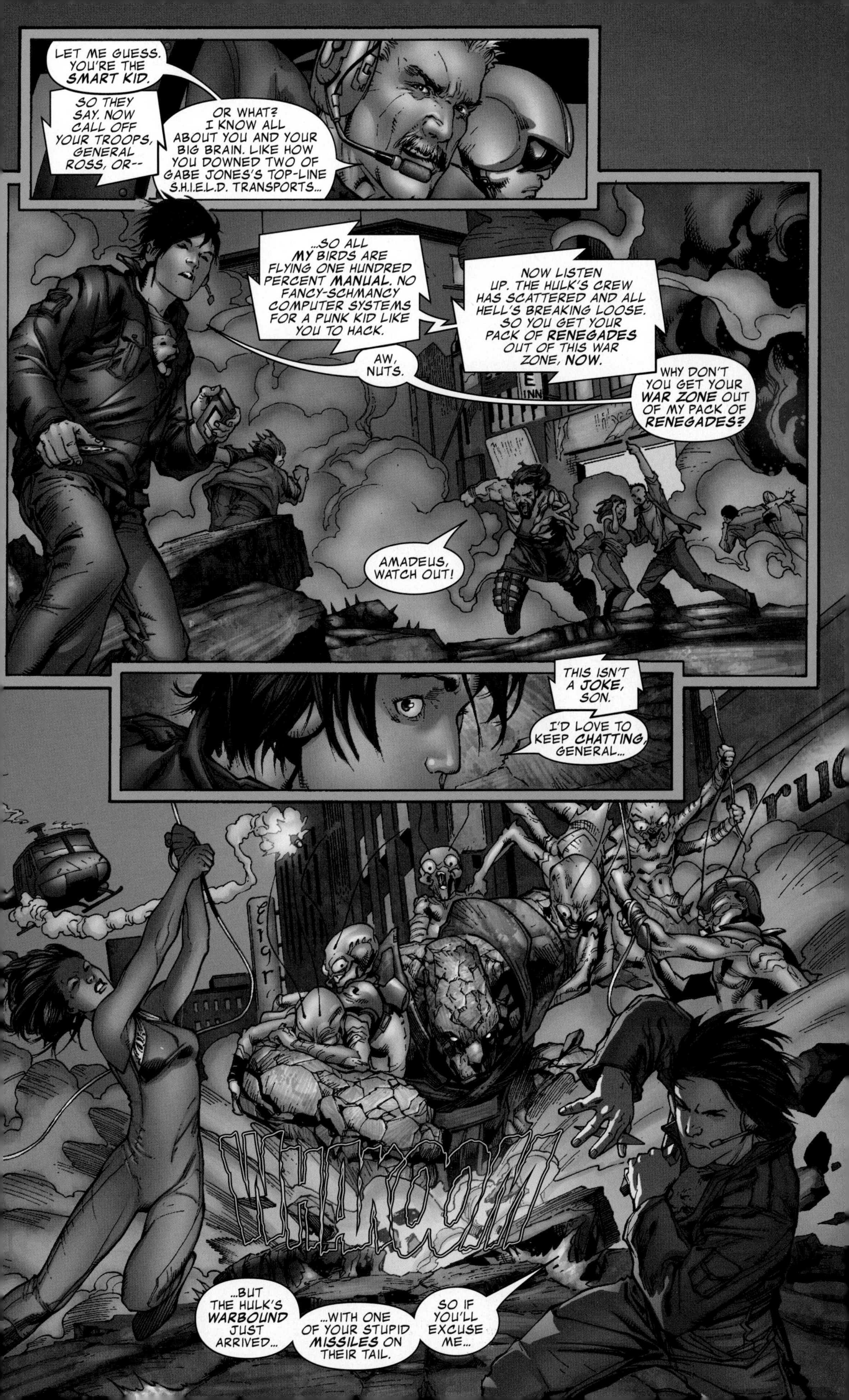
LET ME GUESS. YOU'RE THE SMART KID.
SO THEY SAY. NOW CALL OFF YOUR TROOPS, GENERAL ROSS, OR--
OR WHAT? I KNOW ALL ABOUT YOU AND YOUR BIG BRAIN. LIKE HOW YOU DOWNED TWO OF GABE JONES'S TOP-LINE S.H.I.E.L.D. TRANSPORTS...
...SO ALL MY BIRDS ARE FLYING ONE HUNDRED PERCENT MANUAL. NO FANCY-SCHMANCY COMPUTER SYSTEMS FOR A PUNK KID LIKE YOU TO HACK.
AW, NUTS.
NOW LISTEN UP. THE HULK'S CREW HAS SCATTERED AND ALL HELL'S BREAKING LOOSE. SO YOU GET YOUR PACK OF RENEGADES OUT OF THIS WAR ZONE, NOW.
WHY DON'T YOU GET YOUR WAR ZONE OUT OF MY PACK OF RENEGADES?
AMADEUS, WATCH OUT!
THIS ISN'T A JOKE, SON.
I'D LOVE TO KEEP CHATTING, GENERAL...
...BUT THE HULK'S WARBOUND JUST ARRIVED...
...WITH ONE OF YOUR STUPID MISSILES ON THEIR TAIL.
SO IF YOU'LL EXCUSE ME...

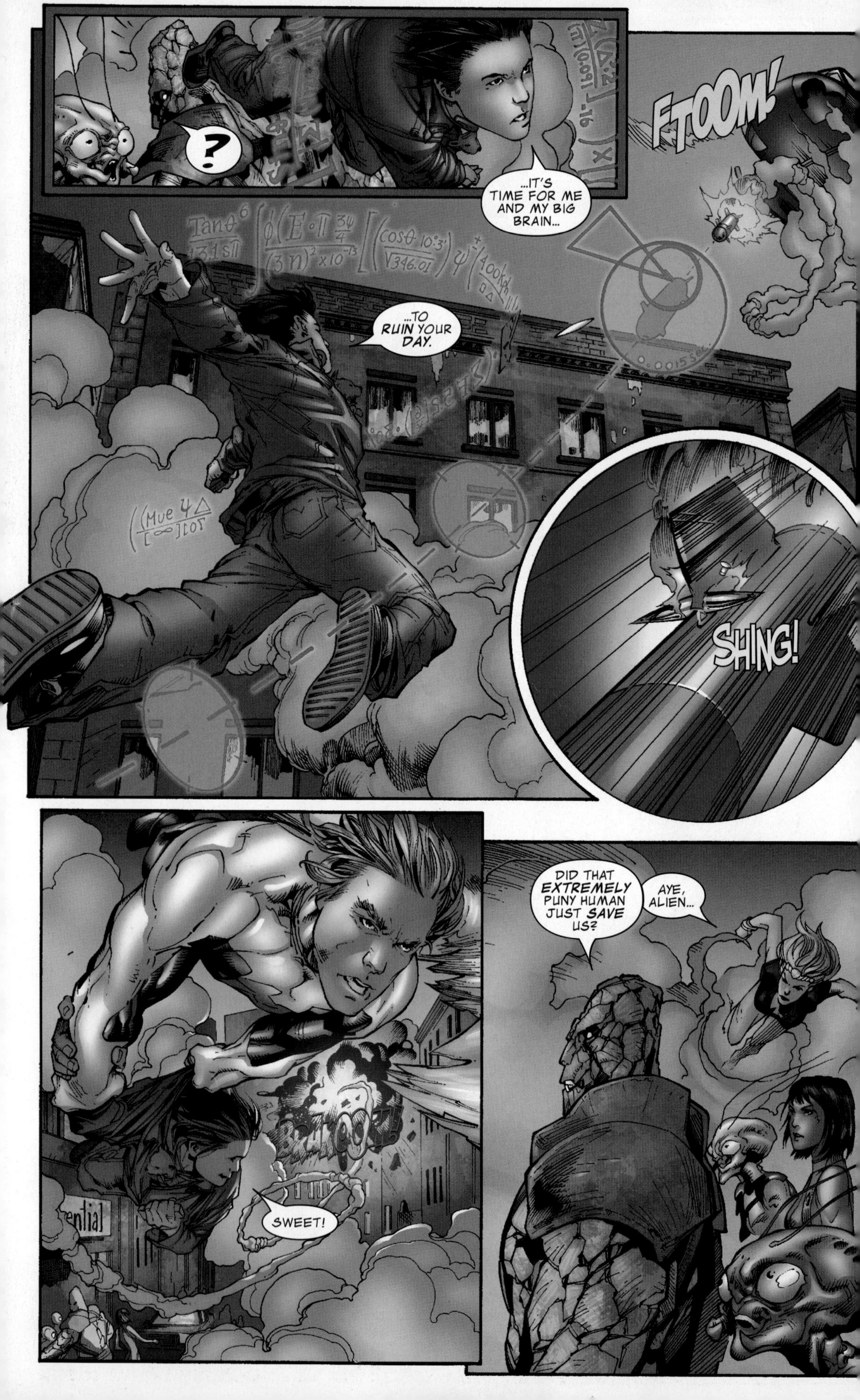
?
...IT'S TIME FOR ME AND MY BIG BRAIN...
FTOOM!
...TO RUIN YOUR DAY.
SHING!
SWEET!
DID THAT EXTREMELY PUNY HUMAN JUST SAVE US?
AYE, ALIEN...

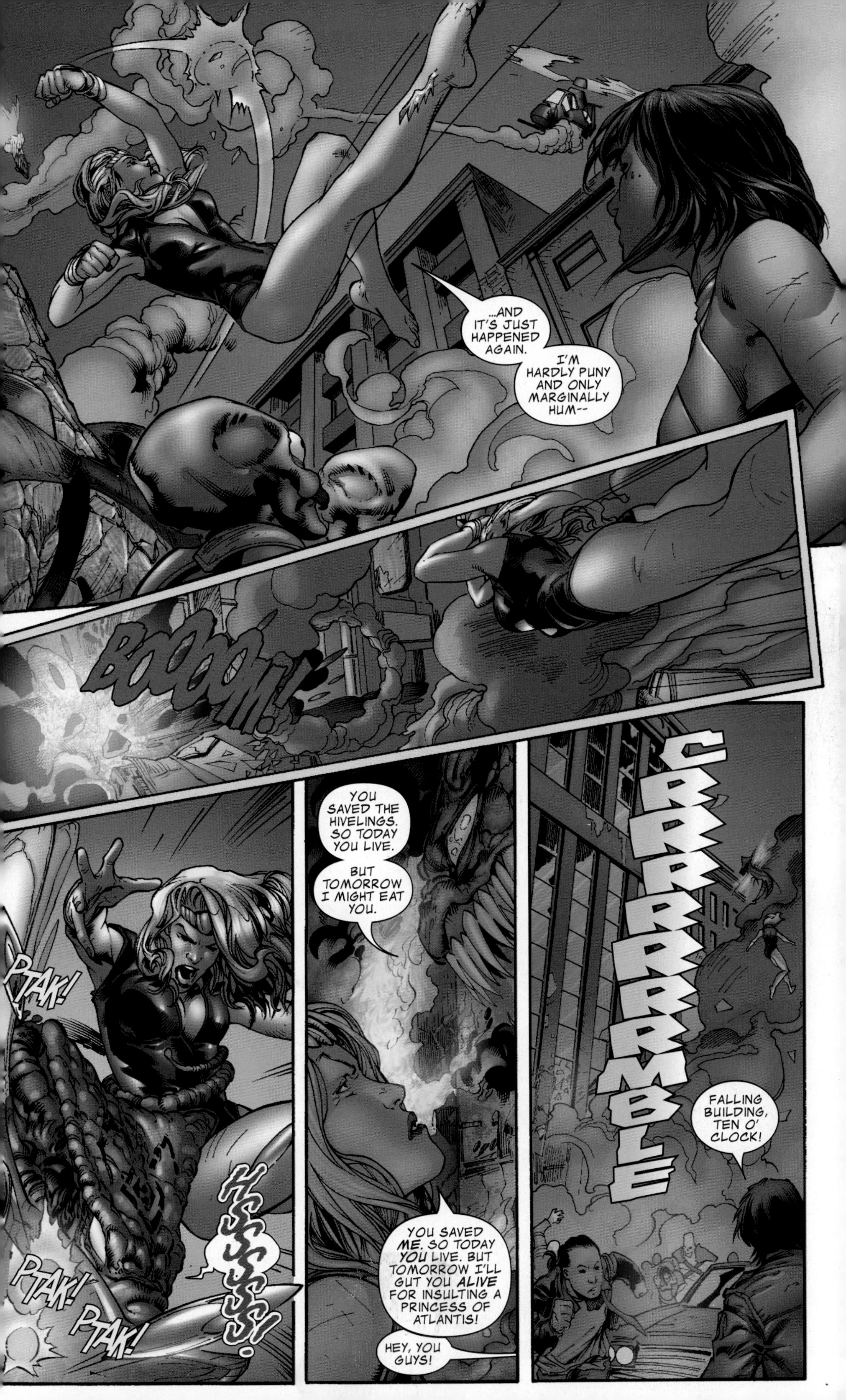
...AND IT'S JUST HAPPENED AGAIN.
I'M HARDLY PUNY AND ONLY MARGINALLY HUM--
BOOOOM!!
PTAK!
YOU SAVED THE HIVELINGS. SO TODAY YOU LIVE.
BUT TOMORROW I MIGHT EAT YOU.
CRRRRRRMBLE
FALLING BUILDING, TEN O' CLOCK!
HSSSSSS!
PTAK! PTAK!
YOU SAVED ME. SO TODAY YOU LIVE. BUT TOMORROW I'LL GUT YOU ALIVE FOR INSULTING A PRINCESS OF ATLANTIS!
HEY, YOU GUYS!

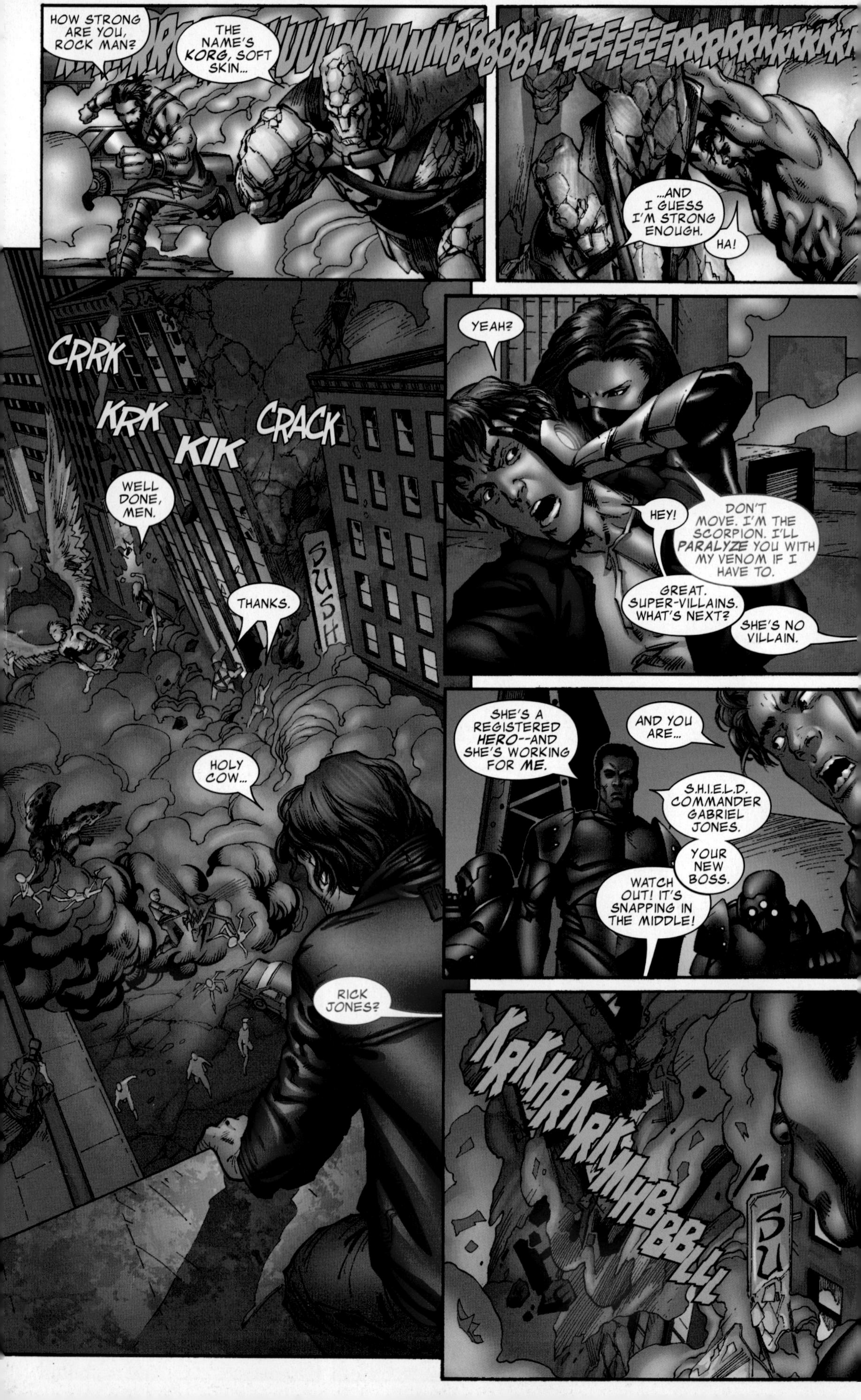
HOW STRONG ARE YOU, ROCK MAN?
THE NAME'S KORG, SOFT SKIN...
...AND I GUESS I'M STRONG ENOUGH.
HA!
CRRK
KRK
KIK
CRACK
WELL DONE, MEN.
THANKS.
HOLY COW...
RICK JONES?
YEAH?
HEY!
DON'T MOVE. I'M THE SCORPION. I'LL PARALYZE YOU WITH MY VENOM IF I HAVE TO.
GREAT. SUPER-VILLAINS. WHAT'S NEXT?
SHE'S NO VILLAIN.
SHE'S A REGISTERED HERO--AND SHE'S WORKING FOR ME.
AND YOU ARE...
S.H.I.E.L.D. COMMANDER GABRIEL JONES.
YOUR NEW BOSS.
WATCH OUT! IT'S SNAPPING IN THE MIDDLE!

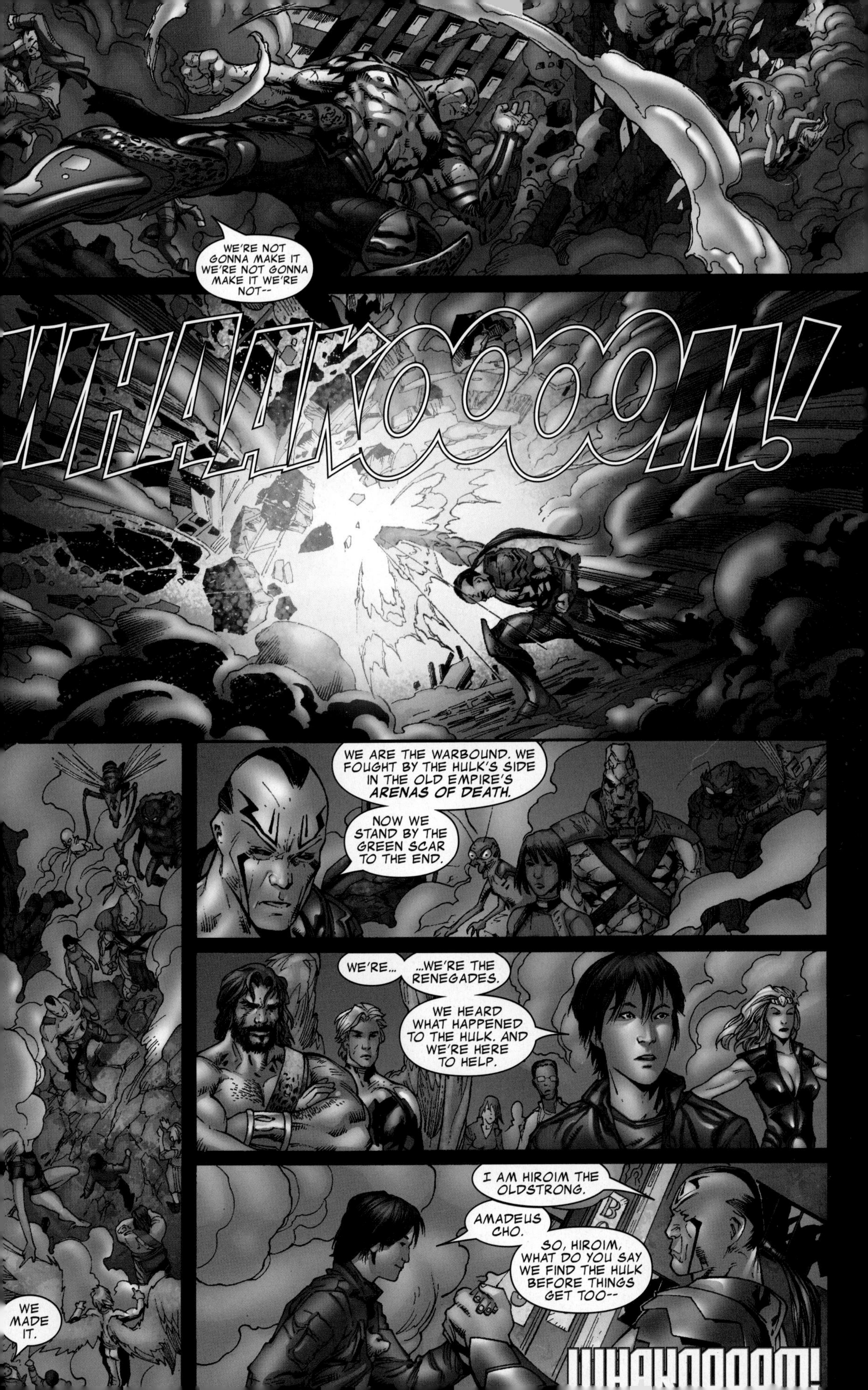
WE'RE NOT GONNA MAKE IT WE'RE NOT GONNA MAKE IT WE'RE NOT--
WHAKOOOOM!
WE ARE THE WARBOUND. WE FOUGHT BY THE HULK'S SIDE IN THE OLD EMPIRE'S ARENAS OF DEATH.
NOW WE STAND BY THE GREEN SCAR TO THE END.
WE'RE...
...WE'RE THE RENEGADES.
WE HEARD WHAT HAPPENED TO THE HULK. AND WE'RE HERE TO HELP.
WE MADE IT.
I AM HIROIM THE OLDSTRONG.
AMADEUS CHO.
SO, HIROIM, WHAT DO YOU SAY WE FIND THE HULK BEFORE THINGS GET TOO--
WHAKOOOOM!

WHAKOOOOM!

I THINK HE'S FOUND US.

STUPID.

PUNY.

HUMANS.

AW, SNAP...

EEEEEEEEEEEEEEEEEEEEEEEEEEEEEEEEEEEE

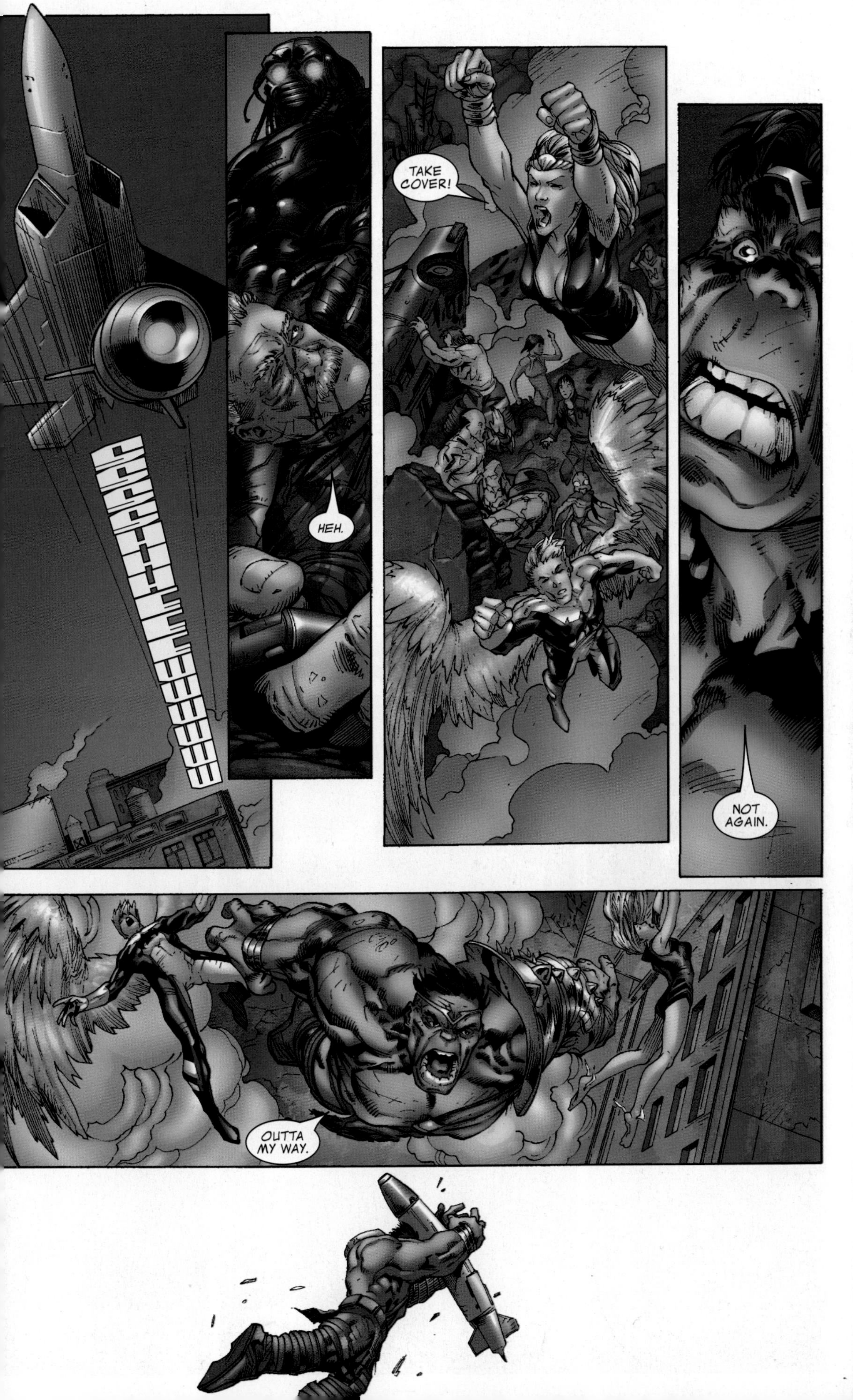
SSSSHHHEEEWWWWWW
HEH.
TAKE COVER!
NOT AGAIN.
OUTTA MY WAY.

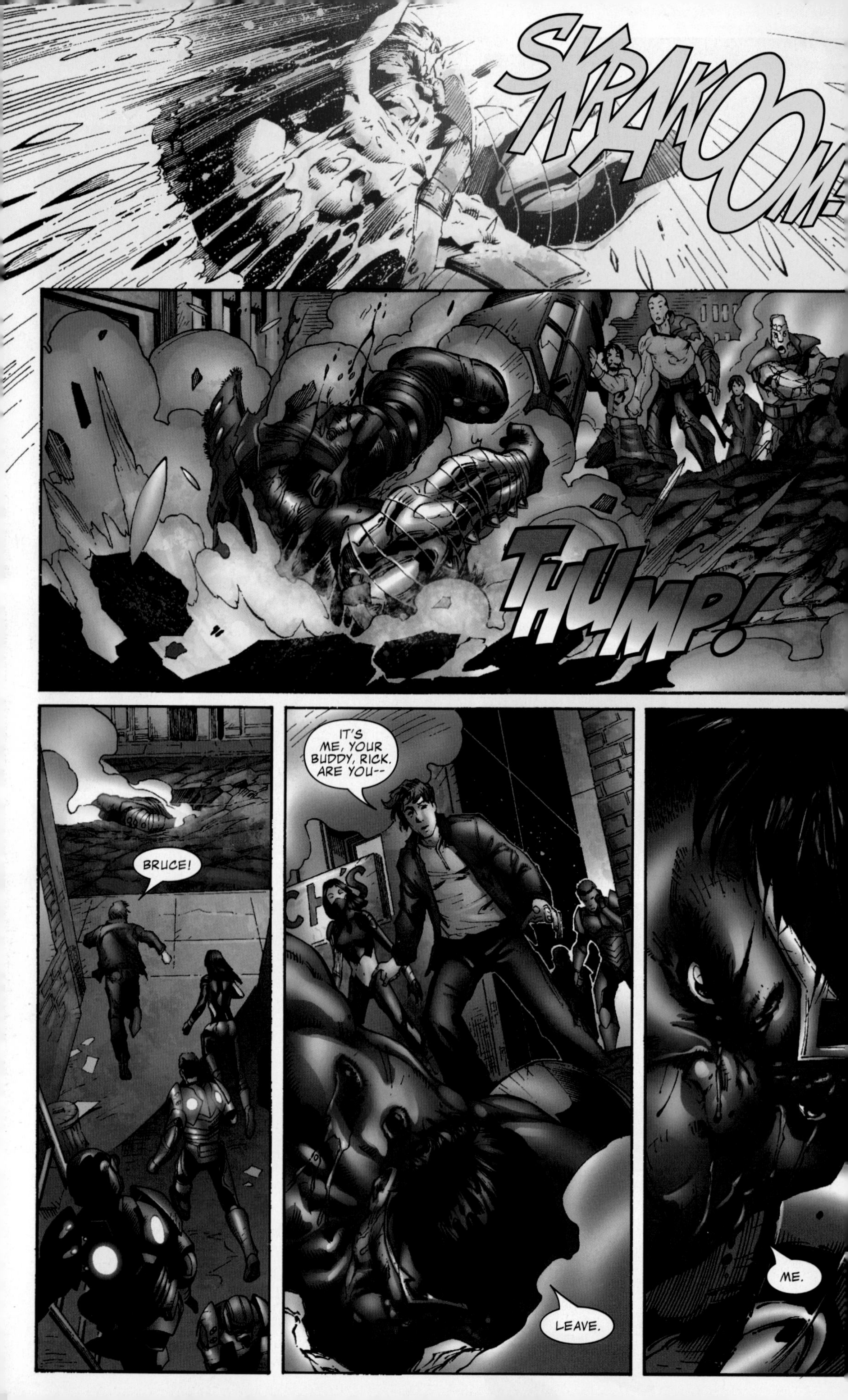
SKRAKOOM!
THUMP!
BRUCE!
IT'S ME, YOUR BUDDY, RICK. ARE YOU--
LEAVE.
ME.

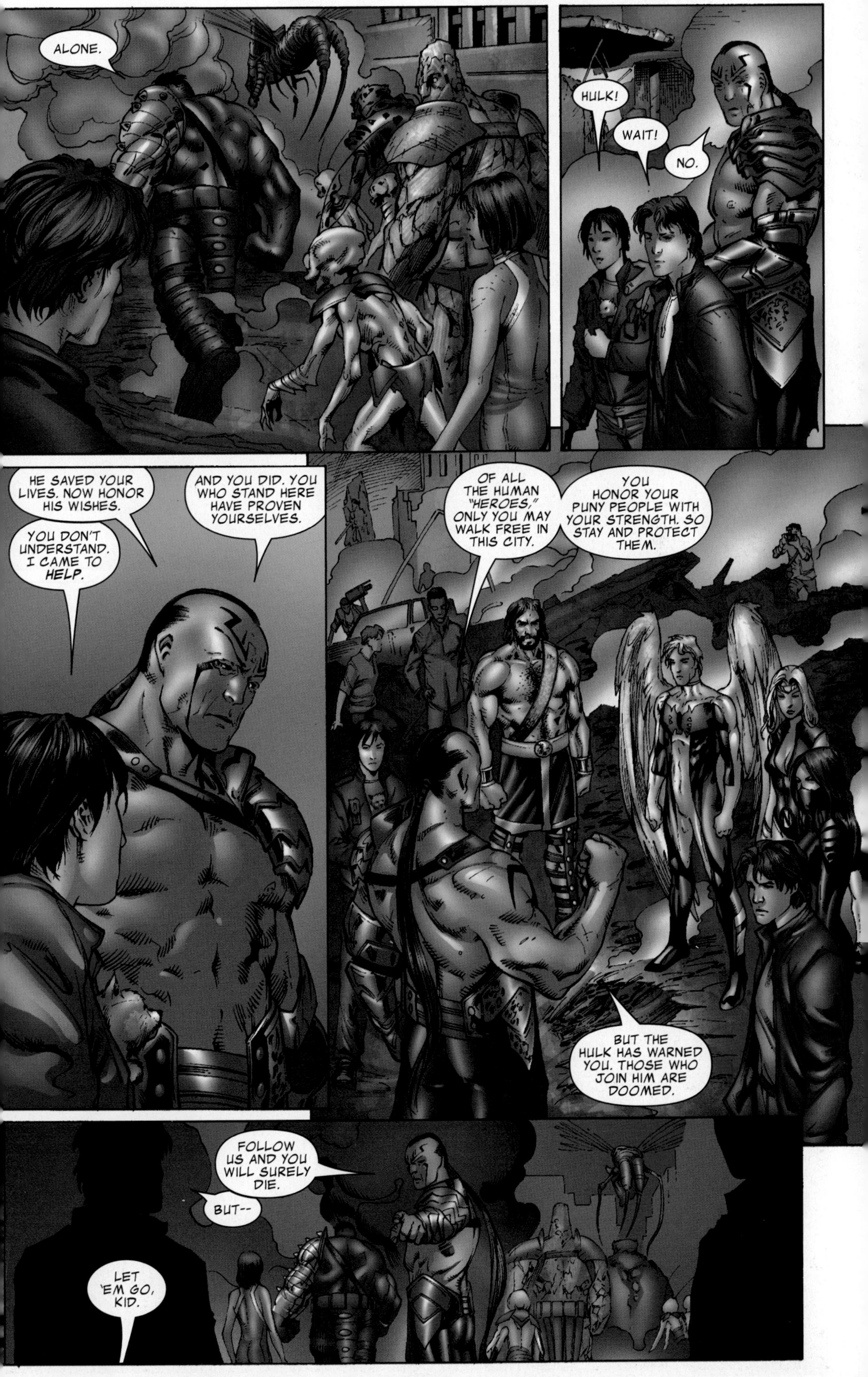
ALONE.
HULK!
WAIT!
NO.
HE SAVED YOUR LIVES. NOW HONOR HIS WISHES.
YOU DON'T UNDERSTAND. I CAME TO HELP.
AND YOU DID. YOU WHO STAND HERE HAVE PROVEN YOURSELVES.
OF ALL THE HUMAN "HEROES," ONLY YOU MAY WALK FREE IN THIS CITY.
YOU HONOR YOUR PUNY PEOPLE WITH YOUR STRENGTH. SO STAY AND PROTECT THEM.
BUT THE HULK HAS WARNED YOU. THOSE WHO JOIN HIM ARE DOOMED.
FOLLOW US AND YOU WILL SURELY DIE.
BUT--
LET 'EM GO, KID.

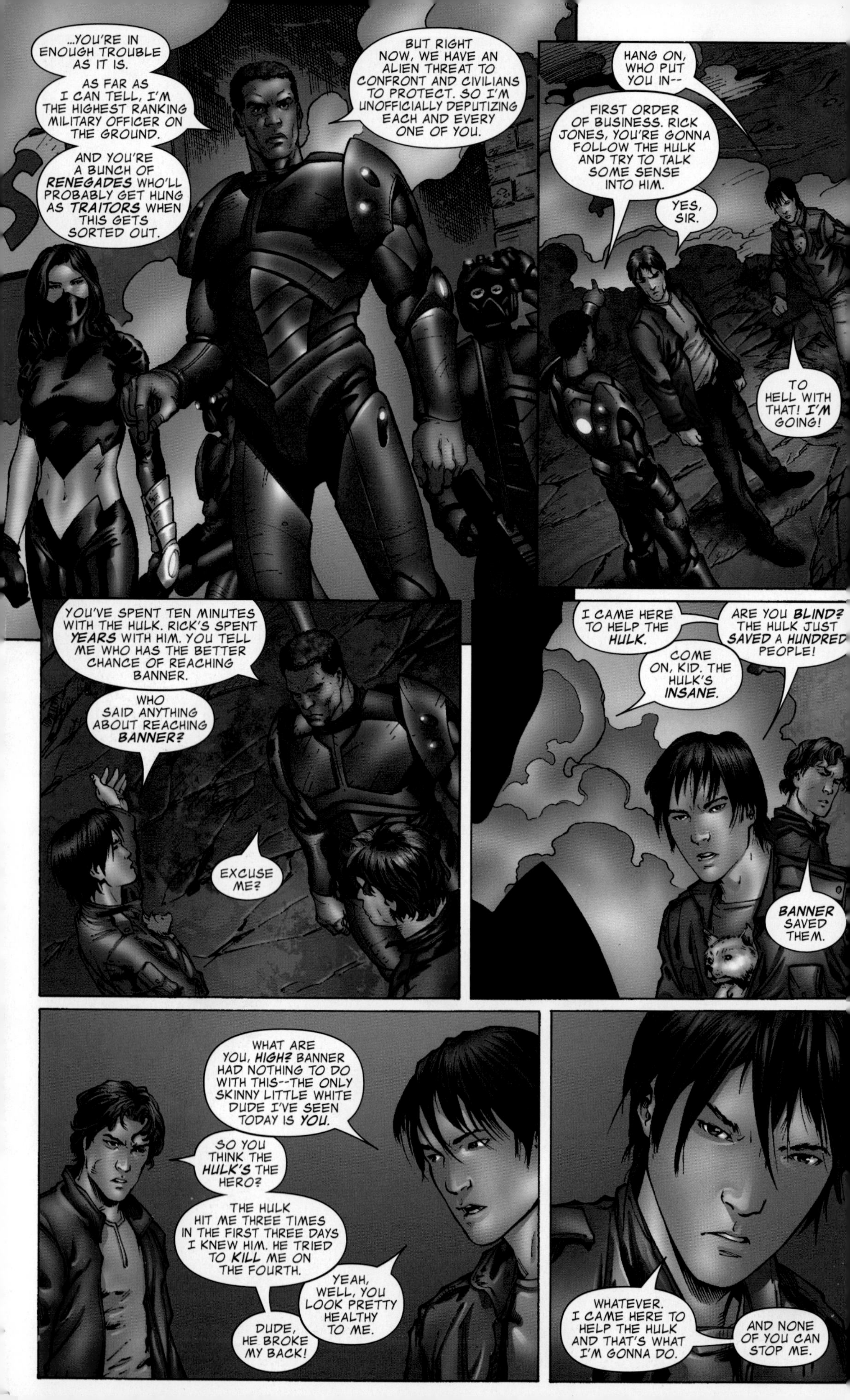
...YOU'RE IN ENOUGH TROUBLE AS IT IS.
AS FAR AS I CAN TELL, I'M THE HIGHEST RANKING MILITARY OFFICER ON THE GROUND.
AND YOU'RE A BUNCH OF RENEGADES WHO'LL PROBABLY GET HUNG AS TRAITORS WHEN THIS GETS SORTED OUT.
BUT RIGHT NOW, WE HAVE AN ALIEN THREAT TO CONFRONT AND CIVILIANS TO PROTECT. SO I'M UNOFFICIALLY DEPUTIZING EACH AND EVERY ONE OF YOU.
HANG ON, WHO PUT YOU IN--
FIRST ORDER OF BUSINESS. RICK JONES, YOU'RE GONNA FOLLOW THE HULK AND TRY TO TALK SOME SENSE INTO HIM.
YES, SIR.
TO HELL WITH THAT! I'M GOING!
YOU'VE SPENT TEN MINUTES WITH THE HULK. RICK'S SPENT YEARS WITH HIM. YOU TELL ME WHO HAS THE BETTER CHANCE OF REACHING BANNER.
WHO SAID ANYTHING ABOUT REACHING BANNER?
EXCUSE ME?
I CAME HERE TO HELP THE HULK.
COME ON, KID. THE HULK'S INSANE.
ARE YOU BLIND? THE HULK JUST SAVED A HUNDRED PEOPLE!
BANNER SAVED THEM.
WHAT ARE YOU, HIGH? BANNER HAD NOTHING TO DO WITH THIS--THE ONLY SKINNY LITTLE WHITE DUDE I'VE SEEN TODAY IS YOU.
SO YOU THINK THE HULK'S THE HERO?
THE HULK HIT ME THREE TIMES IN THE FIRST THREE DAYS I KNEW HIM. HE TRIED TO KILL ME ON THE FOURTH.
YEAH, WELL, YOU LOOK PRETTY HEALTHY TO ME.
DUDE, HE BROKE MY BACK!
WHATEVER. I CAME HERE TO HELP THE HULK AND THAT'S WHAT I'M GONNA DO.
AND NONE OF YOU CAN STOP ME.

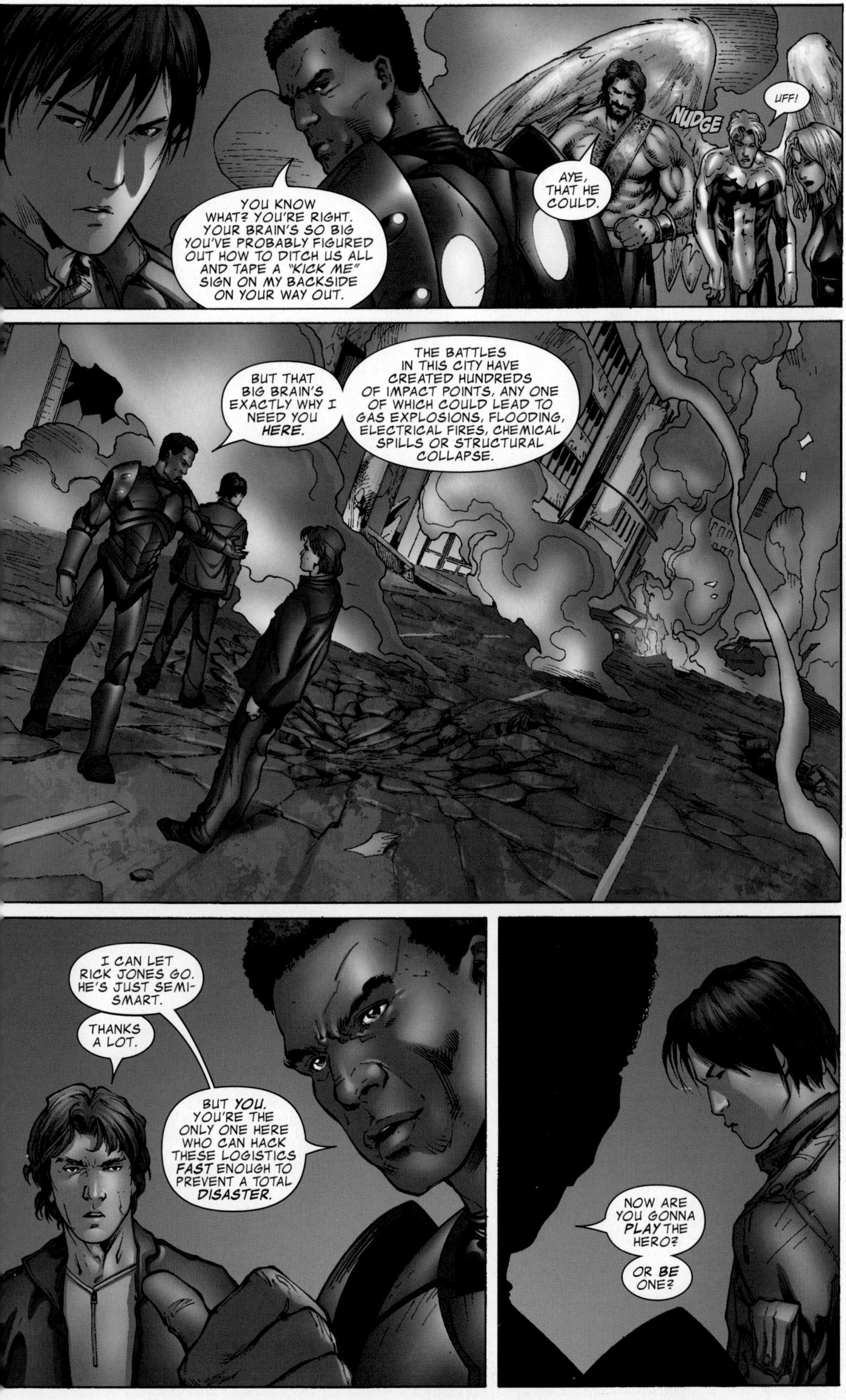

YOU KNOW WHAT? YOU'RE RIGHT. YOUR BRAIN'S SO BIG YOU'VE PROBABLY FIGURED OUT HOW TO DITCH US ALL AND TAPE A "KICK ME" SIGN ON MY BACKSIDE ON YOUR WAY OUT.
AYE, THAT HE COULD.
NUDGE
UFF!
BUT THAT BIG BRAIN'S EXACTLY WHY I NEED YOU HERE.
THE BATTLES IN THIS CITY HAVE CREATED HUNDREDS OF IMPACT POINTS, ANY ONE OF WHICH COULD LEAD TO GAS EXPLOSIONS, FLOODING, ELECTRICAL FIRES, CHEMICAL SPILLS OR STRUCTURAL COLLAPSE.
I CAN LET RICK JONES GO. HE'S JUST SEMI-SMART.
THANKS A LOT.
BUT YOU. YOU'RE THE ONLY ONE HERE WHO CAN HACK THESE LOGISTICS FAST ENOUGH TO PREVENT A TOTAL DISASTER.
NOW ARE YOU GONNA PLAY THE HERO?
OR BE ONE?

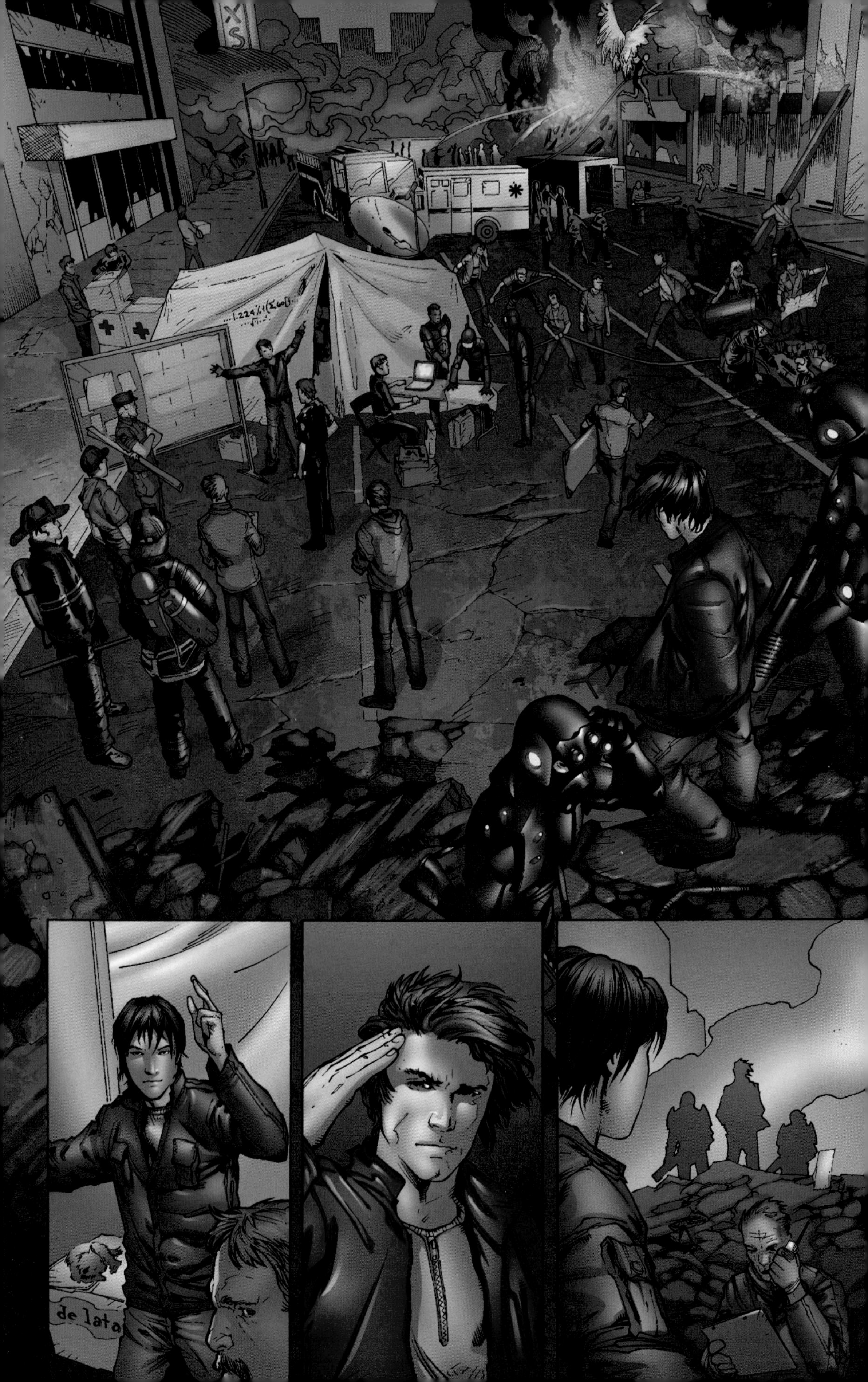
de lata

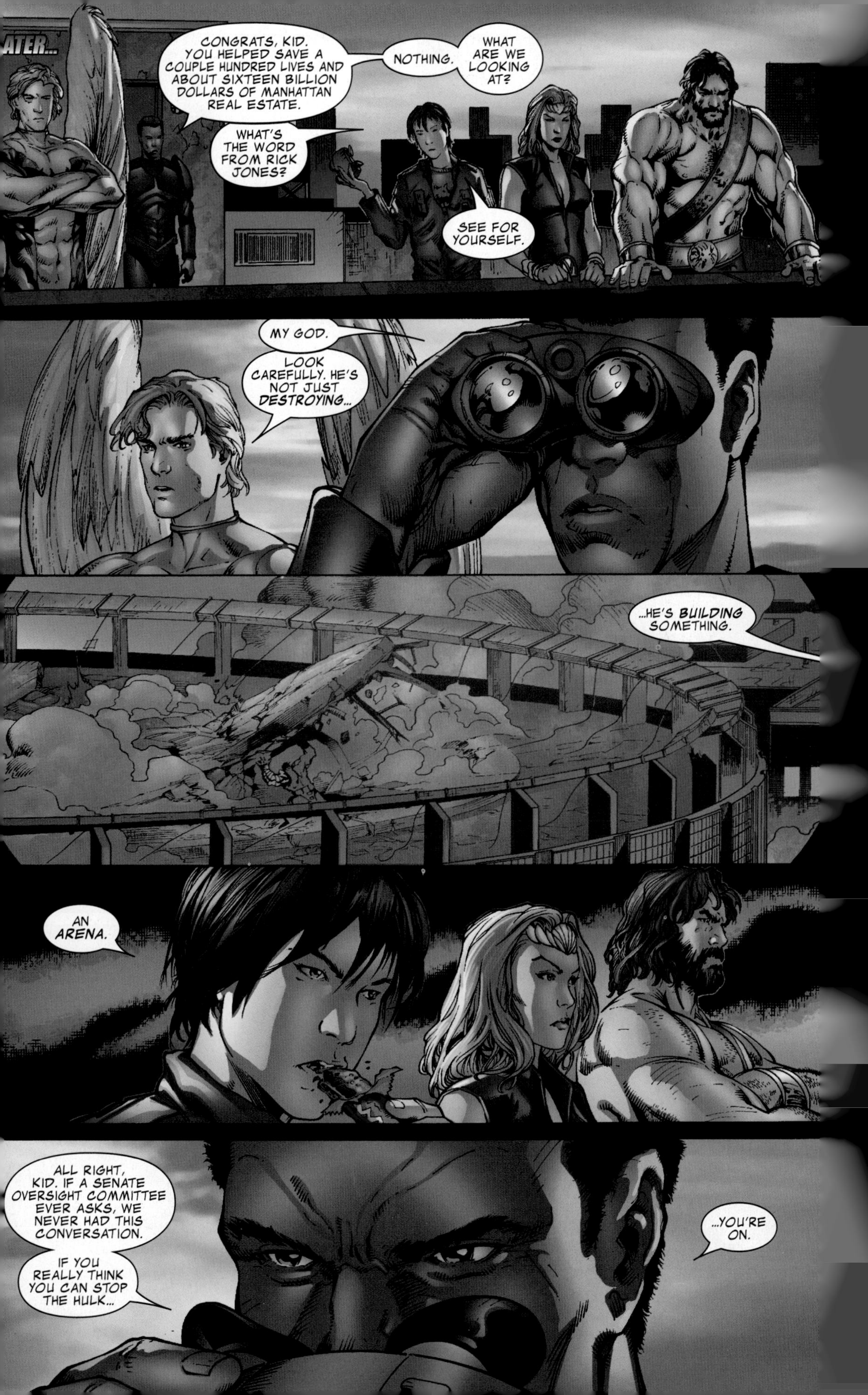
LATER...
CONGRATS, KID. YOU HELPED SAVE A COUPLE HUNDRED LIVES AND ABOUT SIXTEEN BILLION DOLLARS OF MANHATTAN REAL ESTATE.
NOTHING.
WHAT ARE WE LOOKING AT?
WHAT'S THE WORD FROM RICK JONES?
SEE FOR YOURSELF.
MY GOD.
LOOK CAREFULLY. HE'S NOT JUST DESTROYING...
...HE'S BUILDING SOMETHING.
AN ARENA.
ALL RIGHT, KID. IF A SENATE OVERSIGHT COMMITTEE EVER ASKS, WE NEVER HAD THIS CONVERSATION.
IF YOU REALLY THINK YOU CAN STOP THE HULK...
...YOU'RE ON.

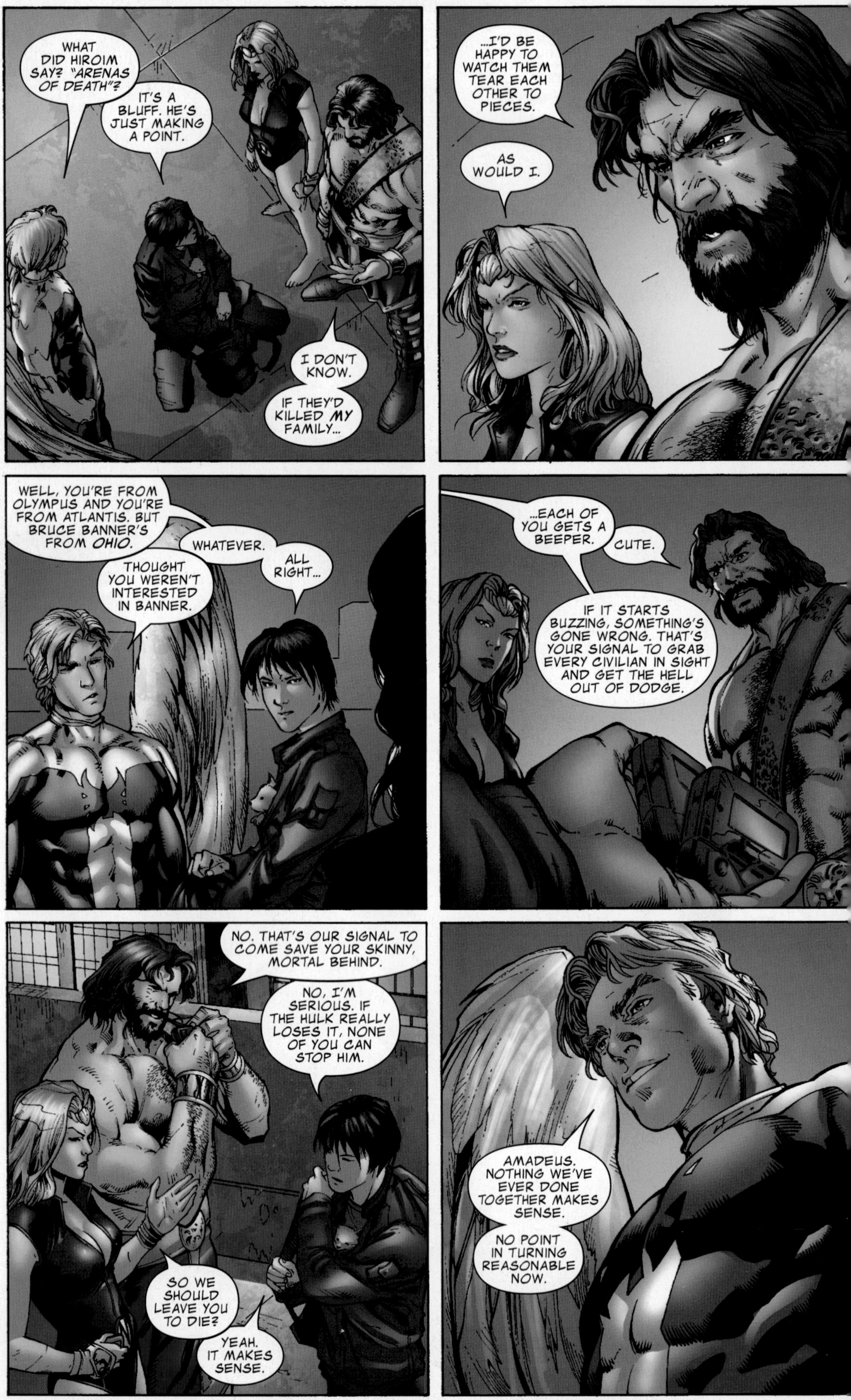
WHAT DID HIROIM SAY? "ARENAS OF DEATH"?
IT'S A BLUFF. HE'S JUST MAKING A POINT.
I DON'T KNOW.
IF THEY'D KILLED MY FAMILY...
...I'D BE HAPPY TO WATCH THEM TEAR EACH OTHER TO PIECES.
AS WOULD I.
WELL, YOU'RE FROM OLYMPUS AND YOU'RE FROM ATLANTIS. BUT BRUCE BANNER'S FROM OHIO.
WHATEVER.
THOUGHT YOU WEREN'T INTERESTED IN BANNER.
ALL RIGHT...
...EACH OF YOU GETS A BEEPER.
CUTE.
IF IT STARTS BUZZING, SOMETHING'S GONE WRONG. THAT'S YOUR SIGNAL TO GRAB EVERY CIVILIAN IN SIGHT AND GET THE HELL OUT OF DODGE.
NO. THAT'S OUR SIGNAL TO COME SAVE YOUR SKINNY, MORTAL BEHIND.
NO, I'M SERIOUS. IF THE HULK REALLY LOSES IT, NONE OF YOU CAN STOP HIM.
SO WE SHOULD LEAVE YOU TO DIE?
YEAH. IT MAKES SENSE.
AMADEUS. NOTHING WE'VE EVER DONE TOGETHER MAKES SENSE.
NO POINT IN TURNING REASONABLE NOW.

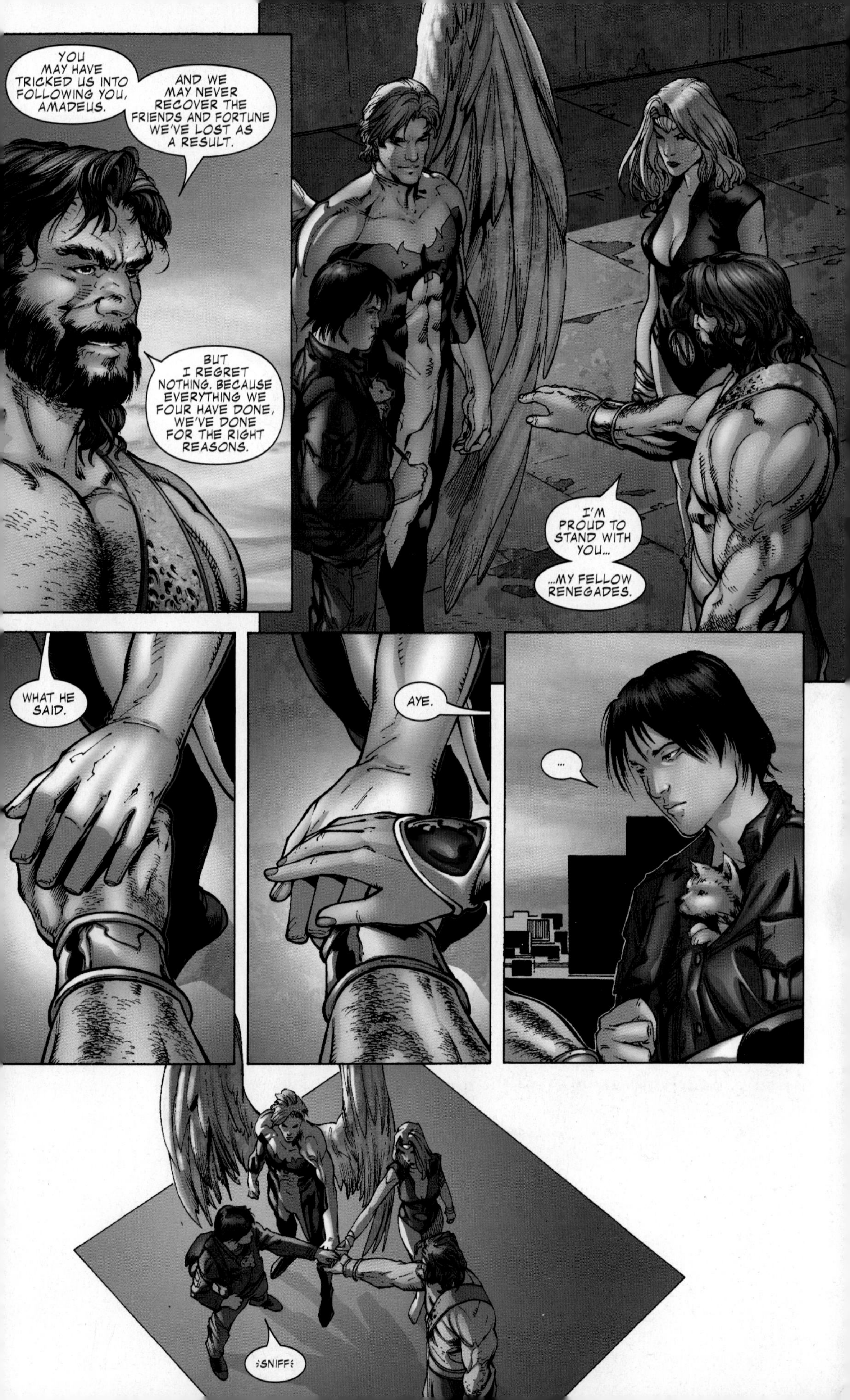
YOU MAY HAVE TRICKED US INTO FOLLOWING YOU, AMADEUS.
AND WE MAY NEVER RECOVER THE FRIENDS AND FORTUNE WE'VE LOST AS A RESULT.
BUT I REGRET NOTHING. BECAUSE EVERYTHING WE FOUR HAVE DONE, WE'VE DONE FOR THE RIGHT REASONS.
I'M PROUD TO STAND WITH YOU...
...MY FELLOW RENEGADES.
WHAT HE SAID.
AYE.
...
SNIFF

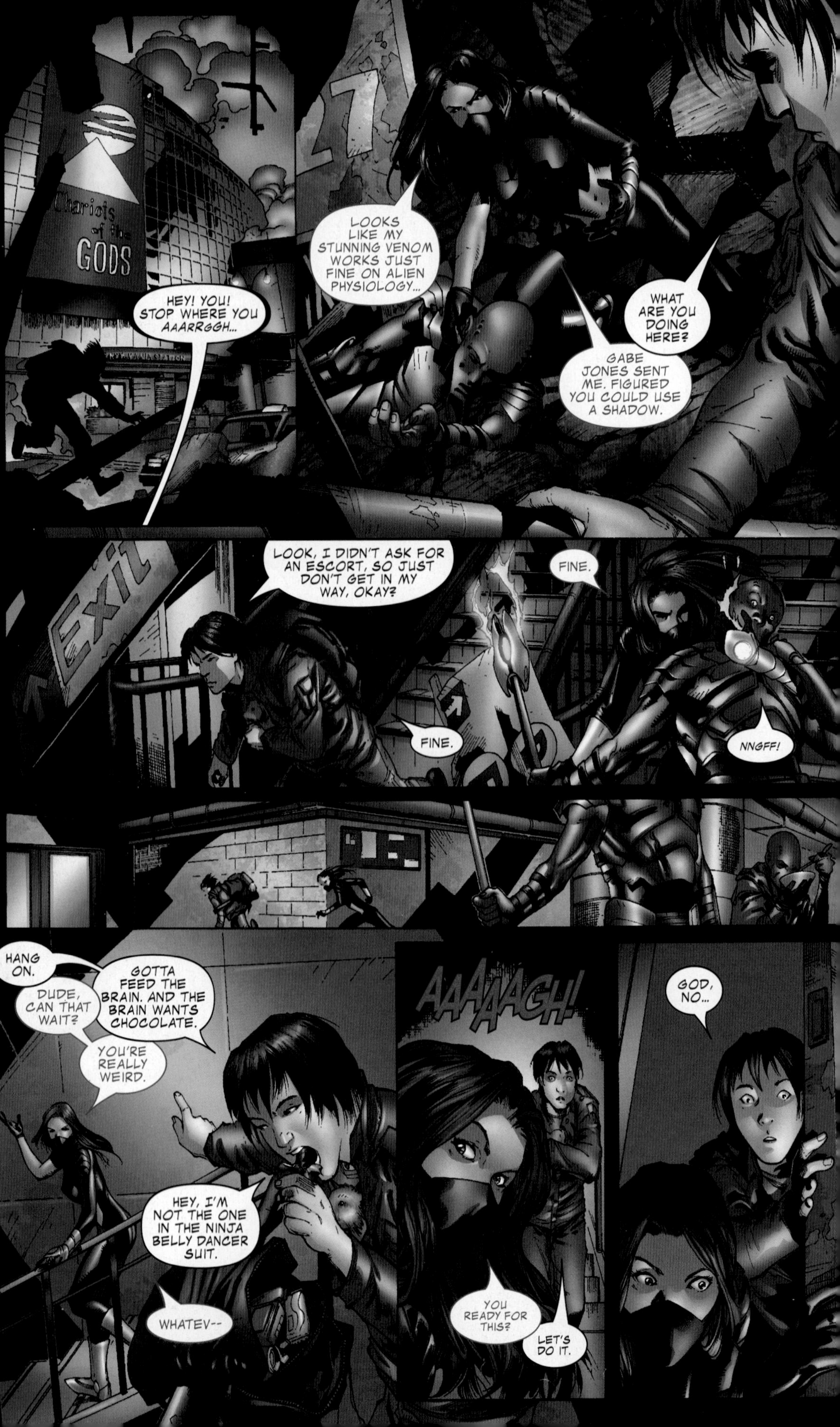
Chariots of the GODS
HEY! YOU! STOP WHERE YOU AAARRGGH...
LOOKS LIKE MY STUNNING VENOM WORKS JUST FINE ON ALIEN PHYSIOLOGY...
WHAT ARE YOU DOING HERE?
GABE JONES SENT ME. FIGURED YOU COULD USE A SHADOW.
EXIT
LOOK, I DIDN'T ASK FOR AN ESCORT, SO JUST DON'T GET IN MY WAY, OKAY?
FINE.
FINE.
NNGFF!
HANG ON.
GOTTA FEED THE BRAIN. AND THE BRAIN WANTS CHOCOLATE.
DUDE, CAN THAT WAIT?
YOU'RE REALLY WEIRD.
HEY, I'M NOT THE ONE IN THE NINJA BELLY DANCER SUIT.
WHATEV--
AAAAAGH!
YOU READY FOR THIS?
LET'S DO IT.
GOD, NO...

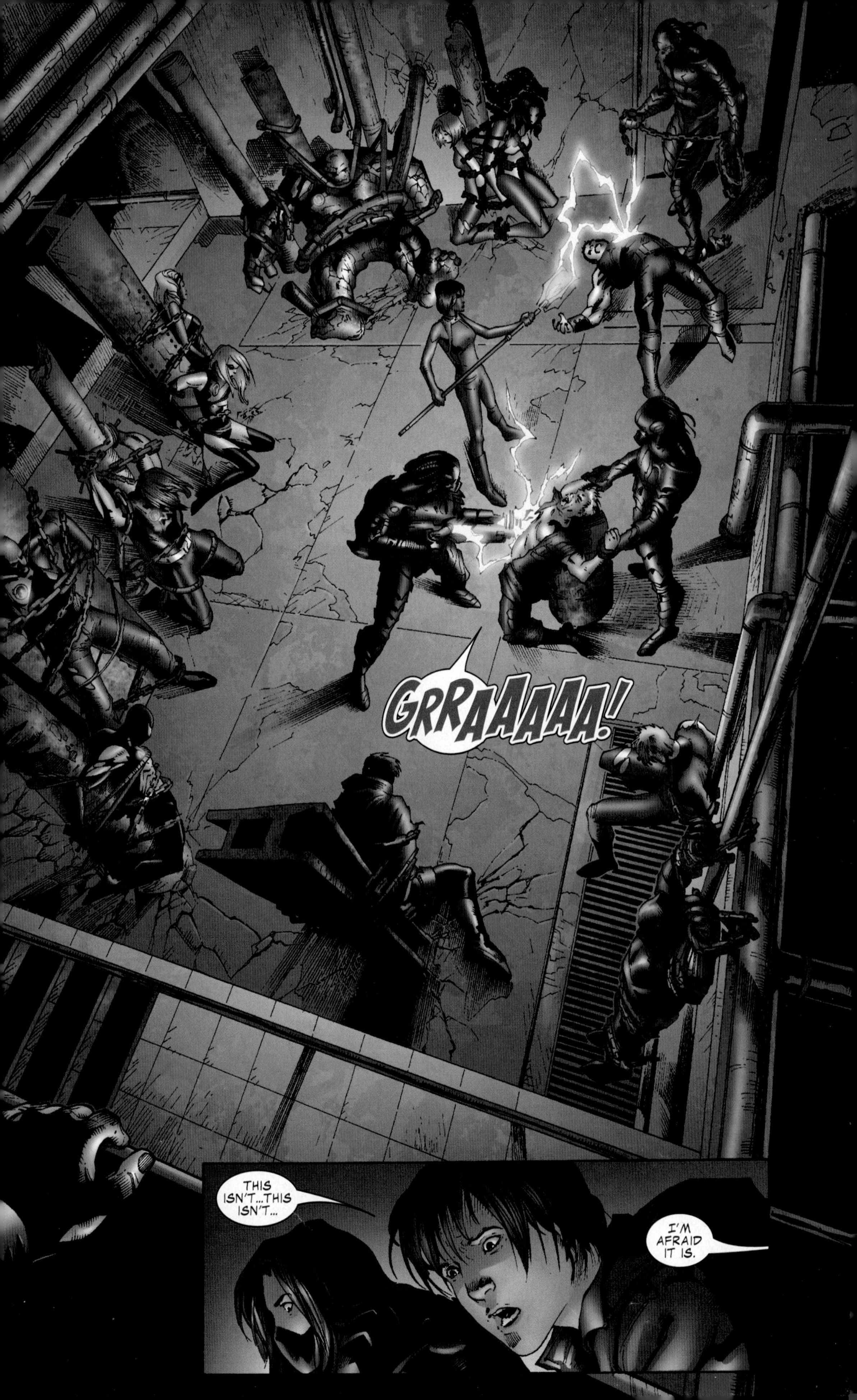
GRRAAAAA!
THIS ISN'T...THIS ISN'T...
I'M AFRAID IT IS.

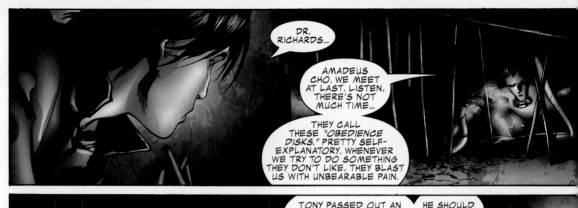

DR. RICHARDS...

AMADEUS CHO. WE MEET AT LAST. LISTEN, THERE'S NOT MUCH TIME...

THEY CALL THESE "OBEDIENCE DISKS." PRETTY SELF-EXPLANATORY. WHENEVER WE TRY TO DO SOMETHING THEY DON'T LIKE, THEY BLAST US WITH UNBEARABLE PAIN.

TONY PASSED OUT AN HOUR AGO, BUT HIS DISK IS STILL SPARKING. I THINK HE'S FIGHTING IT IN HIS SLEEP.

HE SHOULD SAVE HIS STRENGTH.

APPARENTLY, BACK ON SAKAAR, THE RED KING USED THESE DISKS TO FORCE SLAVES TO FIGHT IN THE ARENA...

...TO THE DEATH.

I'VE COME TO FIND THE HULK. I'LL TALK TO HIM. SORT THIS OUT.

TALKING WON'T WORK, AMADEUS.

THE HEROES HAVE FAILED. THE MILITARY CAN'T STRIKE-- ALL THEY HAVE LEFT ARE NUKES, AND THAT'LL JUST MAKE HIM STRONGER.

IT'S UP TO YOU, NOW.

I KNOW YOU IDOLIZE THE HULK. BUT YOU'RE THE SMART KID. I KNOW YOU'VE THOUGHT ABOUT THIS. I KNOW YOU HAVE A PLAN.

YOU HAVE TO END THIS.

OR HE'LL KILL EVERY HERO HERE.

NO. THE HULK...

THE HULK'S NOT A KILLER.

HMPH.

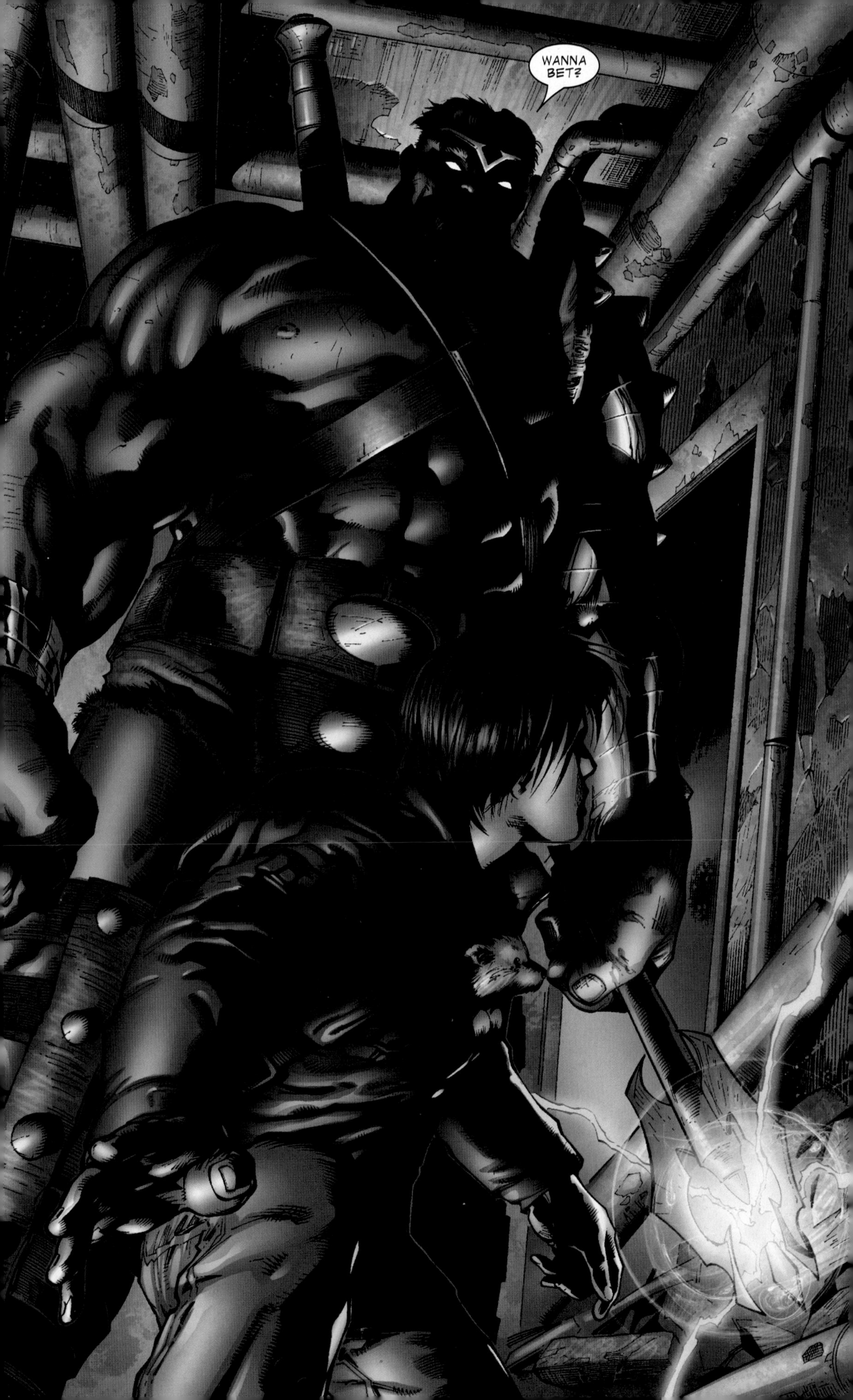
WANNA BET?

110

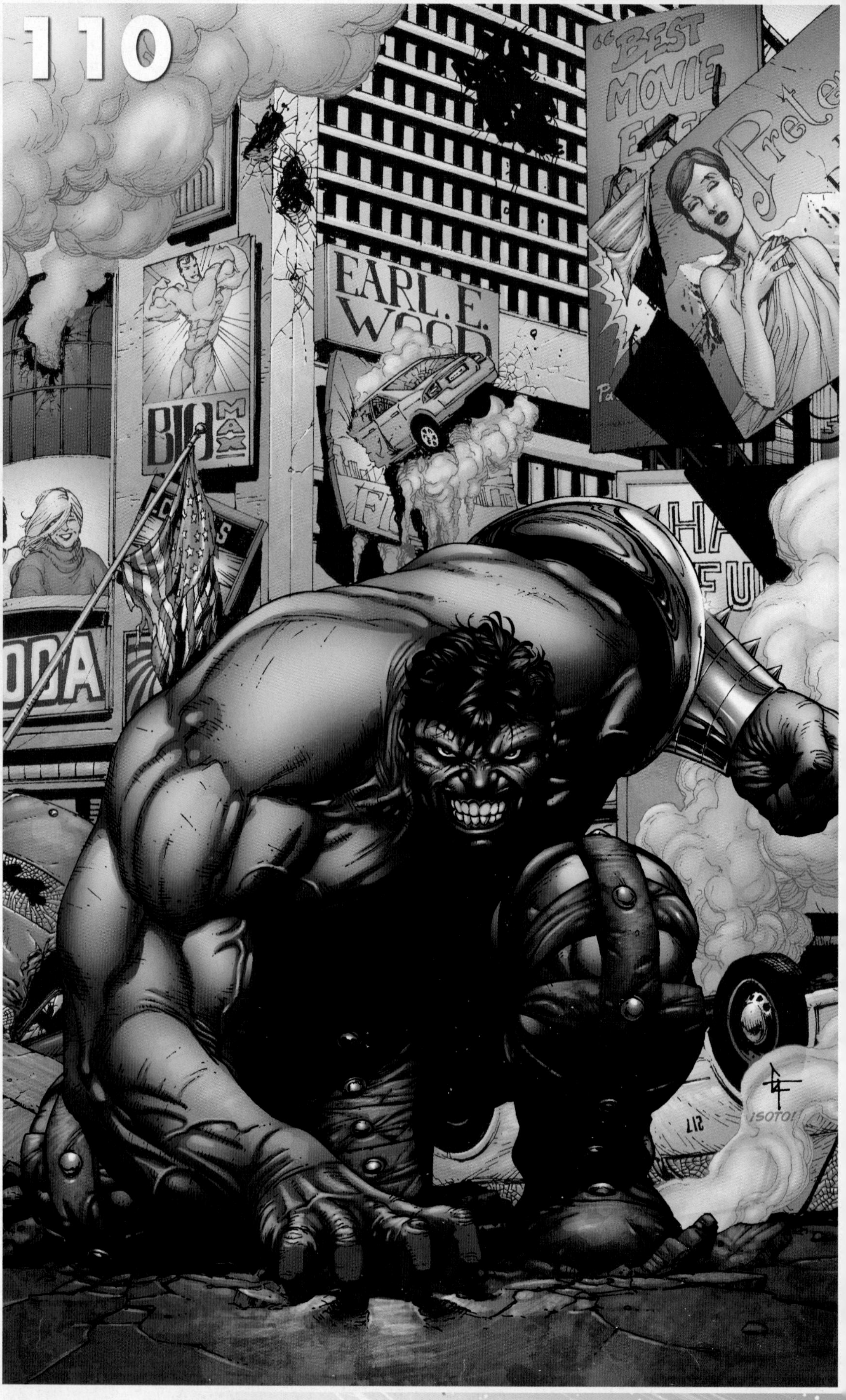
EARL. E. WOOD
BIO MAX

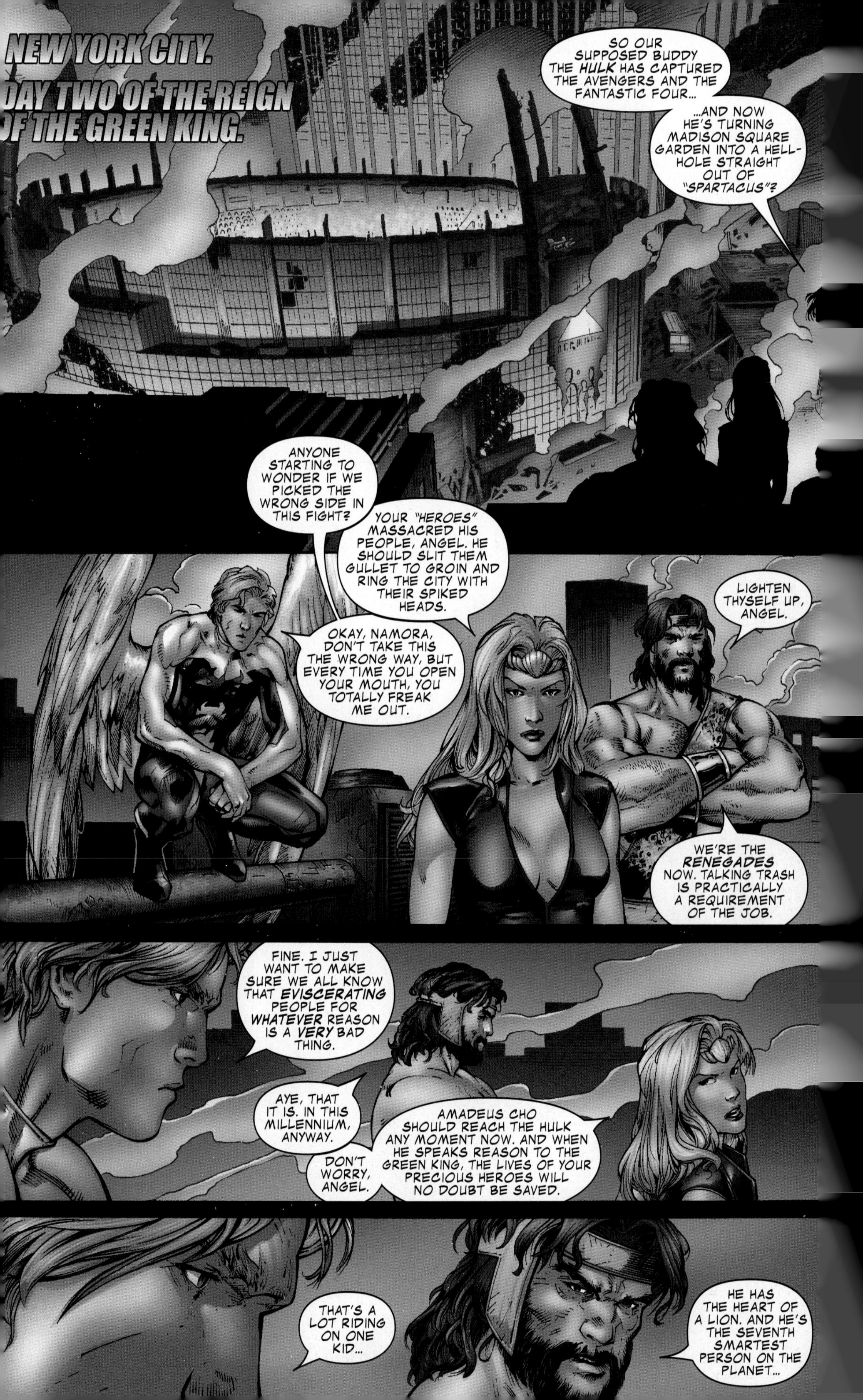
NEW YORK CITY.
DAY TWO OF THE REIGN OF THE GREEN KING.
SO OUR SUPPOSED BUDDY THE HULK HAS CAPTURED THE AVENGERS AND THE FANTASTIC FOUR...
...AND NOW HE'S TURNING MADISON SQUARE GARDEN INTO A HELL-HOLE STRAIGHT OUT OF "SPARTACUS"?
ANYONE STARTING TO WONDER IF WE PICKED THE WRONG SIDE IN THIS FIGHT?
YOUR "HEROES" MASSACRED HIS PEOPLE, ANGEL. HE SHOULD SLIT THEM GULLET TO GROIN AND RING THE CITY WITH THEIR SPIKED HEADS.
OKAY, NAMORA, DON'T TAKE THIS THE WRONG WAY, BUT EVERY TIME YOU OPEN YOUR MOUTH, YOU TOTALLY FREAK ME OUT.
LIGHTEN THYSELF UP, ANGEL.
WE'RE THE RENEGADES NOW. TALKING TRASH IS PRACTICALLY A REQUIREMENT OF THE JOB.
FINE. I JUST WANT TO MAKE SURE WE ALL KNOW THAT EVISCERATING PEOPLE FOR WHATEVER REASON IS A VERY BAD THING.
AYE, THAT IT IS. IN THIS MILLENNIUM, ANYWAY.
DON'T WORRY, ANGEL.
AMADEUS CHO SHOULD REACH THE HULK ANY MOMENT NOW. AND WHEN HE SPEAKS REASON TO THE GREEN KING, THE LIVES OF YOUR PRECIOUS HEROES WILL NO DOUBT BE SAVED.
THAT'S A LOT RIDING ON ONE KID...
HE HAS THE HEART OF A LION. AND HE'S THE SEVENTH SMARTEST PERSON ON THE PLANET...

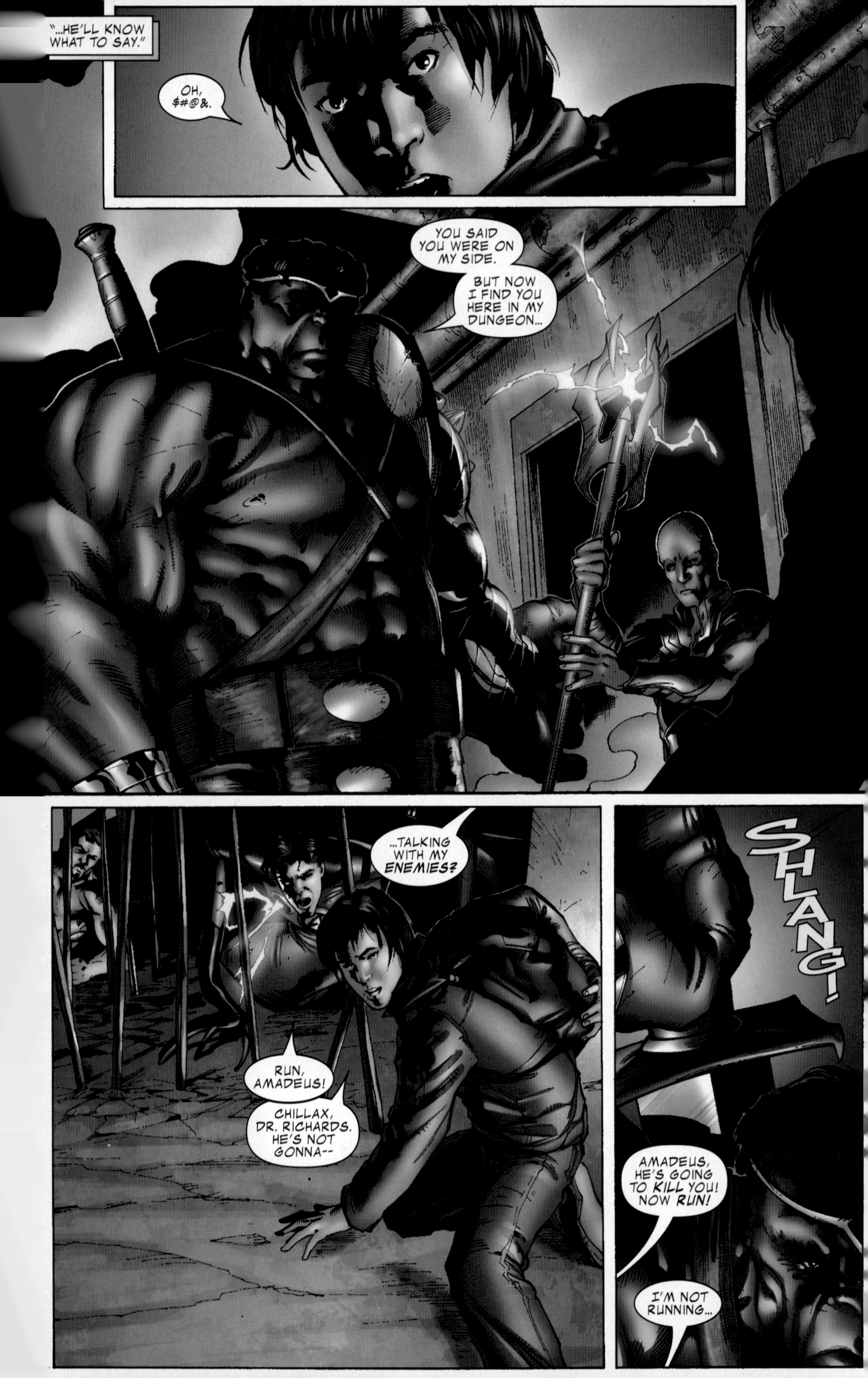
"...HE'LL KNOW WHAT TO SAY."
OH, $#@&.
YOU SAID YOU WERE ON MY SIDE.
BUT NOW I FIND YOU HERE IN MY DUNGEON...
...TALKING WITH MY ENEMIES?
RUN, AMADEUS!
CHILLAX, DR. RICHARDS. HE'S NOT GONNA--
SHLANG!
AMADEUS, HE'S GOING TO KILL YOU! NOW RUN!
I'M NOT RUNNING...

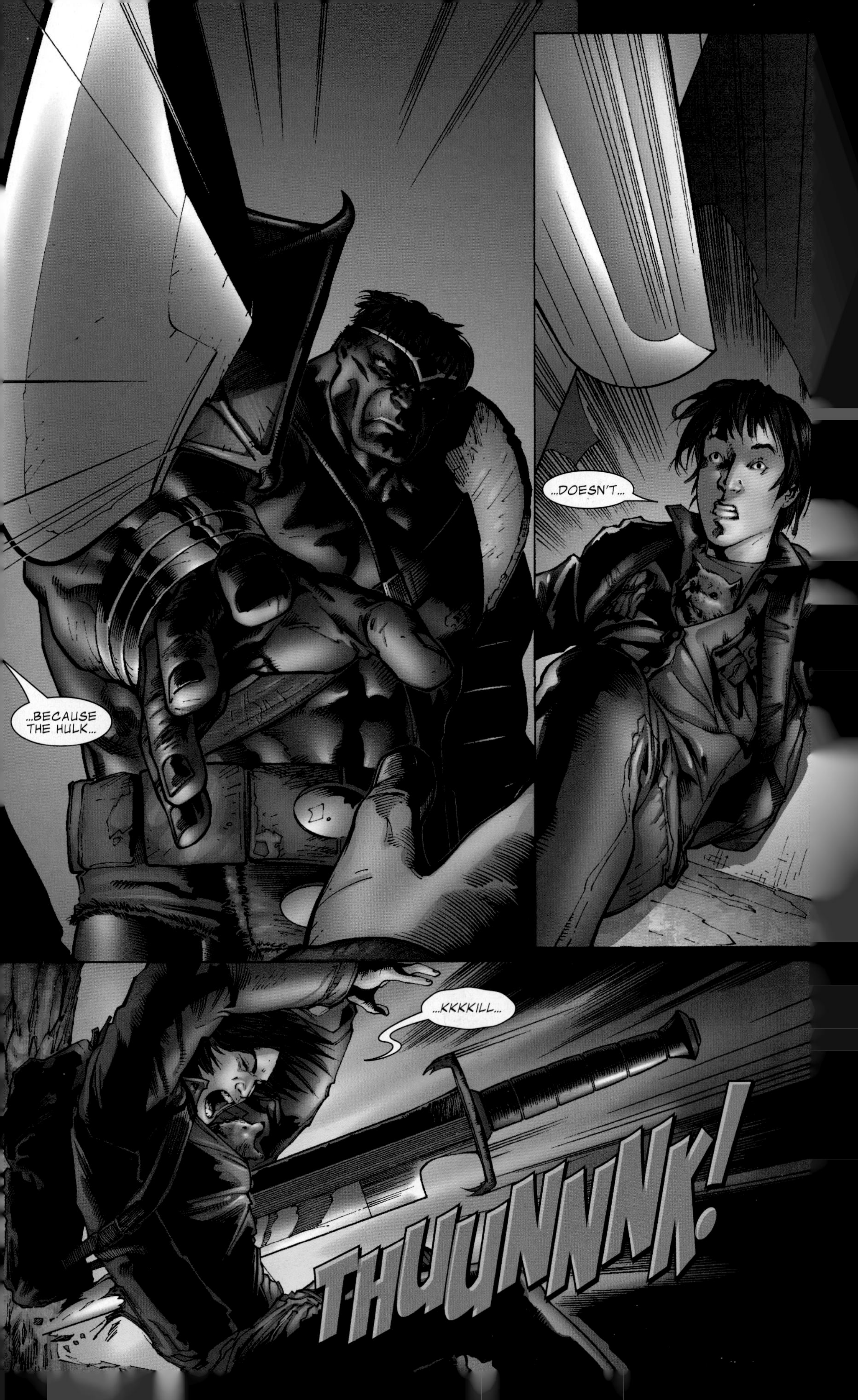
...BECAUSE THE HULK...
...DOESN'T...
...KKKKILL...
THUUNNNK!

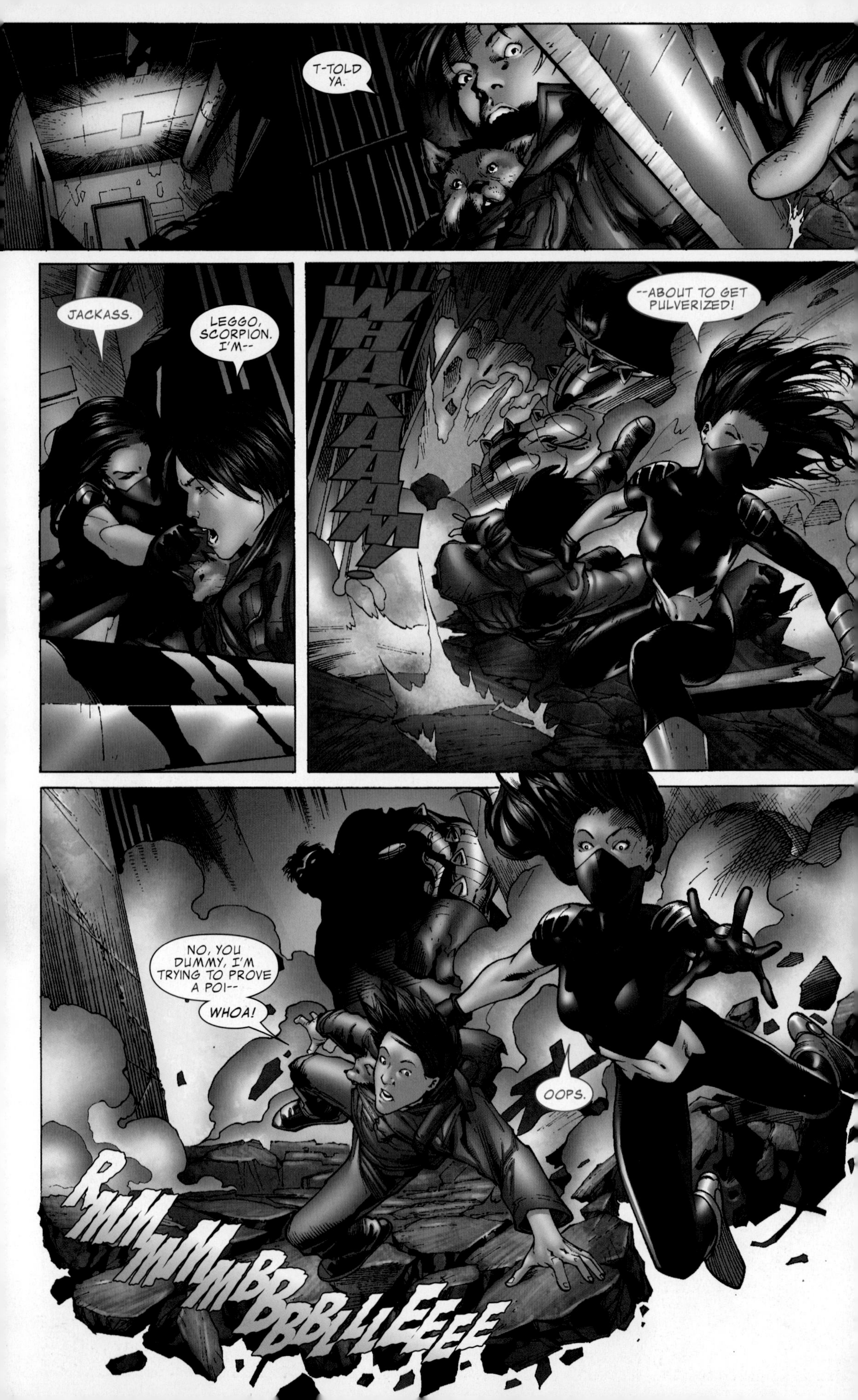
T-TOLD YA.
JACKASS.
LEGGO, SCORPION. I'M--
WHAKAAAM!
--ABOUT TO GET PULVERIZED!
NO, YOU DUMMY, I'M TRYING TO PROVE A POI--
WHOA!
OOPS.
RMMMMMBBBBLLLEEEE

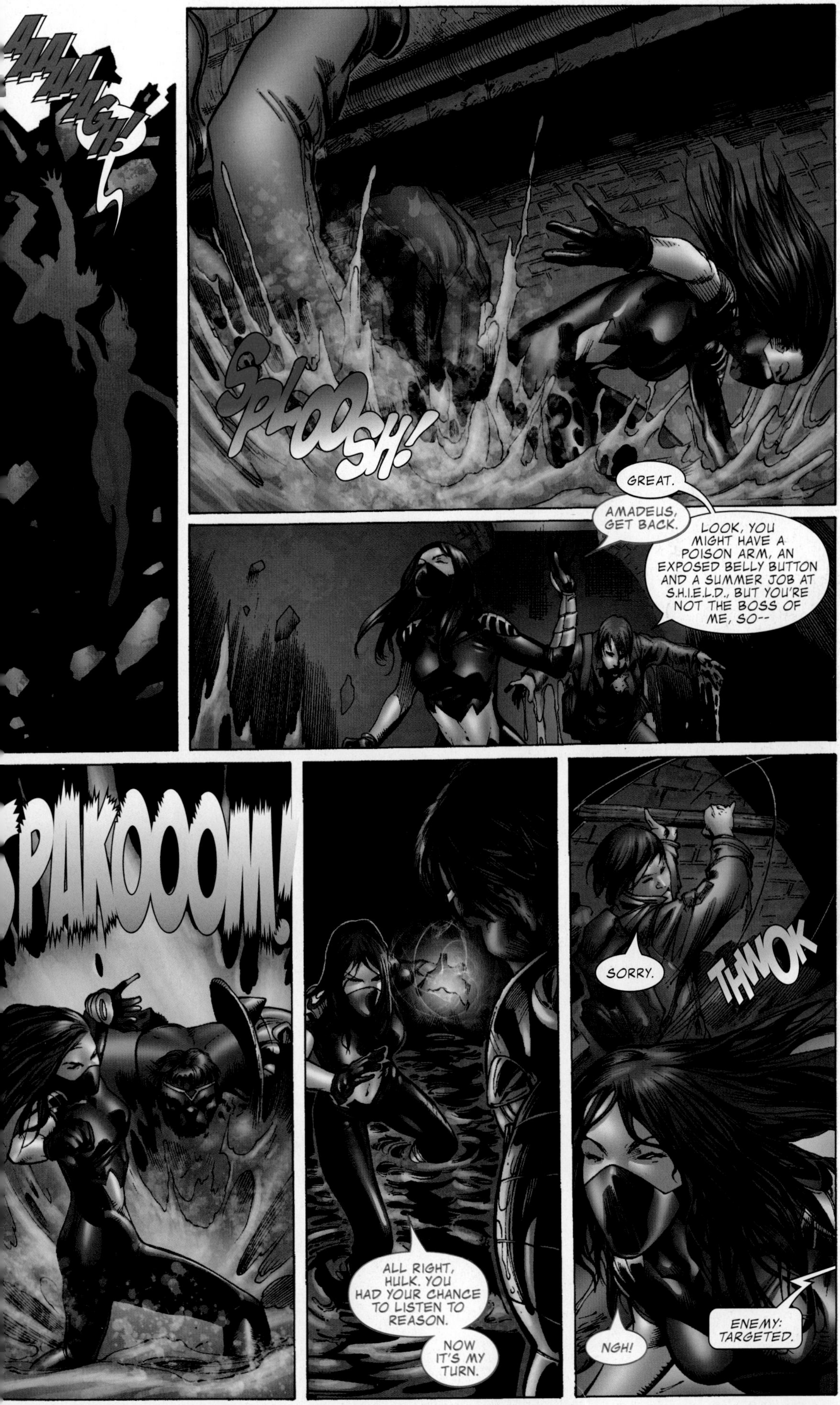
AAAAAAAGH!
SPLOOOSH!
GREAT.
AMADEUS, GET BACK.
LOOK, YOU MIGHT HAVE A POISON ARM, AN EXPOSED BELLY BUTTON AND A SUMMER JOB AT S.H.I.E.L.D., BUT YOU'RE NOT THE BOSS OF ME, SO--
SPAKOOOM!
ALL RIGHT, HULK. YOU HAD YOUR CHANCE TO LISTEN TO REASON.
NOW IT'S MY TURN.
SORRY.
THWOK
NGH!
ENEMY: TARGETED.

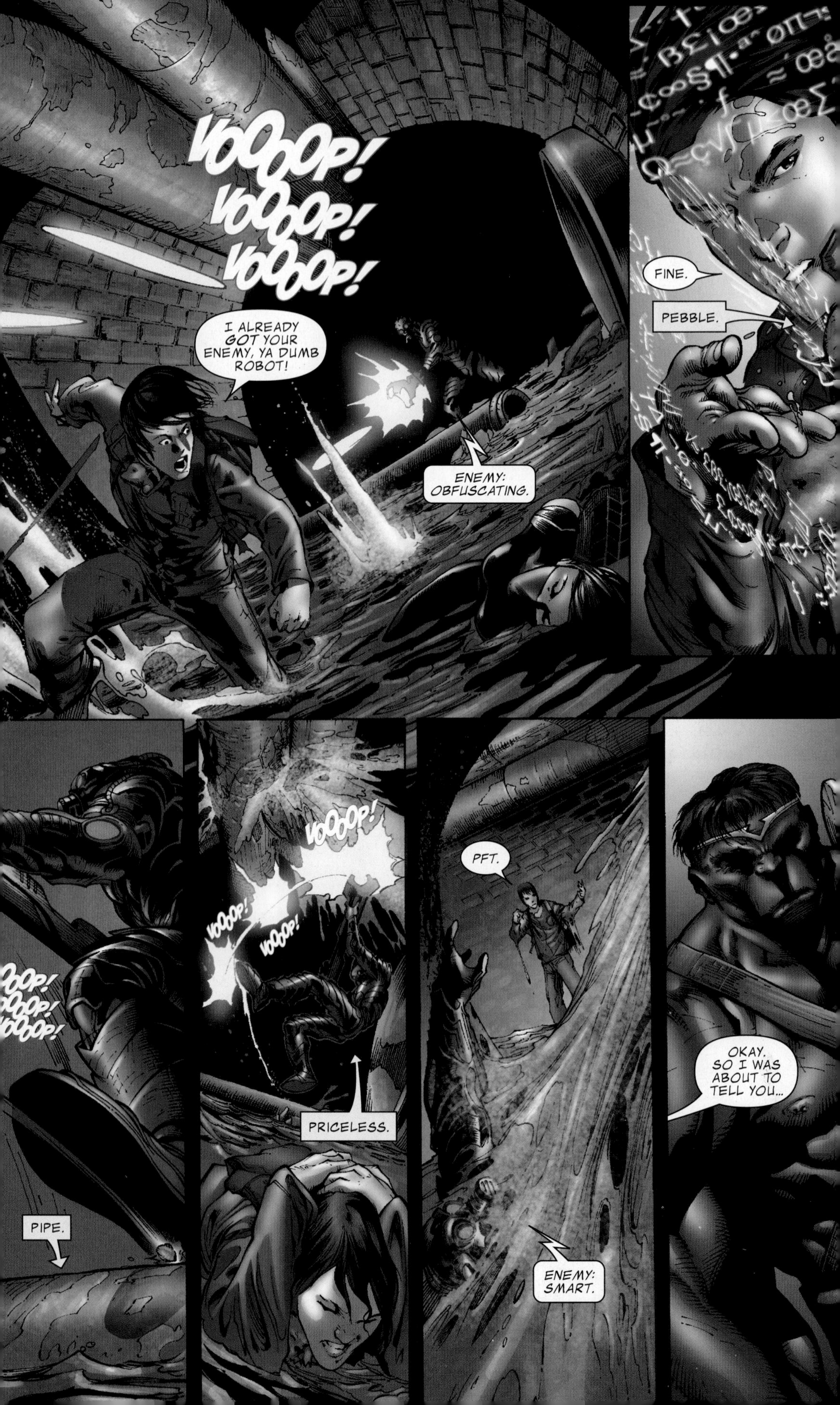
VOOOOP!
VOOOOP!
VOOOOP!
I ALREADY GOT YOUR ENEMY, YA DUMB ROBOT!
ENEMY: OBFUSCATING.
FINE.
PEBBLE.
PIPE.
VOOOOP!
VOOOP!
VOOOP!
PRICELESS.
PFT.
ENEMY: SMART.
OKAY. SO I WAS ABOUT TO TELL YOU...

...SCORPION'S ARM'S PACKED WITH A COCKTAIL OF NEW TOXINS DESIGNED BY S.H.I.E.L.D. TO GOOF UP YOUR GAMMA-POWERED PHYSIOLOGY.

WHICH MEANS **BEFORE** YOUR ROBOT PAL ARRIVED, I'D **ALREADY** SAVED YOUR BIG GREEN CAN, JUST IN CASE YOU NEEDED ANY MORE PROOF THAT I'M ON **YOUR** SIDE.

NOW LISTEN.

I STOLE 1.2 BILLION DOLLARS FROM WARREN WORTHINGTON III AND BOUGHT A FEW THOUSAND ACRES NEAR A DOWNSIZED MILITARY BASE IN THE NEW MEXICO DESERT.

INCLUDING THE OLD ATOMIC TEST SITE WHERE YOU WERE BORN.

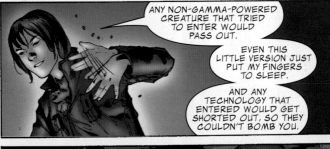

ANY NON-GAMMA-POWERED CREATURE THAT TRIED TO ENTER WOULD PASS OUT.

EVEN THIS LITTLE VERSION JUST PUT MY FINGERS TO SLEEP.

AND ANY TECHNOLOGY THAT ENTERED WOULD GET SHORTED OUT, SO THEY COULDN'T BOMB YOU.

I'VE BEEN WORKING ON THIS DEVICE. THIS IS JUST A TINY VERSION. THE COMPLETED MACHINE WOULD PROJECT A SHIELD OVER THE ENTIRE AREA.

IT'LL BE YOUR PLACE. WHERE THEY'LL FINALLY LEAVE YOU ALONE.

I'M CALLING IT **GAMMAWORLD.**

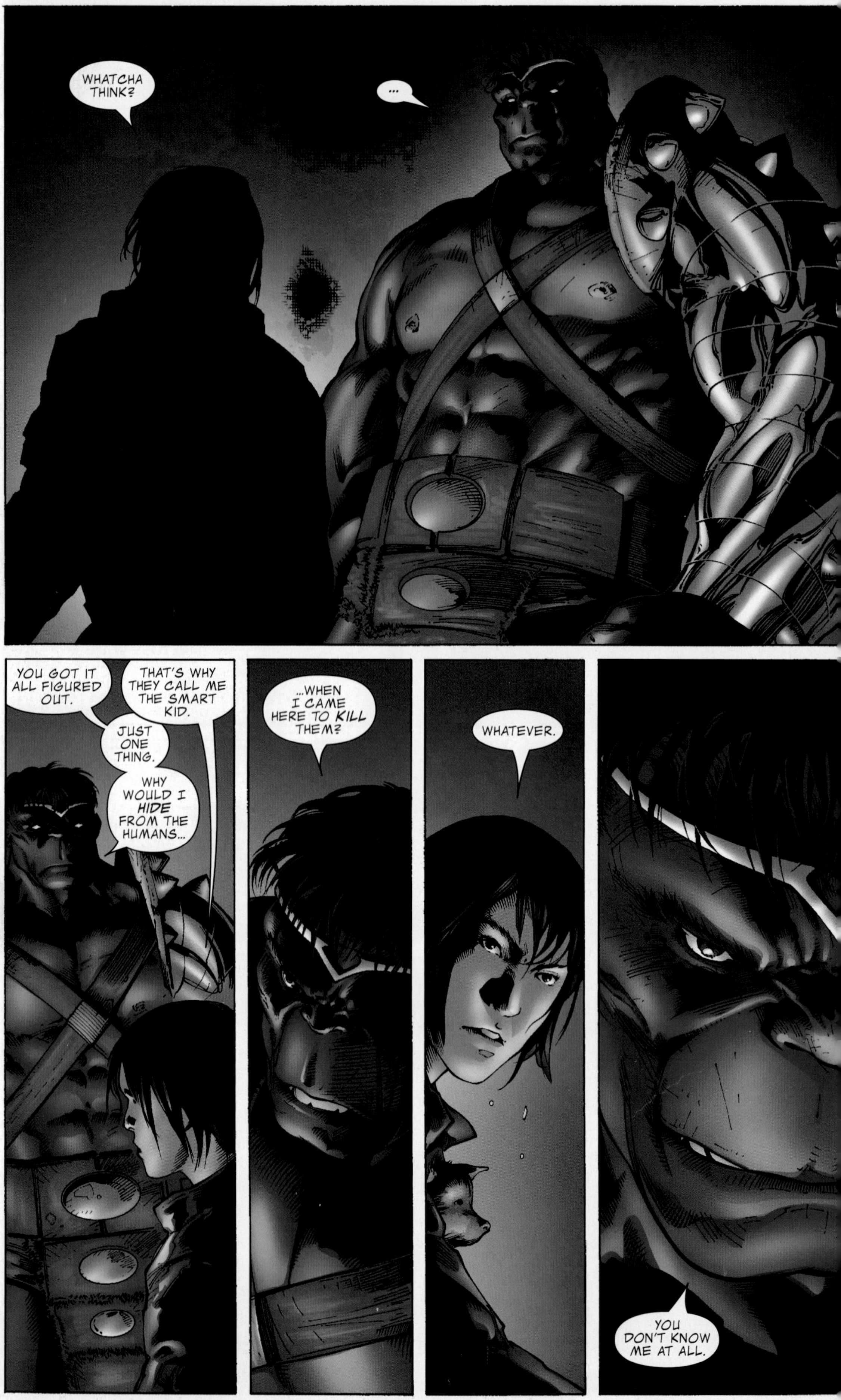
WHATCHA THINK?
...
YOU GOT IT ALL FIGURED OUT.
THAT'S WHY THEY CALL ME THE SMART KID.
JUST ONE THING.
WHY WOULD I HIDE FROM THE HUMANS...
...WHEN I CAME HERE TO KILL THEM?
WHATEVER.
YOU DON'T KNOW ME AT ALL.

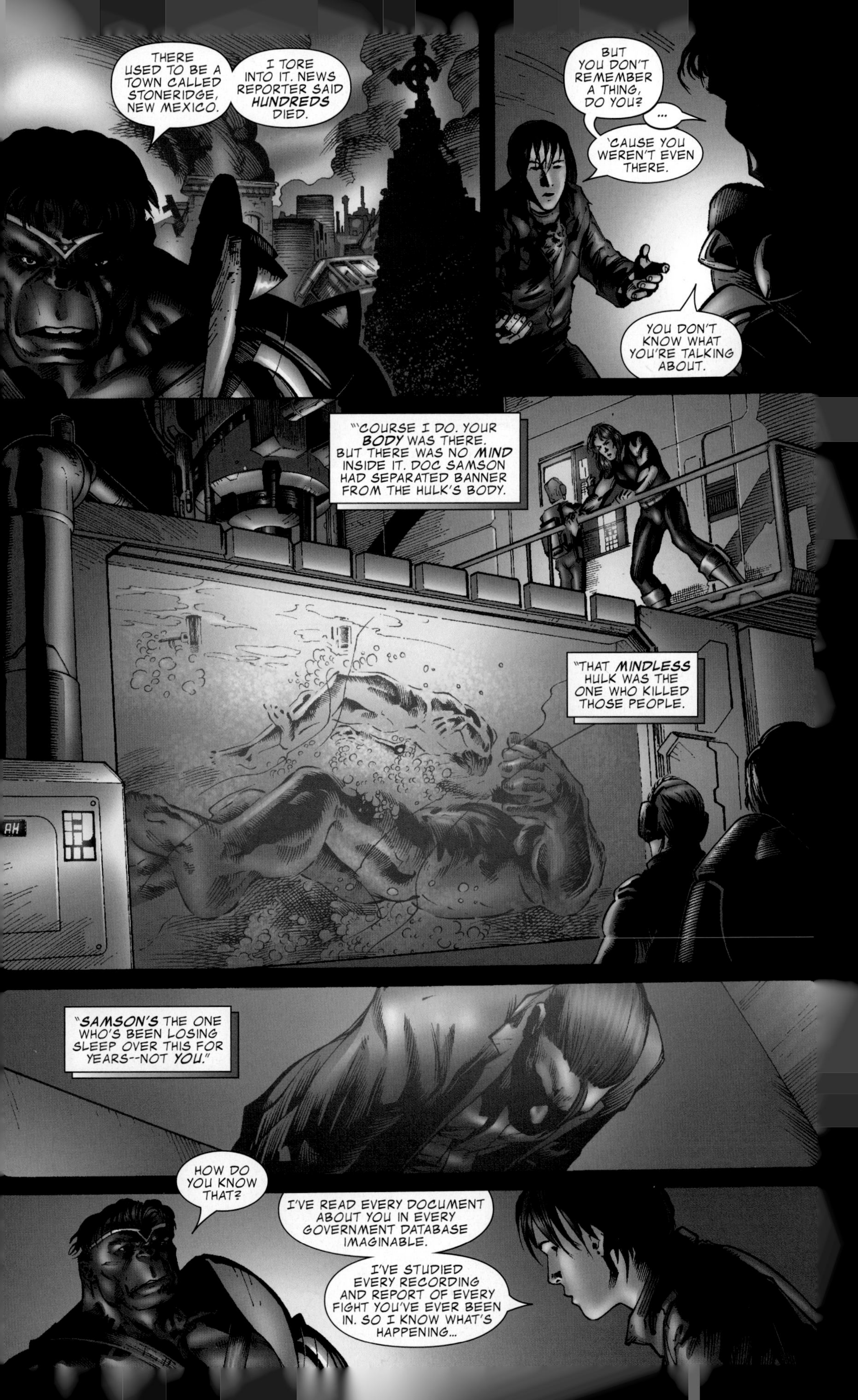
THERE USED TO BE A TOWN CALLED STONERIDGE, NEW MEXICO.
I TORE INTO IT. NEWS REPORTER SAID HUNDREDS DIED.
BUT YOU DON'T REMEMBER A THING, DO YOU?
...
'CAUSE YOU WEREN'T EVEN THERE.
YOU DON'T KNOW WHAT YOU'RE TALKING ABOUT.
"'COURSE I DO. YOUR BODY WAS THERE. BUT THERE WAS NO MIND INSIDE IT. DOC SAMSON HAD SEPARATED BANNER FROM THE HULK'S BODY.
"THAT MINDLESS HULK WAS THE ONE WHO KILLED THOSE PEOPLE.
"SAMSON'S THE ONE WHO'S BEEN LOSING SLEEP OVER THIS FOR YEARS--NOT YOU."
HOW DO YOU KNOW THAT?
I'VE READ EVERY DOCUMENT ABOUT YOU IN EVERY GOVERNMENT DATABASE IMAGINABLE.
I'VE STUDIED EVERY RECORDING AND REPORT OF EVERY FIGHT YOU'VE EVER BEEN IN. SO I KNOW WHAT'S HAPPENING...

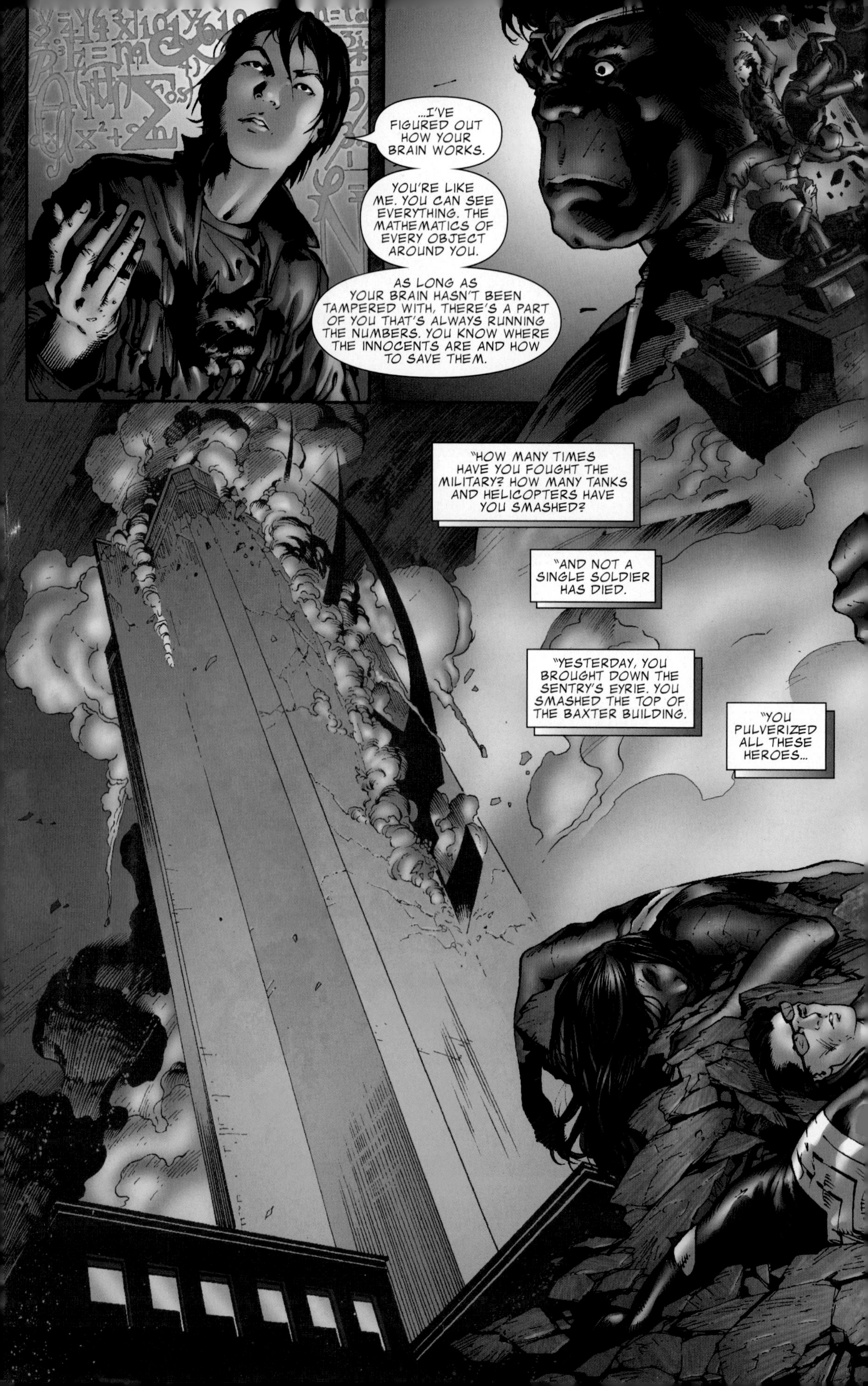
...I'VE FIGURED OUT HOW YOUR BRAIN WORKS.
YOU'RE LIKE ME. YOU CAN SEE EVERYTHING. THE MATHEMATICS OF EVERY OBJECT AROUND YOU.
AS LONG AS YOUR BRAIN HASN'T BEEN TAMPERED WITH, THERE'S A PART OF YOU THAT'S ALWAYS RUNNING THE NUMBERS. YOU KNOW WHERE THE INNOCENTS ARE AND HOW TO SAVE THEM.
"HOW MANY TIMES HAVE YOU FOUGHT THE MILITARY? HOW MANY TANKS AND HELICOPTERS HAVE YOU SMASHED?
"AND NOT A SINGLE SOLDIER HAS DIED.
"YESTERDAY, YOU BROUGHT DOWN THE SENTRY'S EYRIE. YOU SMASHED THE TOP OF THE BAXTER BUILDING.
"YOU PULVERIZED ALL THESE HEROES...

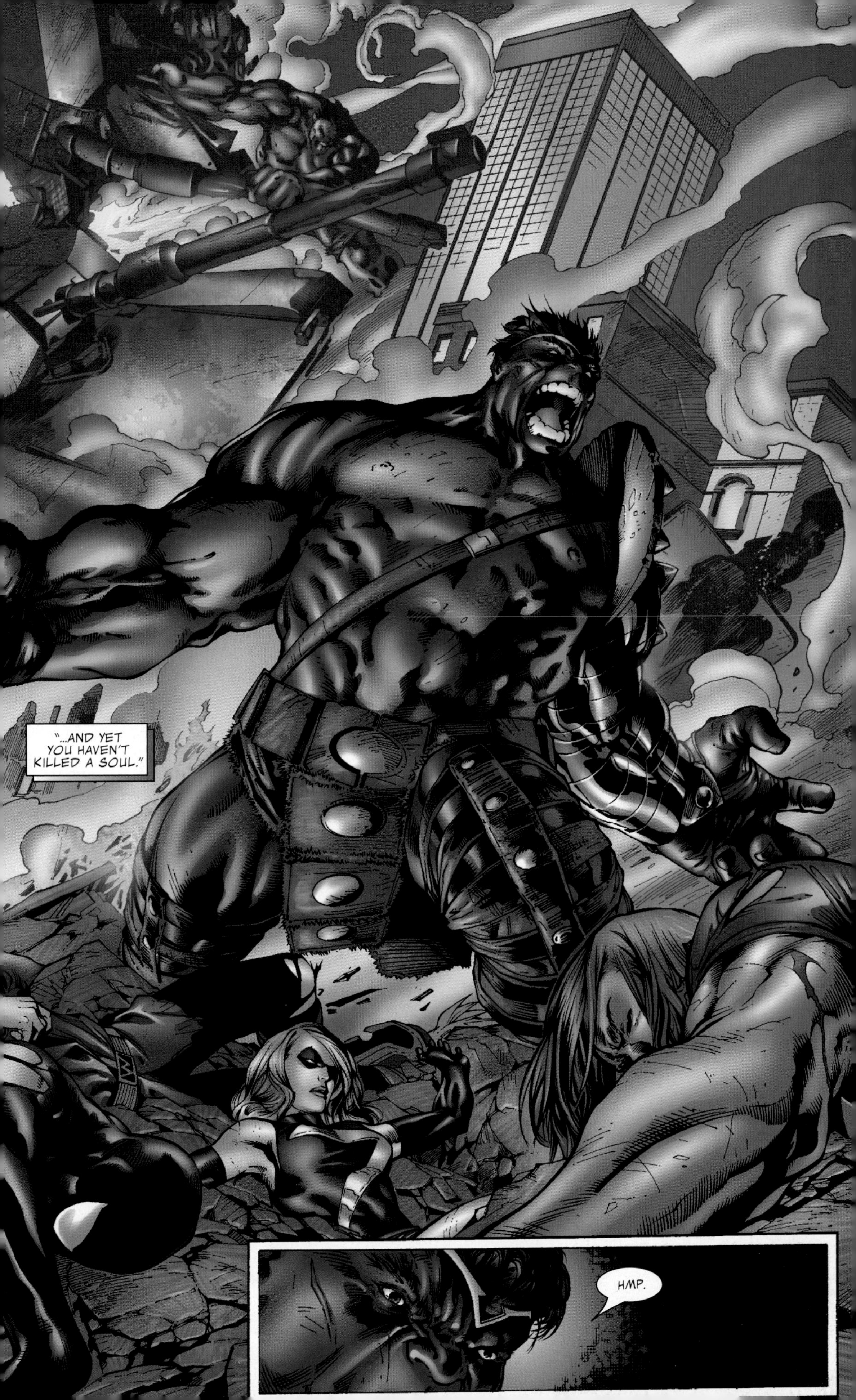
"...AND YET YOU HAVEN'T KILLED A SOUL."
HMP.

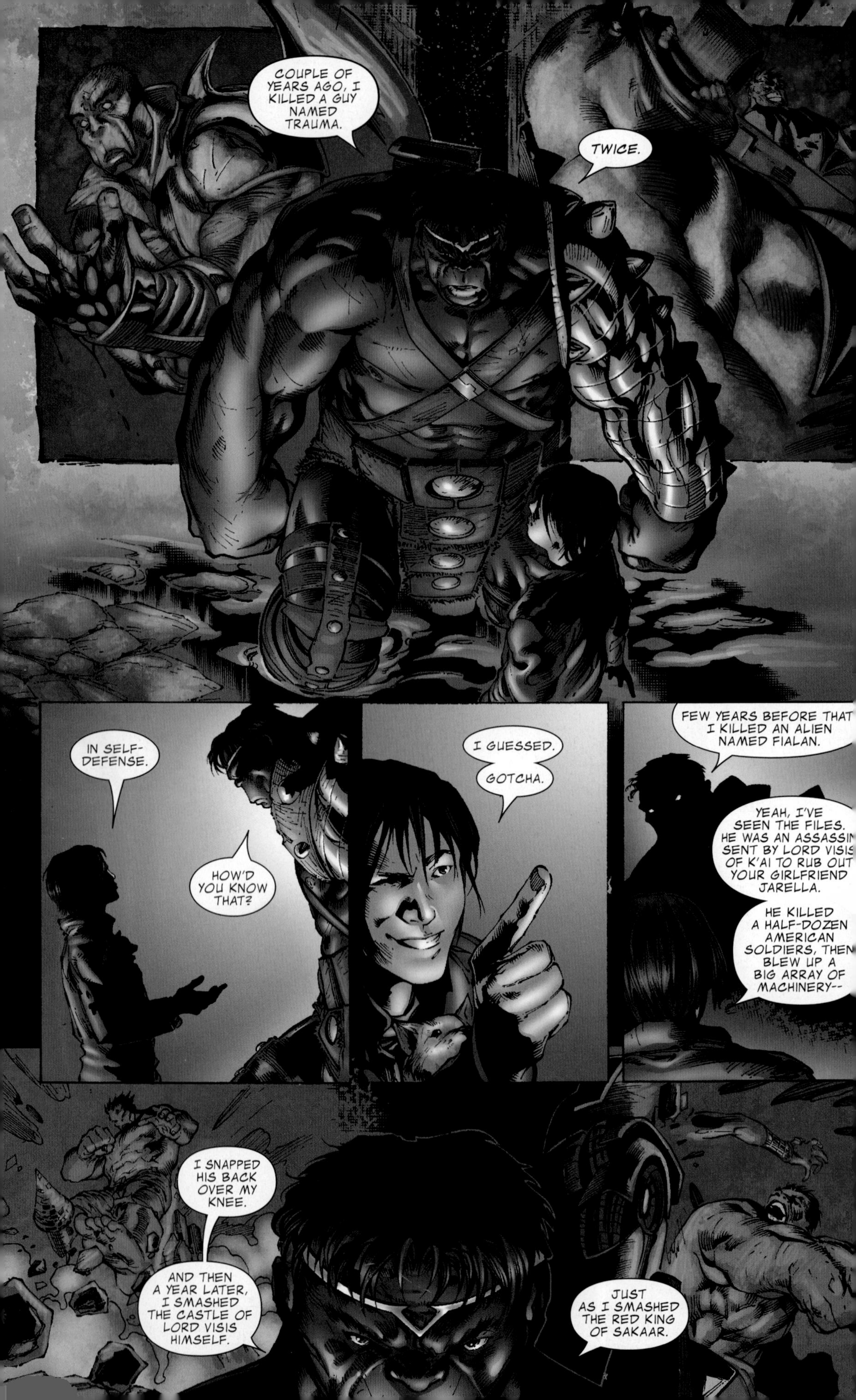
COUPLE OF YEARS AGO, I KILLED A GUY NAMED TRAUMA.
TWICE.
IN SELF-DEFENSE.
HOW'D YOU KNOW THAT?
I GUESSED.
GOTCHA.
FEW YEARS BEFORE THAT I KILLED AN ALIEN NAMED FIALAN.
YEAH, I'VE SEEN THE FILES. HE WAS AN ASSASSIN SENT BY LORD VISIS OF K'AI TO RUB OUT YOUR GIRLFRIEND JARELLA.
HE KILLED A HALF-DOZEN AMERICAN SOLDIERS, THEN BLEW UP A BIG ARRAY OF MACHINERY--
I SNAPPED HIS BACK OVER MY KNEE.
AND THEN A YEAR LATER, I SMASHED THE CASTLE OF LORD VISIS HIMSELF.
JUST AS I SMASHED THE RED KING OF SAKAAR.

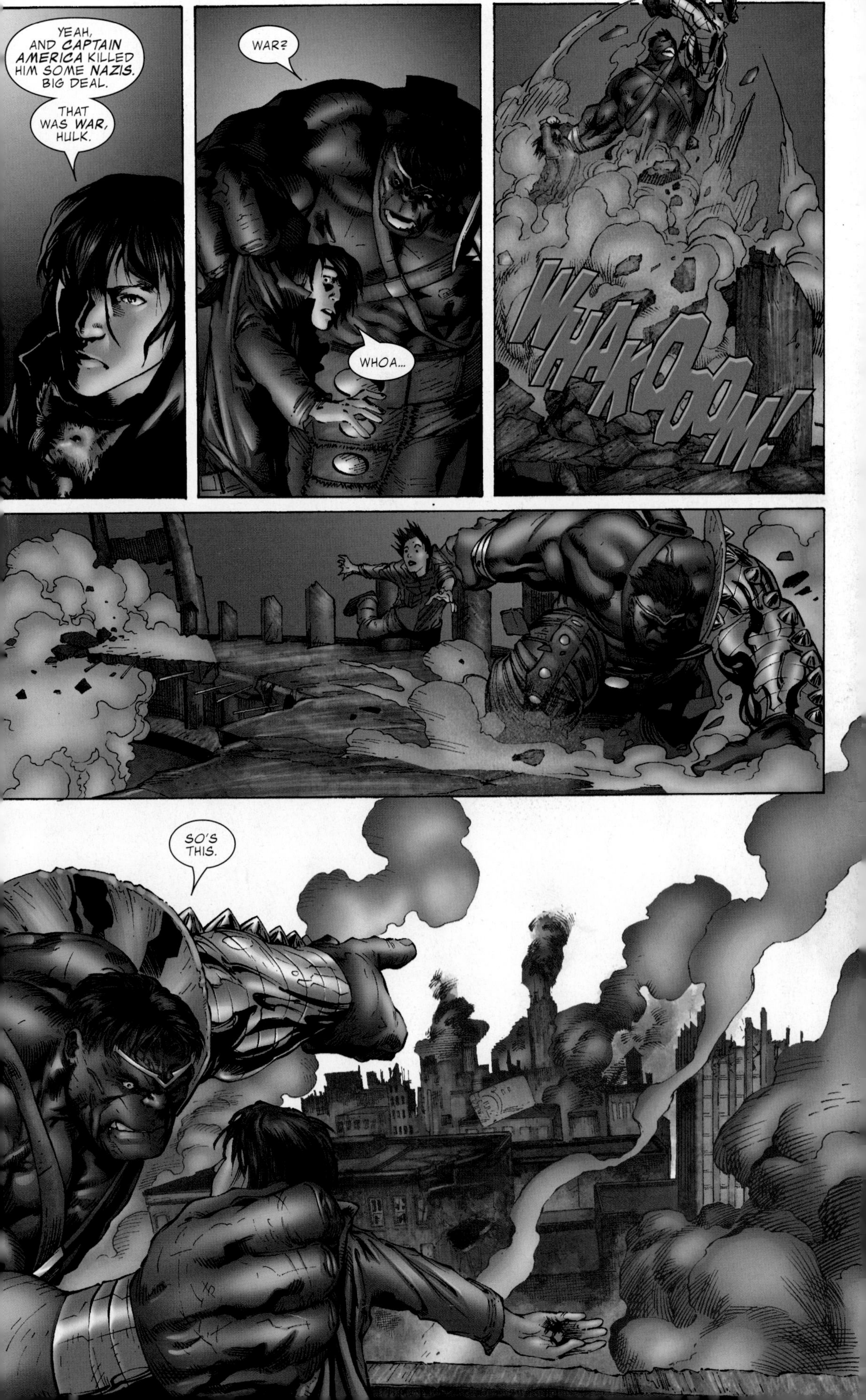
YEAH, AND CAPTAIN AMERICA KILLED HIM SOME NAZIS. BIG DEAL.
THAT WAS WAR, HULK.
WAR?
WHOA...
WHAKOOOM!
SO'S THIS.

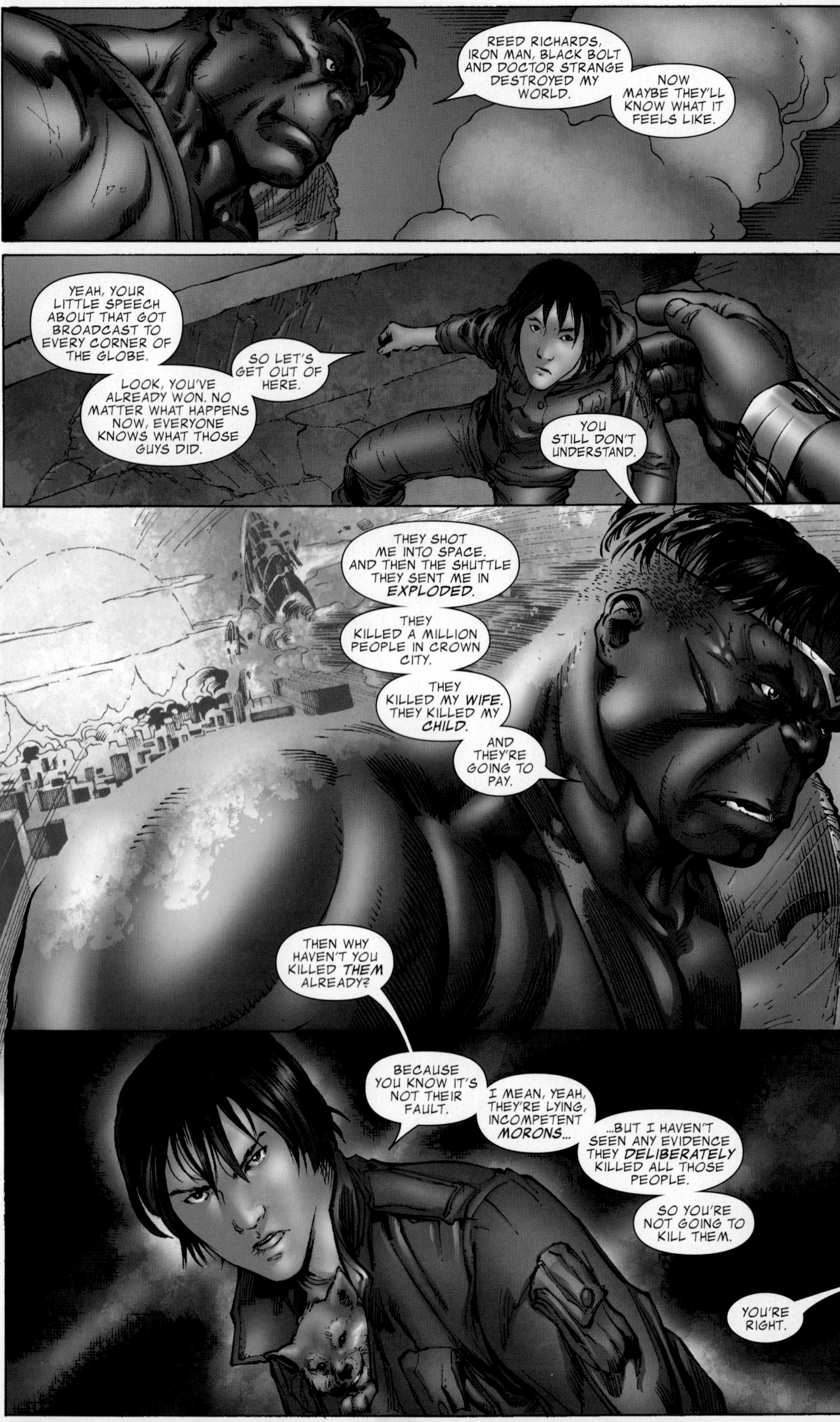

REED RICHARDS, IRON MAN, BLACK BOLT AND DOCTOR STRANGE DESTROYED MY WORLD.
NOW MAYBE THEY'LL KNOW WHAT IT FEELS LIKE.
YEAH, YOUR LITTLE SPEECH ABOUT THAT GOT BROADCAST TO EVERY CORNER OF THE GLOBE.
LOOK, YOU'VE ALREADY WON. NO MATTER WHAT HAPPENS NOW, EVERYONE KNOWS WHAT THOSE GUYS DID.
SO LET'S GET OUT OF HERE.
YOU STILL DON'T UNDERSTAND.
THEY SHOT ME INTO SPACE. AND THEN THE SHUTTLE THEY SENT ME IN EXPLODED.
THEY KILLED A MILLION PEOPLE IN CROWN CITY.
THEY KILLED MY WIFE. THEY KILLED MY CHILD.
AND THEY'RE GOING TO PAY.
THEN WHY HAVEN'T YOU KILLED THEM ALREADY?
BECAUSE YOU KNOW IT'S NOT THEIR FAULT.
I MEAN, YEAH, THEY'RE LYING, INCOMPETENT MORONS...
...BUT I HAVEN'T SEEN ANY EVIDENCE THEY DELIBERATELY KILLED ALL THOSE PEOPLE.
SO YOU'RE NOT GOING TO KILL THEM.
YOU'RE RIGHT.

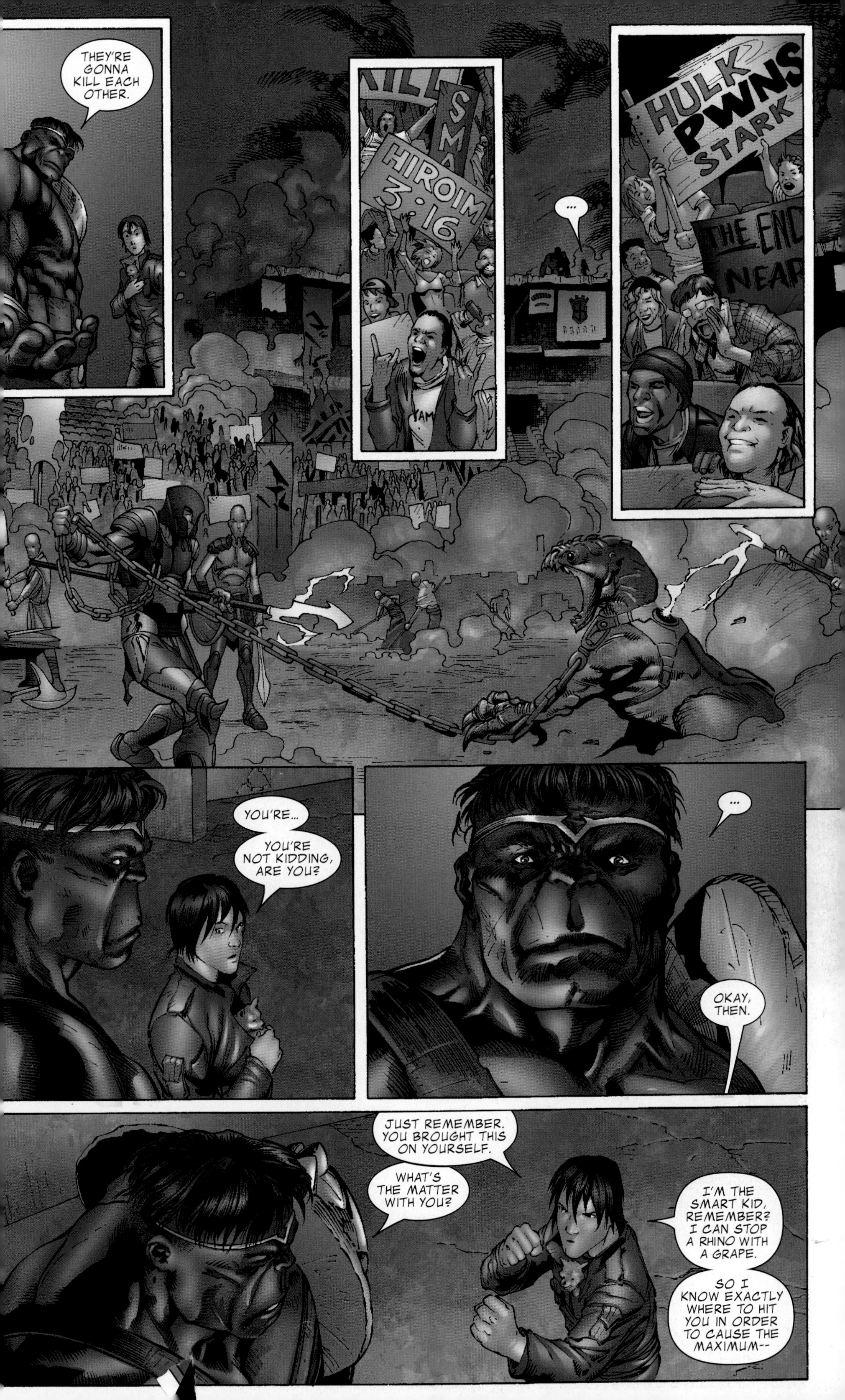
THEY'RE GONNA KILL EACH OTHER.
KILL
SMA
HIROIM 3:16
YAM
...
HULK PWNS STARK
THE END NEAR
YOU'RE...
YOU'RE NOT KIDDING, ARE YOU?
...
OKAY, THEN.
JUST REMEMBER. YOU BROUGHT THIS ON YOURSELF.
WHAT'S THE MATTER WITH YOU?
I'M THE SMART KID, REMEMBER? I CAN STOP A RHINO WITH A GRAPE.
SO I KNOW EXACTLY WHERE TO HIT YOU IN ORDER TO CAUSE THE MAXIMUM--

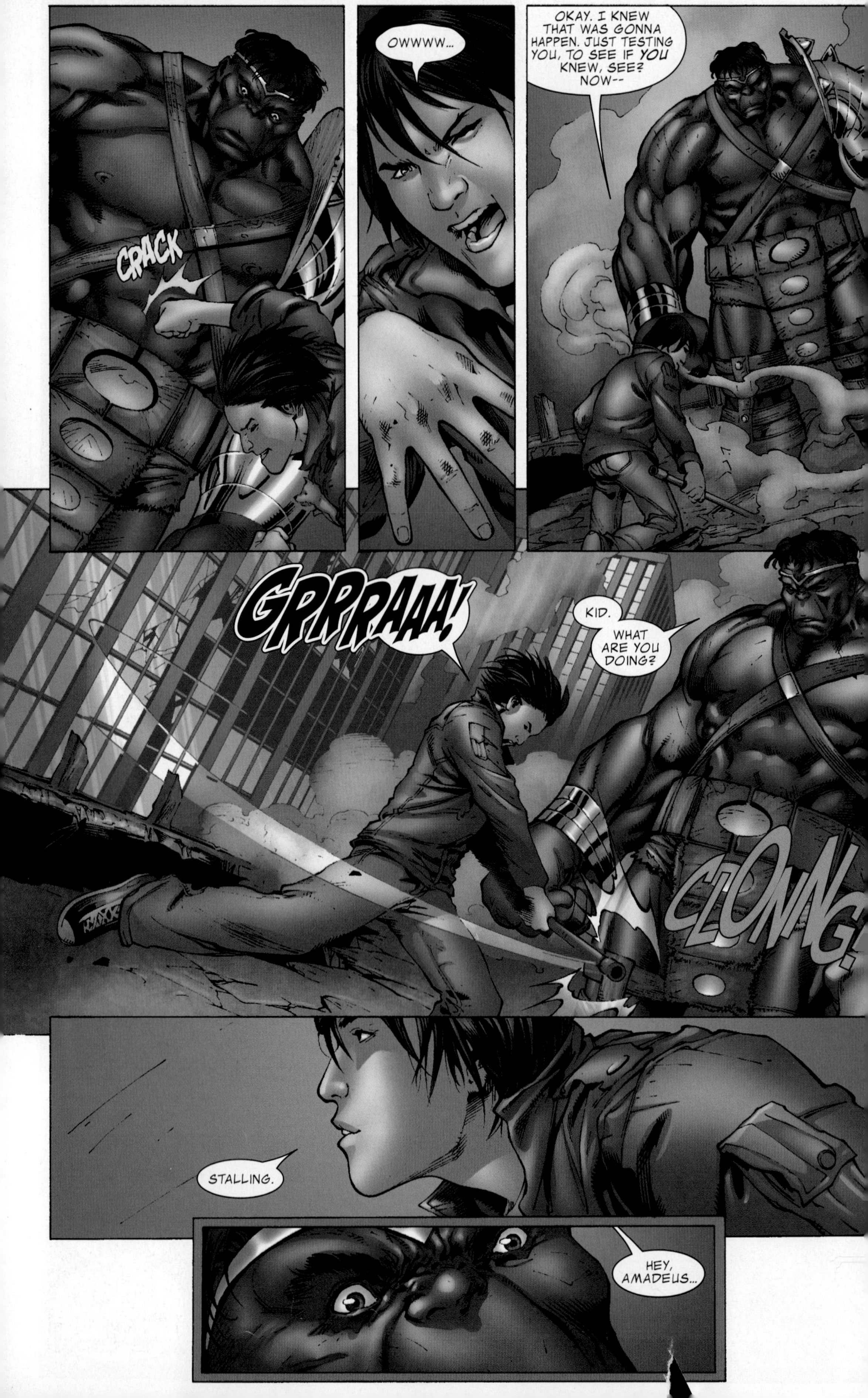
CRACK
OWWWW...
OKAY. I KNEW THAT WAS GONNA HAPPEN. JUST TESTING YOU, TO SEE IF YOU KNEW, SEE? NOW--
GRRRAAA!
KID.
WHAT ARE YOU DOING?
CLONNG!
STALLING.
HEY, AMADEUS...

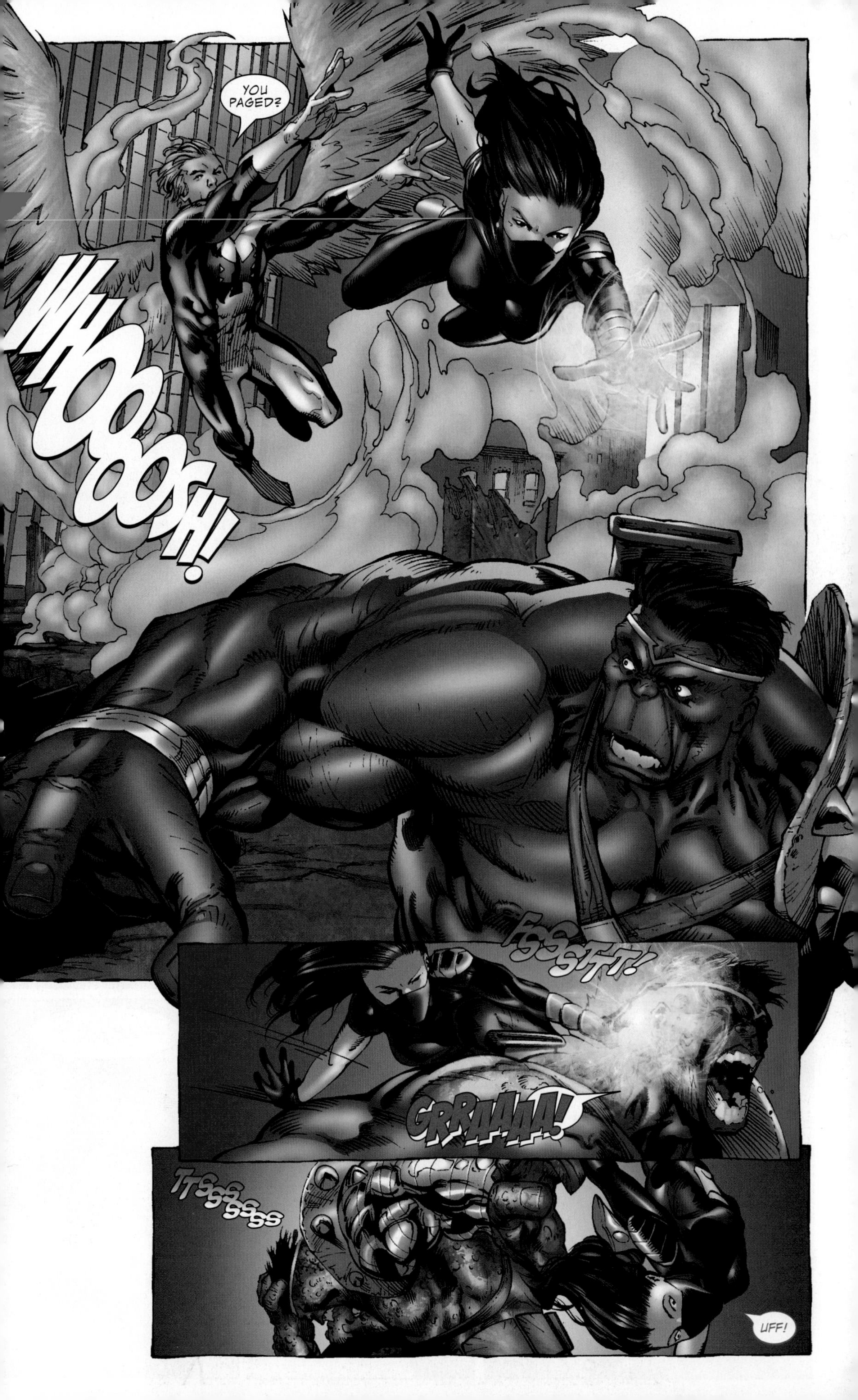
YOU PAGED?
WHOOOOOSH!
FSSSTTT!
GRRAAAAA!
TTSSSSSSSS
UFF!

WHAT THE--

I THOUGHT YOU WERE JUST GOING TO *STUN* HIM!

SSSTSSSS

AAARRGGHHH!!

YOU THOUGHT WRONG, FLYBOY.

THIS IS THE *END*.

YE GODS, GIRL...

NO. HANG ON, HULK. WE'RE GONNA HELP--

NO. WAIT.

WAIT?

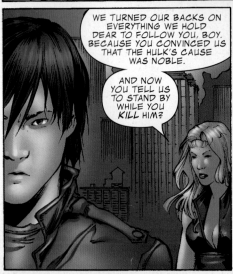

WE TURNED OUR BACKS ON EVERYTHING WE HOLD DEAR TO FOLLOW YOU, BOY. BECAUSE YOU CONVINCED US THAT THE HULK'S CAUSE WAS NOBLE.

AND NOW YOU TELL US TO STAND BY WHILE YOU *KILL* HIM?

JUST...

...TRUST ME.

SSS

AAARGH!

CONGRATULATIONS, TOUGH GUY...

SS

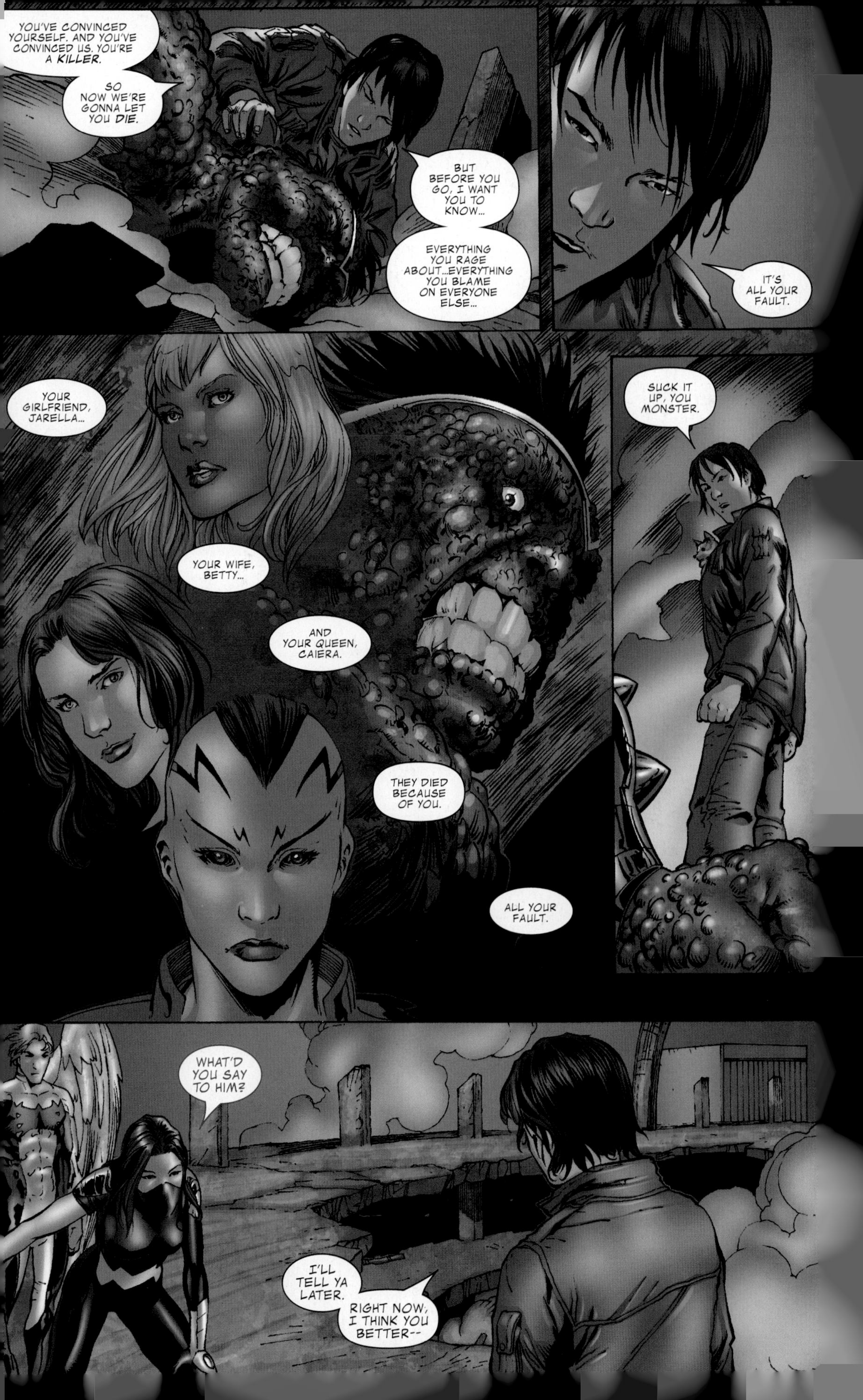
YOU'VE CONVINCED YOURSELF. AND YOU'VE CONVINCED US. YOU'RE A KILLER.
SO NOW WE'RE GONNA LET YOU DIE.
BUT BEFORE YOU GO, I WANT YOU TO KNOW...
EVERYTHING YOU RAGE ABOUT...EVERYTHING YOU BLAME ON EVERYONE ELSE...
IT'S ALL YOUR FAULT.
YOUR GIRLFRIEND, JARELLA...
YOUR WIFE, BETTY...
AND YOUR QUEEN, CAIERA.
THEY DIED BECAUSE OF YOU.
ALL YOUR FAULT.
SUCK IT UP, YOU MONSTER.
WHAT'D YOU SAY TO HIM?
I'LL TELL YA LATER.
RIGHT NOW, I THINK YOU BETTER--

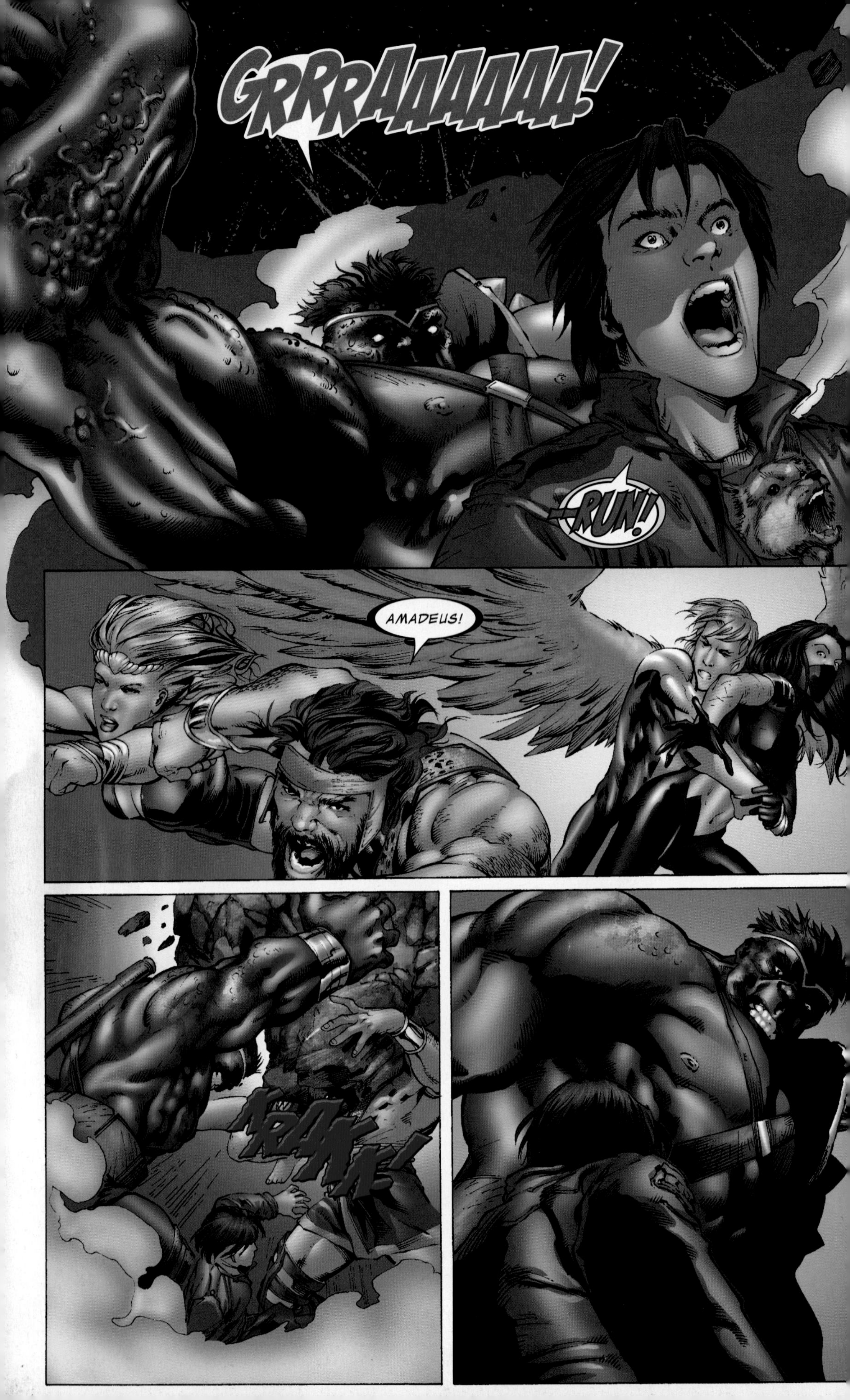
GRRRAAAAAA!
RUN!
AMADEUS!

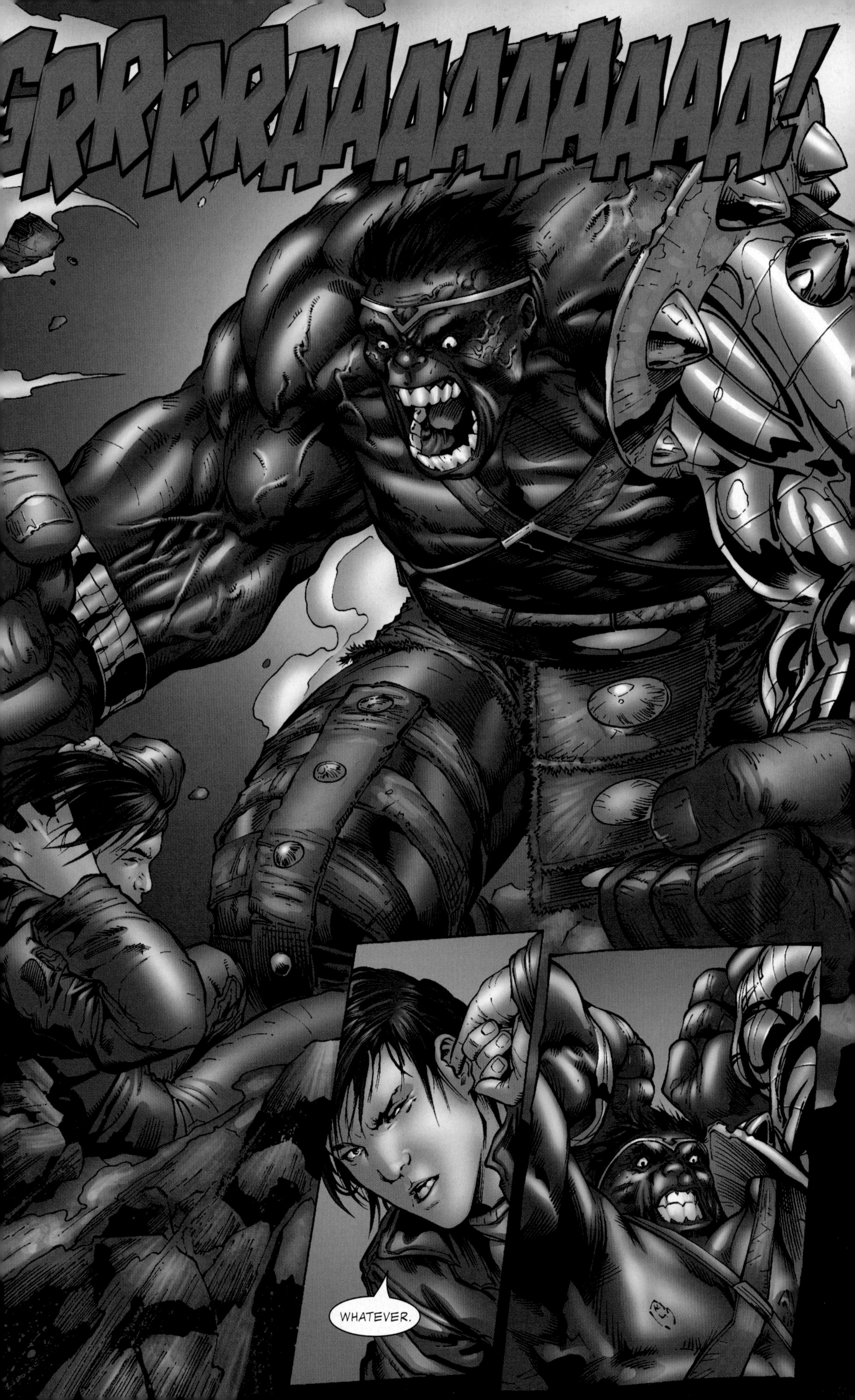
GRRRRAAAAAAAAAAAA!
WHATEVER.

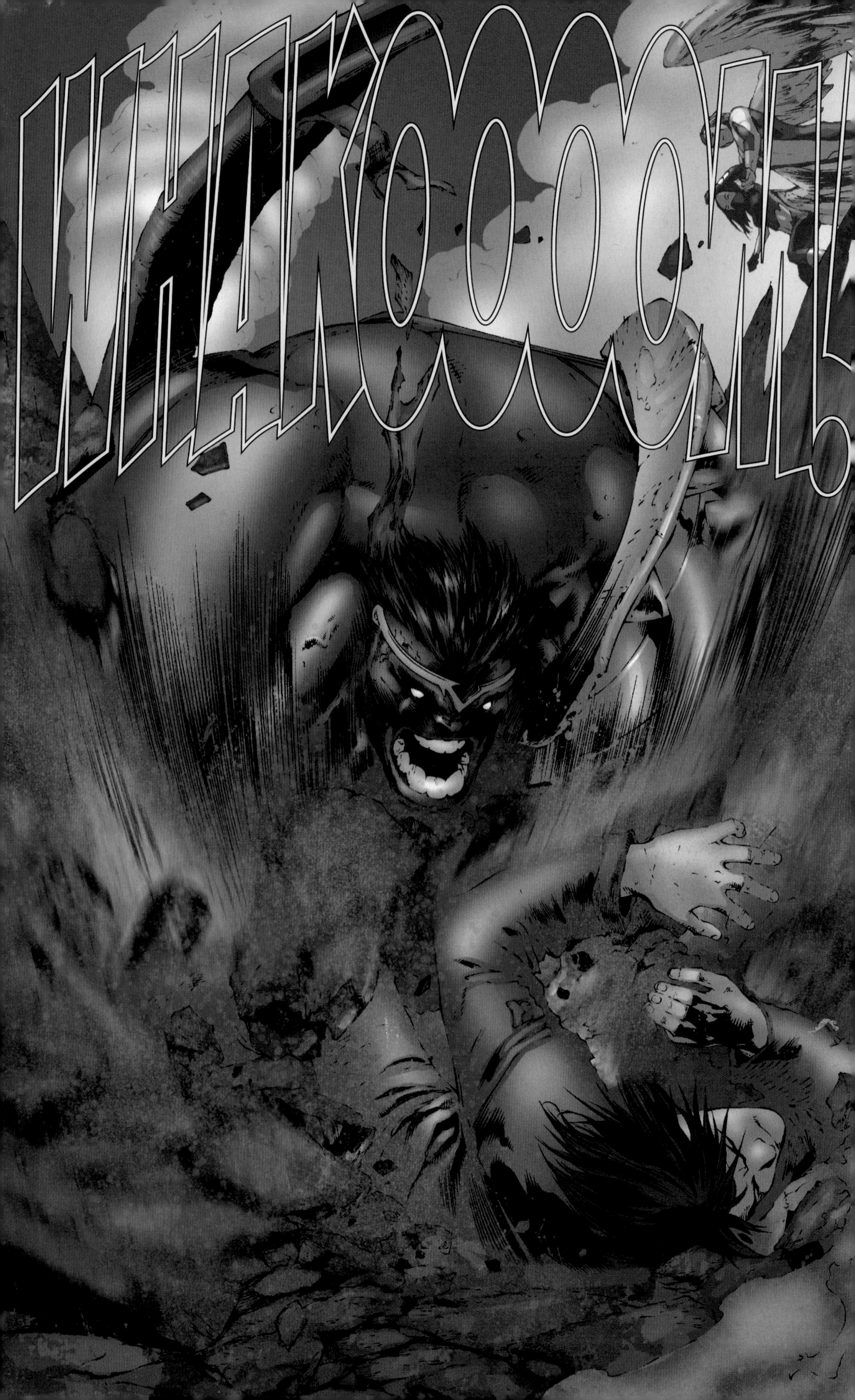
WHAKOOOOM!

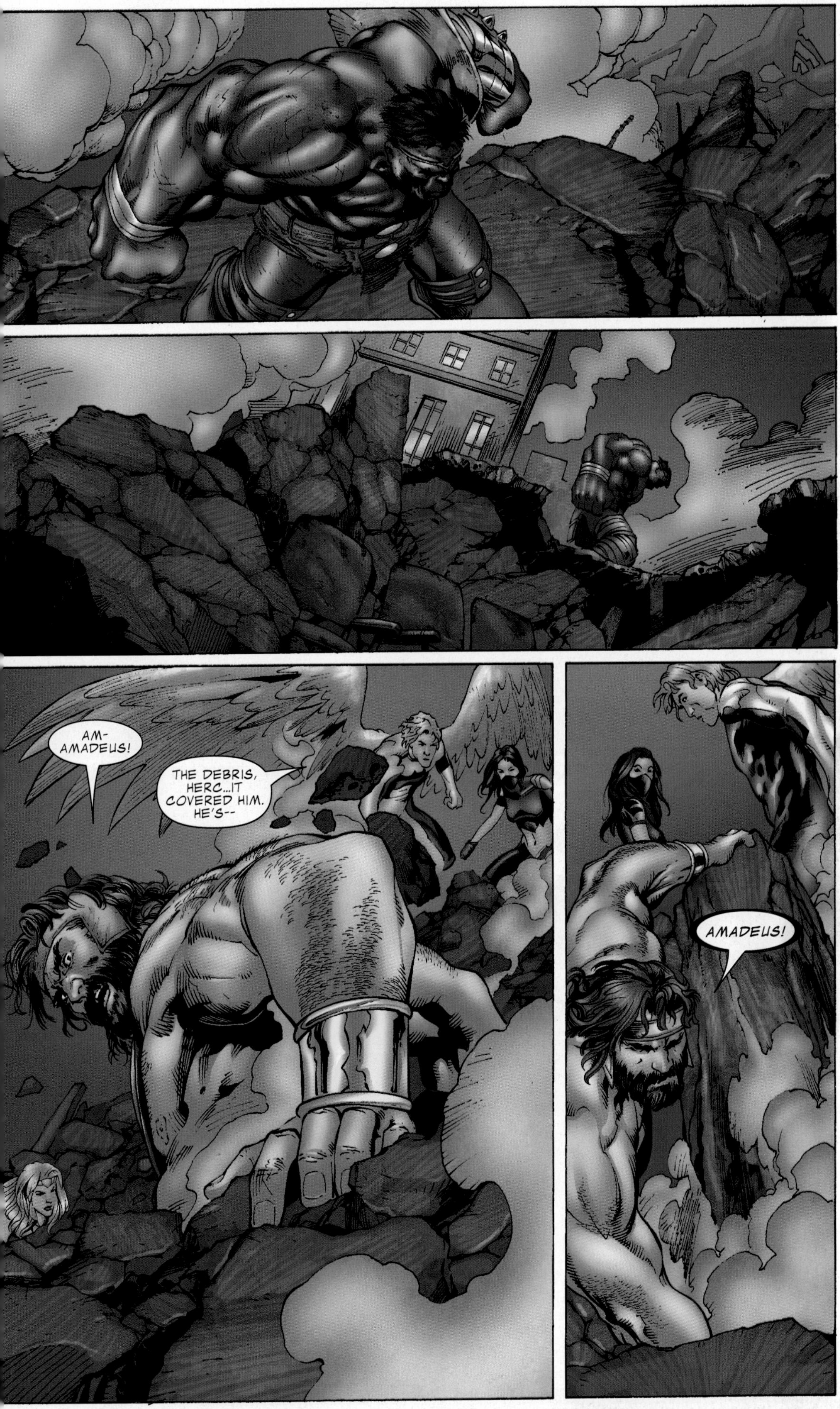
AM-
AMADEUS!
THE DEBRIS, HERC...IT COVERED HIM. HE'S--
AMADEUS!

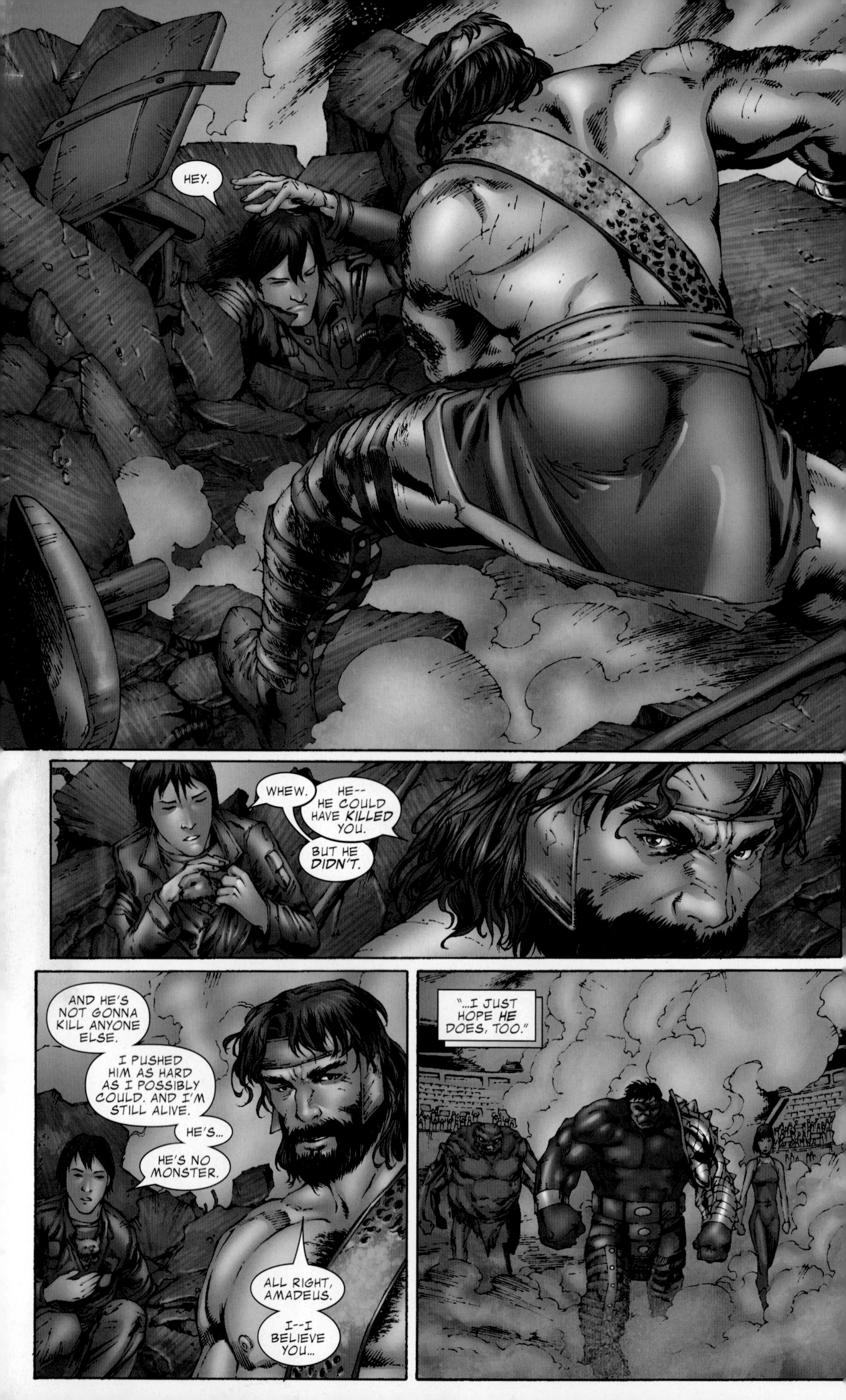
HEY.
WHEW.
HE-- HE COULD HAVE KILLED YOU.
BUT HE DIDN'T.
AND HE'S NOT GONNA KILL ANYONE ELSE.
I PUSHED HIM AS HARD AS I POSSIBLY COULD. AND I'M STILL ALIVE.
HE'S...
HE'S NO MONSTER.
ALL RIGHT, AMADEUS.
I--I BELIEVE YOU...
"...I JUST HOPE HE DOES, TOO."

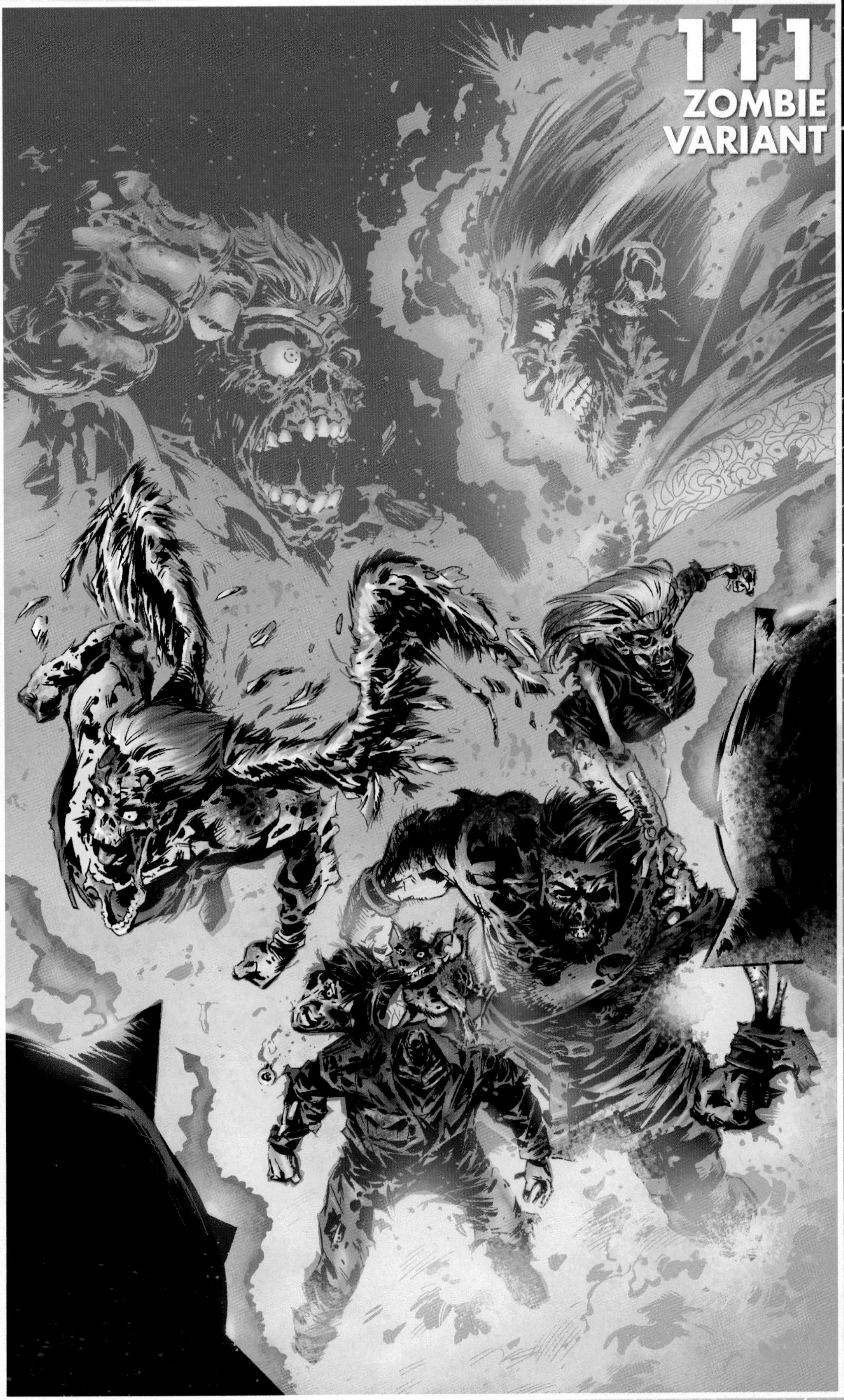
111
ZOMBIE
VARIANT

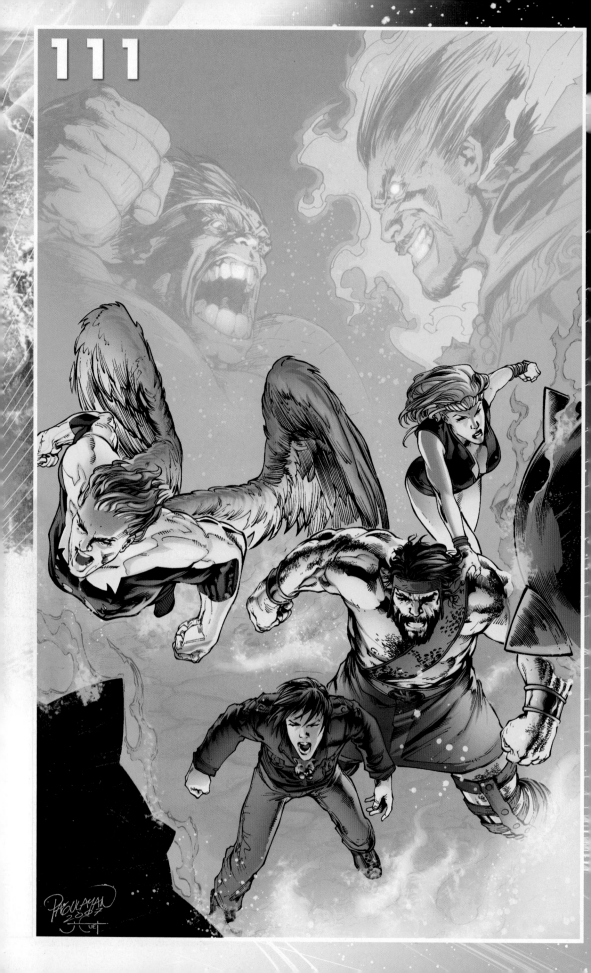

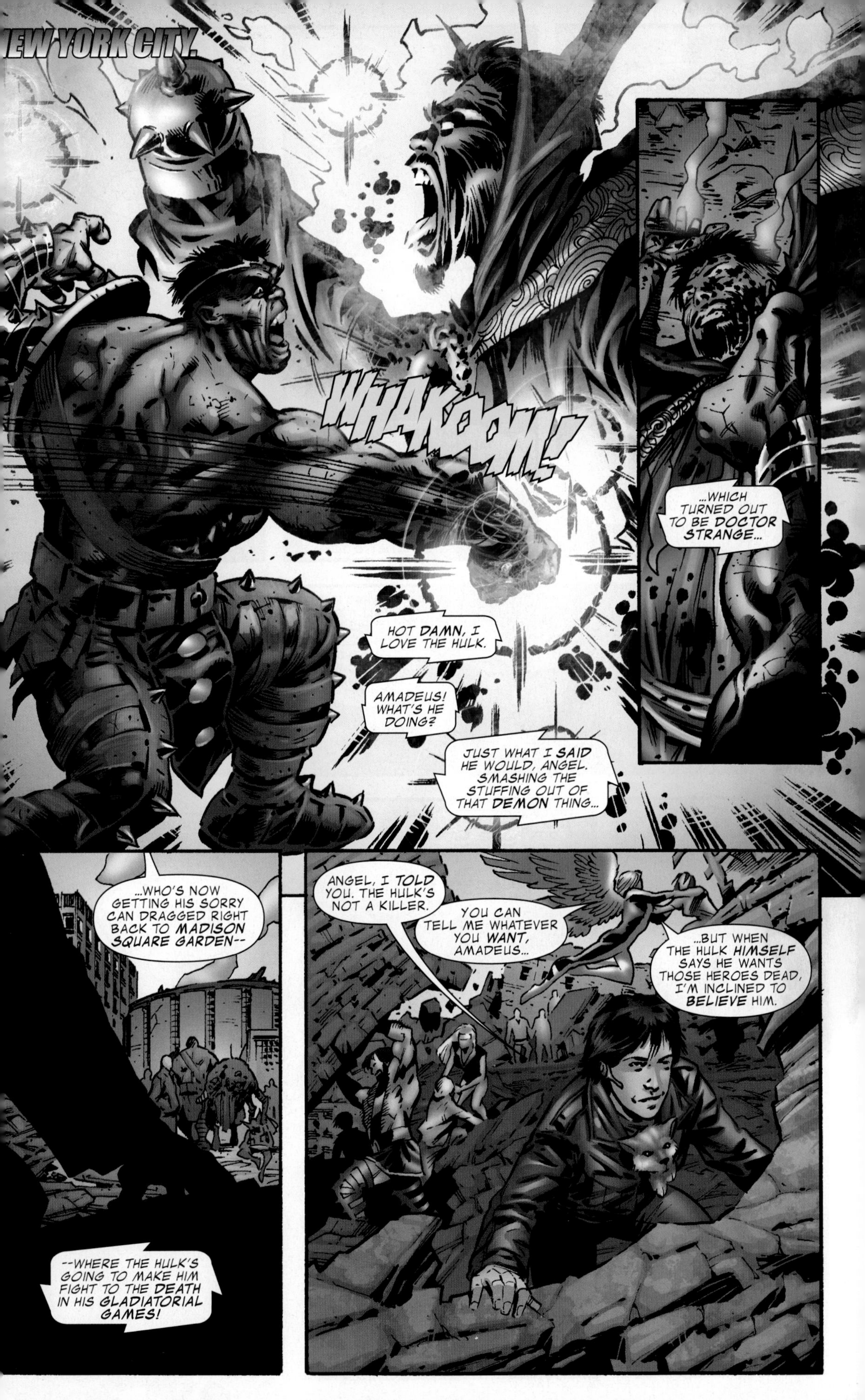

NEW YORK CITY.
WHAKOOM!
...WHICH TURNED OUT TO BE DOCTOR STRANGE...
HOT DAMN, I LOVE THE HULK.
AMADEUS! WHAT'S HE DOING?
JUST WHAT I SAID HE WOULD, ANGEL. SMASHING THE STUFFING OUT OF THAT DEMON THING...
...WHO'S NOW GETTING HIS SORRY CAN DRAGGED RIGHT BACK TO MADISON SQUARE GARDEN--
--WHERE THE HULK'S GOING TO MAKE HIM FIGHT TO THE DEATH IN HIS GLADIATORIAL GAMES!
ANGEL, I TOLD YOU. THE HULK'S NOT A KILLER.
YOU CAN TELL ME WHATEVER YOU WANT, AMADEUS...
...BUT WHEN THE HULK HIMSELF SAYS HE WANTS THOSE HEROES DEAD, I'M INCLINED TO BELIEVE HIM.

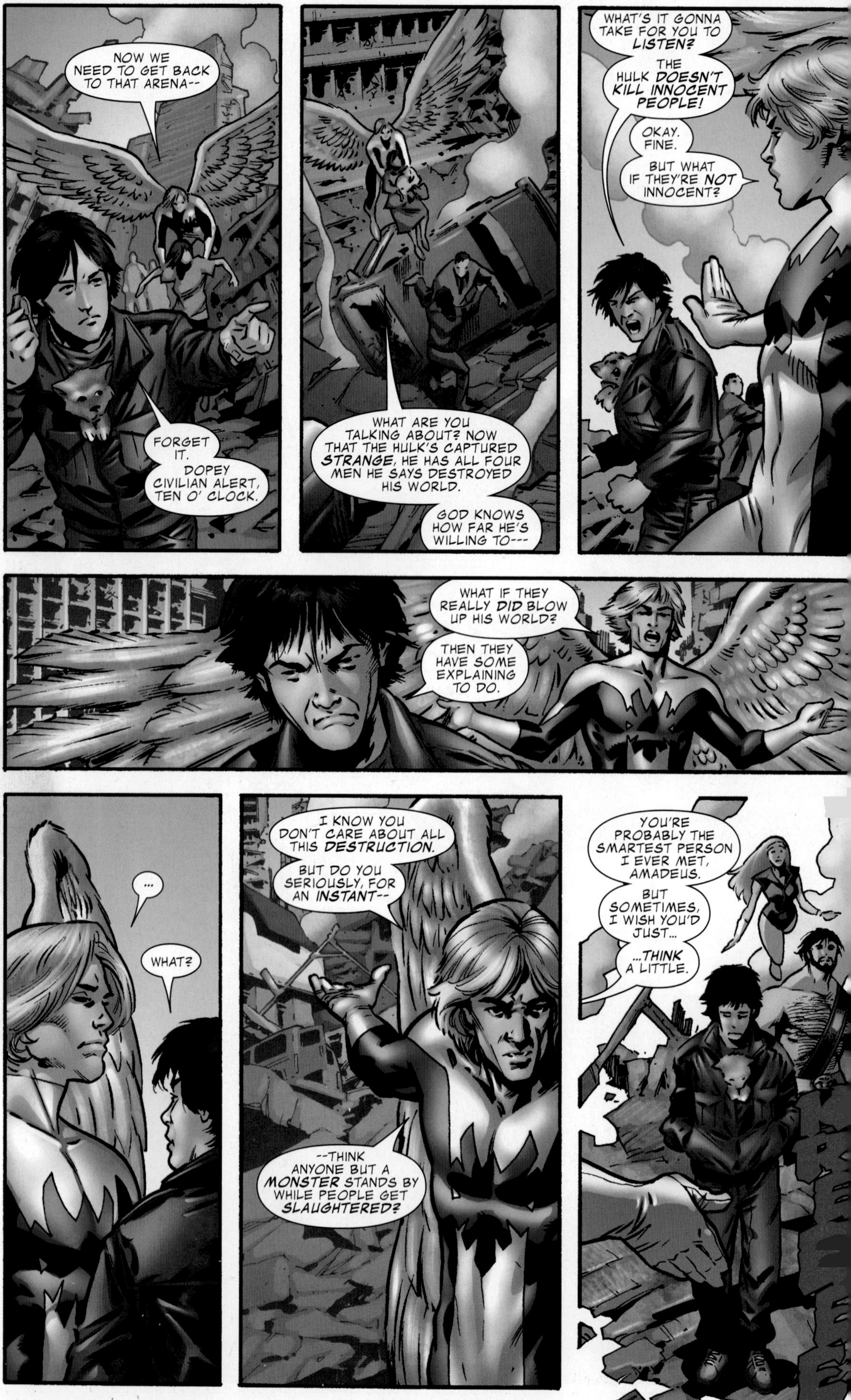
NOW WE NEED TO GET BACK TO THAT ARENA--
FORGET IT.
DOPEY CIVILIAN ALERT, TEN O' CLOCK.
WHAT ARE YOU TALKING ABOUT? NOW THAT THE HULK'S CAPTURED STRANGE, HE HAS ALL FOUR MEN HE SAYS DESTROYED HIS WORLD.
GOD KNOWS HOW FAR HE'S WILLING TO---
WHAT'S IT GONNA TAKE FOR YOU TO LISTEN?
THE HULK DOESN'T KILL INNOCENT PEOPLE!
OKAY. FINE.
BUT WHAT IF THEY'RE NOT INNOCENT?
WHAT IF THEY REALLY DID BLOW UP HIS WORLD?
THEN THEY HAVE SOME EXPLAINING TO DO.
...
WHAT?
I KNOW YOU DON'T CARE ABOUT ALL THIS DESTRUCTION.
BUT DO YOU SERIOUSLY, FOR AN INSTANT--
--THINK ANYONE BUT A MONSTER STANDS BY WHILE PEOPLE GET SLAUGHTERED?
YOU'RE PROBABLY THE SMARTEST PERSON I EVER MET, AMADEUS.
BUT SOMETIMES, I WISH YOU'D JUST...
...THINK A LITTLE.

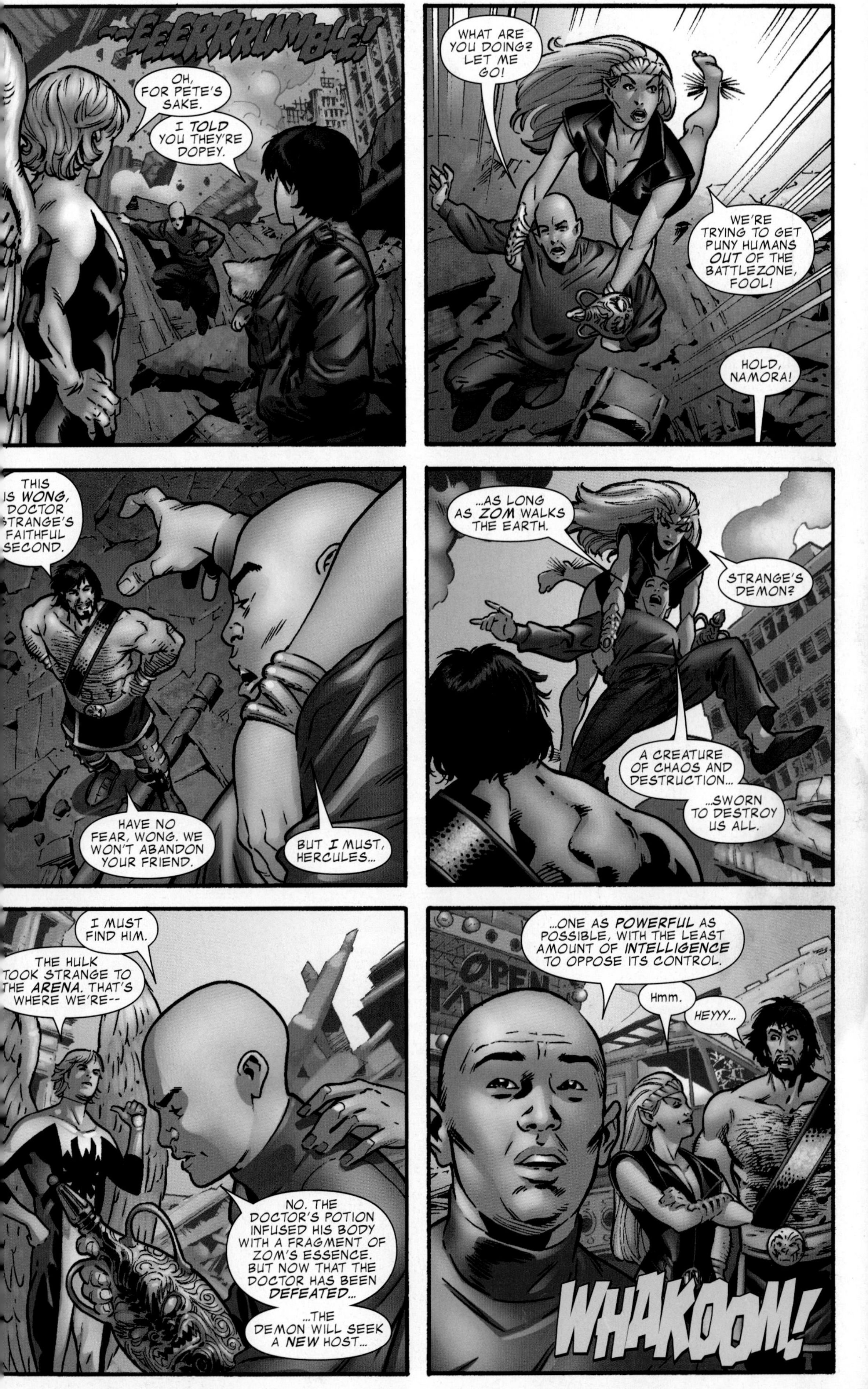
--EEERRRRUMBLE!
OH, FOR PETE'S SAKE.
I TOLD YOU THEY'RE DOPEY.
WHAT ARE YOU DOING? LET ME GO!
WE'RE TRYING TO GET PUNY HUMANS OUT OF THE BATTLEZONE, FOOL!
HOLD, NAMORA!
THIS IS WONG, DOCTOR STRANGE'S FAITHFUL SECOND.
HAVE NO FEAR, WONG. WE WON'T ABANDON YOUR FRIEND.
BUT I MUST, HERCULES...
...AS LONG AS ZOM WALKS THE EARTH.
STRANGE'S DEMON?
A CREATURE OF CHAOS AND DESTRUCTION...
...SWORN TO DESTROY US ALL.
I MUST FIND HIM.
THE HULK TOOK STRANGE TO THE ARENA. THAT'S WHERE WE'RE--
NO. THE DOCTOR'S POTION INFUSED HIS BODY WITH A FRAGMENT OF ZOM'S ESSENCE. BUT NOW THAT THE DOCTOR HAS BEEN DEFEATED...
...THE DEMON WILL SEEK A NEW HOST...
...ONE AS POWERFUL AS POSSIBLE, WITH THE LEAST AMOUNT OF INTELLIGENCE TO OPPOSE ITS CONTROL.
Hmm.
HEYYY...
WHAKOOM!

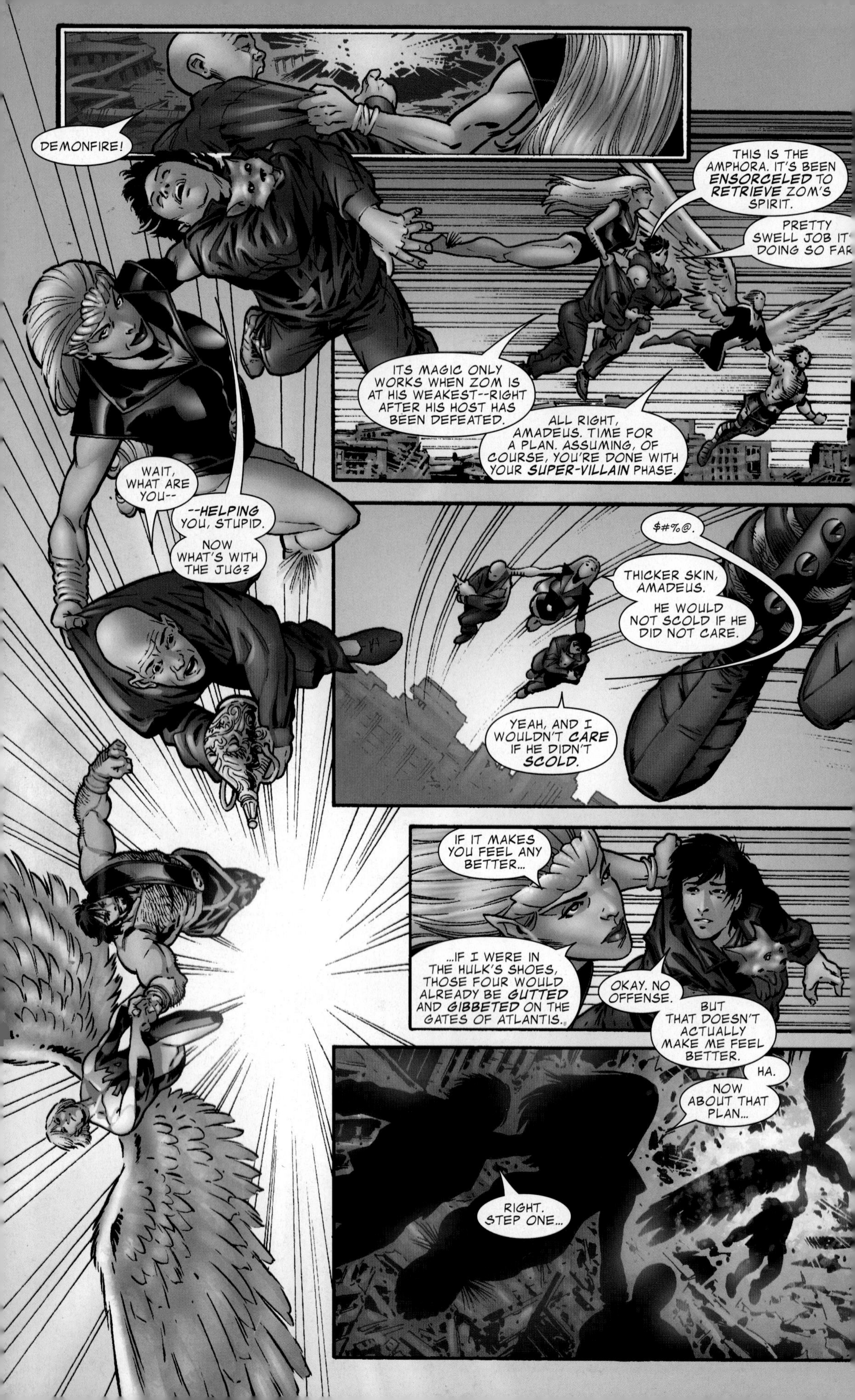
DEMONFIRE!
THIS IS THE AMPHORA. IT'S BEEN ENSORCELED TO RETRIEVE ZOM'S SPIRIT.
PRETTY SWELL JOB IT'S DOING SO FAR.
ITS MAGIC ONLY WORKS WHEN ZOM IS AT HIS WEAKEST--RIGHT AFTER HIS HOST HAS BEEN DEFEATED.
ALL RIGHT, AMADEUS. TIME FOR A PLAN. ASSUMING, OF COURSE, YOU'RE DONE WITH YOUR SUPER-VILLAIN PHASE.
WAIT, WHAT ARE YOU--
--HELPING YOU, STUPID.
NOW WHAT'S WITH THE JUG?
$#%@.
THICKER SKIN, AMADEUS.
HE WOULD NOT SCOLD IF HE DID NOT CARE.
YEAH, AND I WOULDN'T CARE IF HE DIDN'T SCOLD.
IF IT MAKES YOU FEEL ANY BETTER...
...IF I WERE IN THE HULK'S SHOES, THOSE FOUR WOULD ALREADY BE GUTTED AND GIBBETED ON THE GATES OF ATLANTIS.
OKAY. NO OFFENSE.
BUT THAT DOESN'T ACTUALLY MAKE ME FEEL BETTER.
HA.
NOW ABOUT THAT PLAN...
RIGHT. STEP ONE...

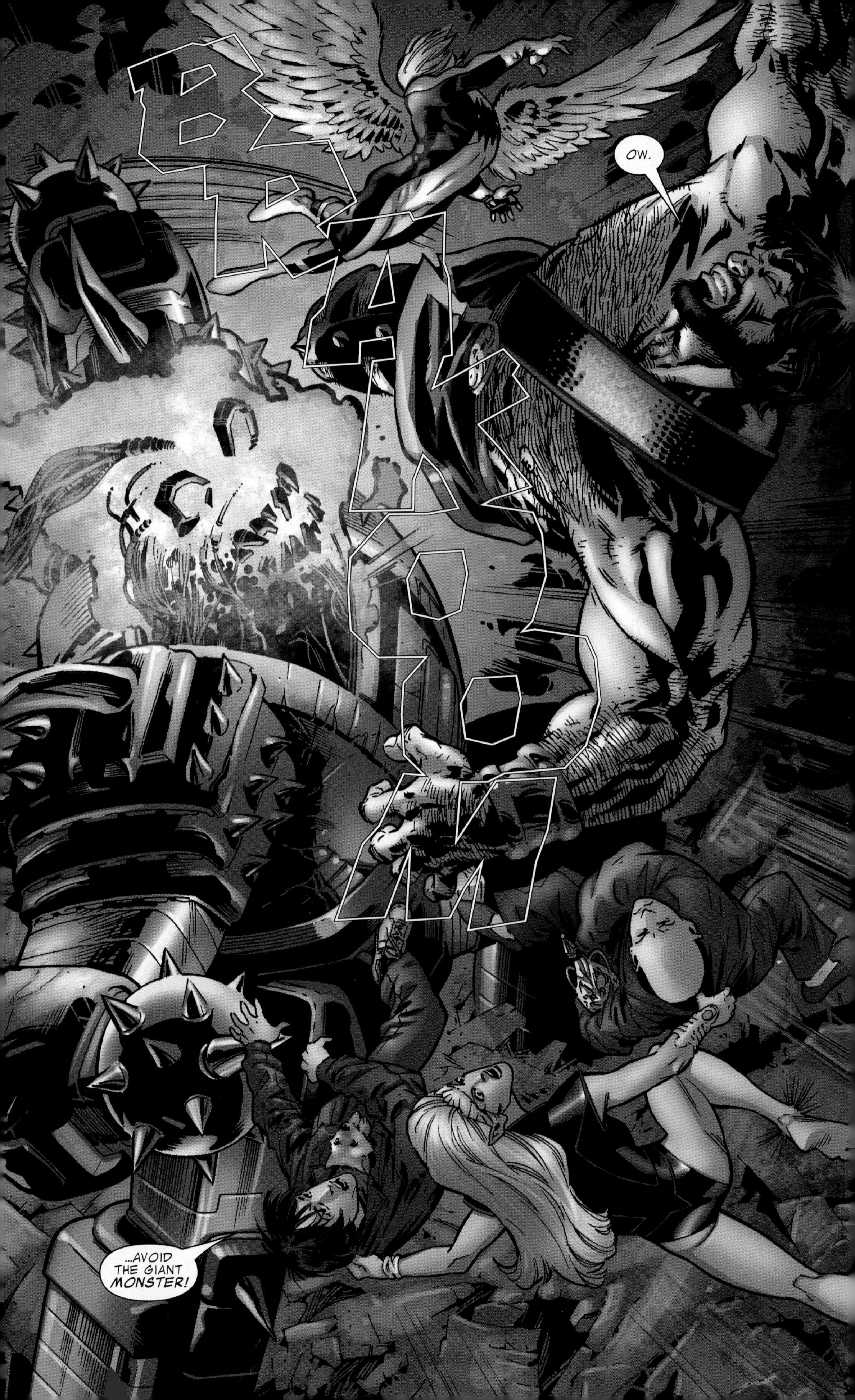
OW.
...AVOID THE GIANT MONSTER!

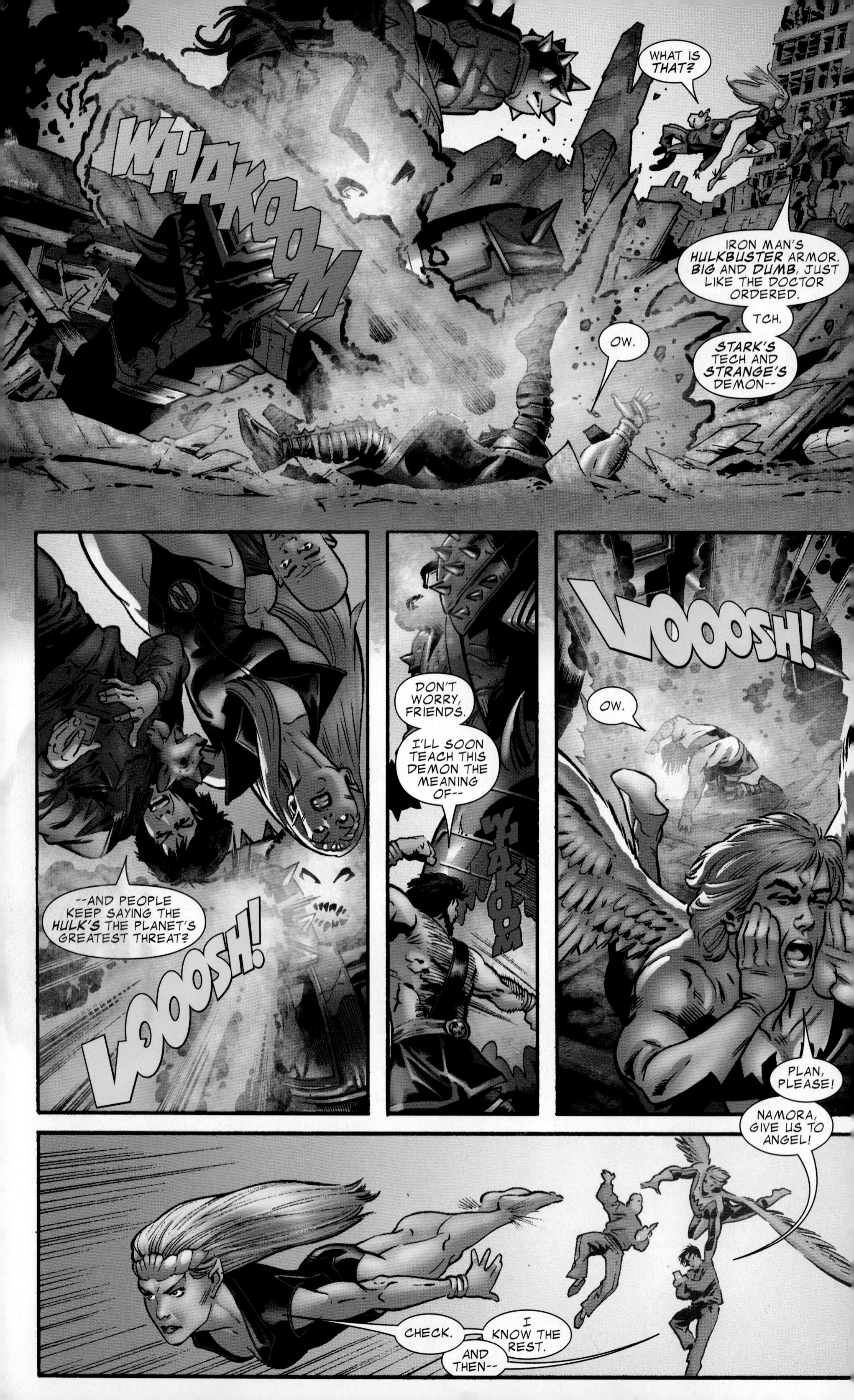
WHAKOOM
WHAT IS THAT?
IRON MAN'S HULKBUSTER ARMOR. BIG AND DUMB, JUST LIKE THE DOCTOR ORDERED.
TCH.
STARK'S TECH AND STRANGE'S DEMON--
OW.
--AND PEOPLE KEEP SAYING THE HULK'S THE PLANET'S GREATEST THREAT?
VOOOSH!
DON'T WORRY, FRIENDS.
I'LL SOON TEACH THIS DEMON THE MEANING OF--
WHAKOOM
VOOOSH!
OW.
PLAN, PLEASE!
NAMORA, GIVE US TO ANGEL!
CHECK.
I KNOW THE REST.
AND THEN--

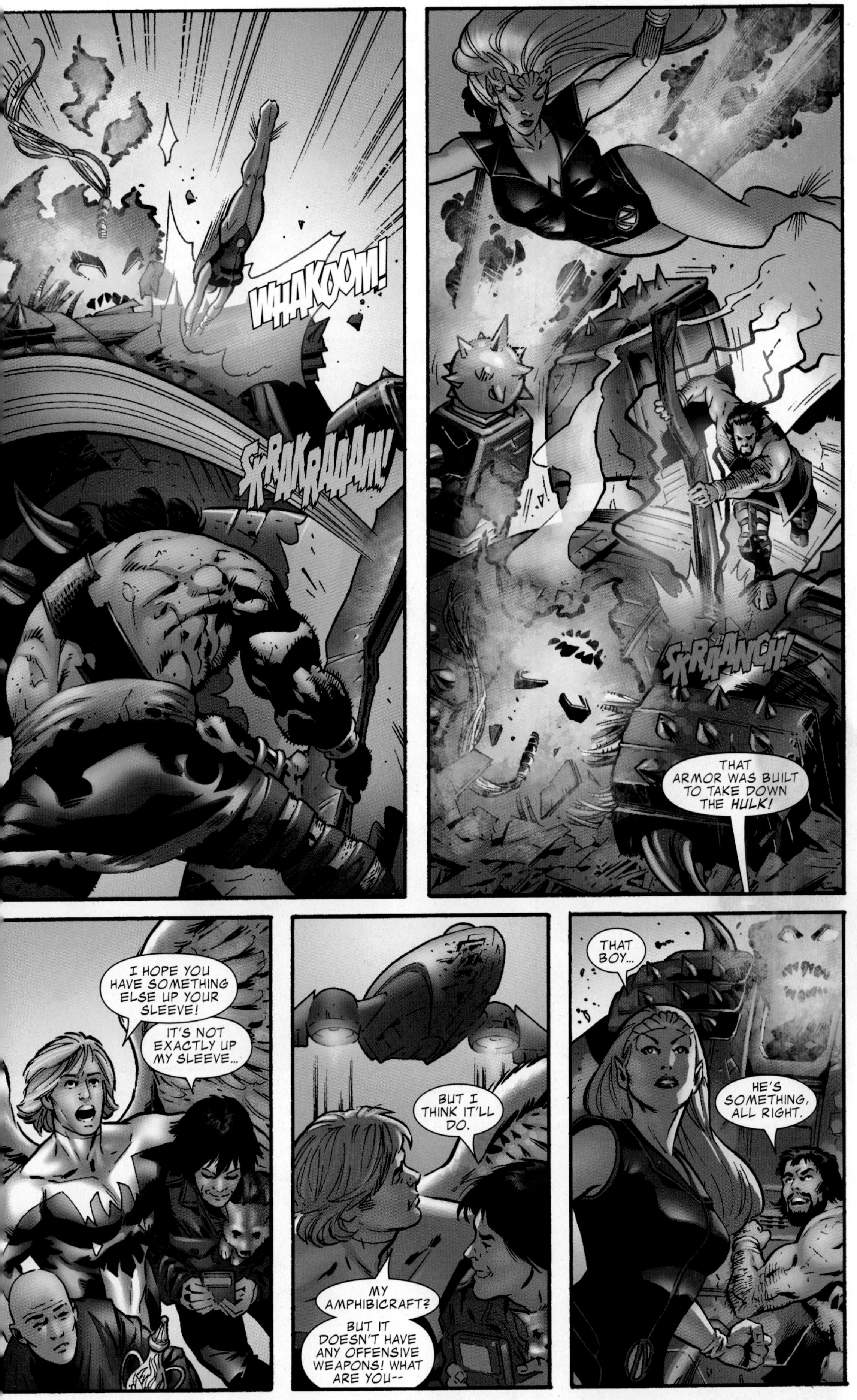
WHAKOOM!
SKRAKRAAAM!
SKRAANCH!
THAT ARMOR WAS BUILT TO TAKE DOWN THE HULK!
I HOPE YOU HAVE SOMETHING ELSE UP YOUR SLEEVE!
IT'S NOT EXACTLY UP MY SLEEVE...
BUT I THINK IT'LL DO.
MY AMPHIBICRAFT?
BUT IT DOESN'T HAVE ANY OFFENSIVE WEAPONS! WHAT ARE YOU--
THAT BOY...
HE'S SOMETHING, ALL RIGHT.

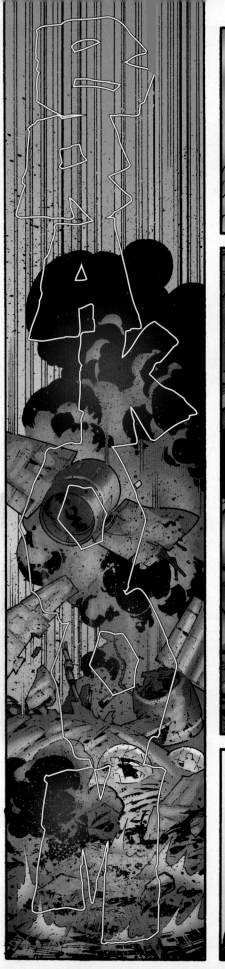

ARE YOU *INSANE*?

COME ON, ANGEL...

HERC'S THE PRINCE OF POWER! AND NAMORA'S AN INVULNERABLE ATLANTEAN MUTANT! THEY *LIVE* FOR THIS STUFF!

RRAAAAAA HA HA HA!

LET'S JUST FINISH THIS.

THE DEMON IS DOWN. THE AMPHORA SHOULD SUCK UP HIS ESSENCE, RIGHT, WONG?

THAT'S THE IDEA...

KREEEE...

OH, BOY.

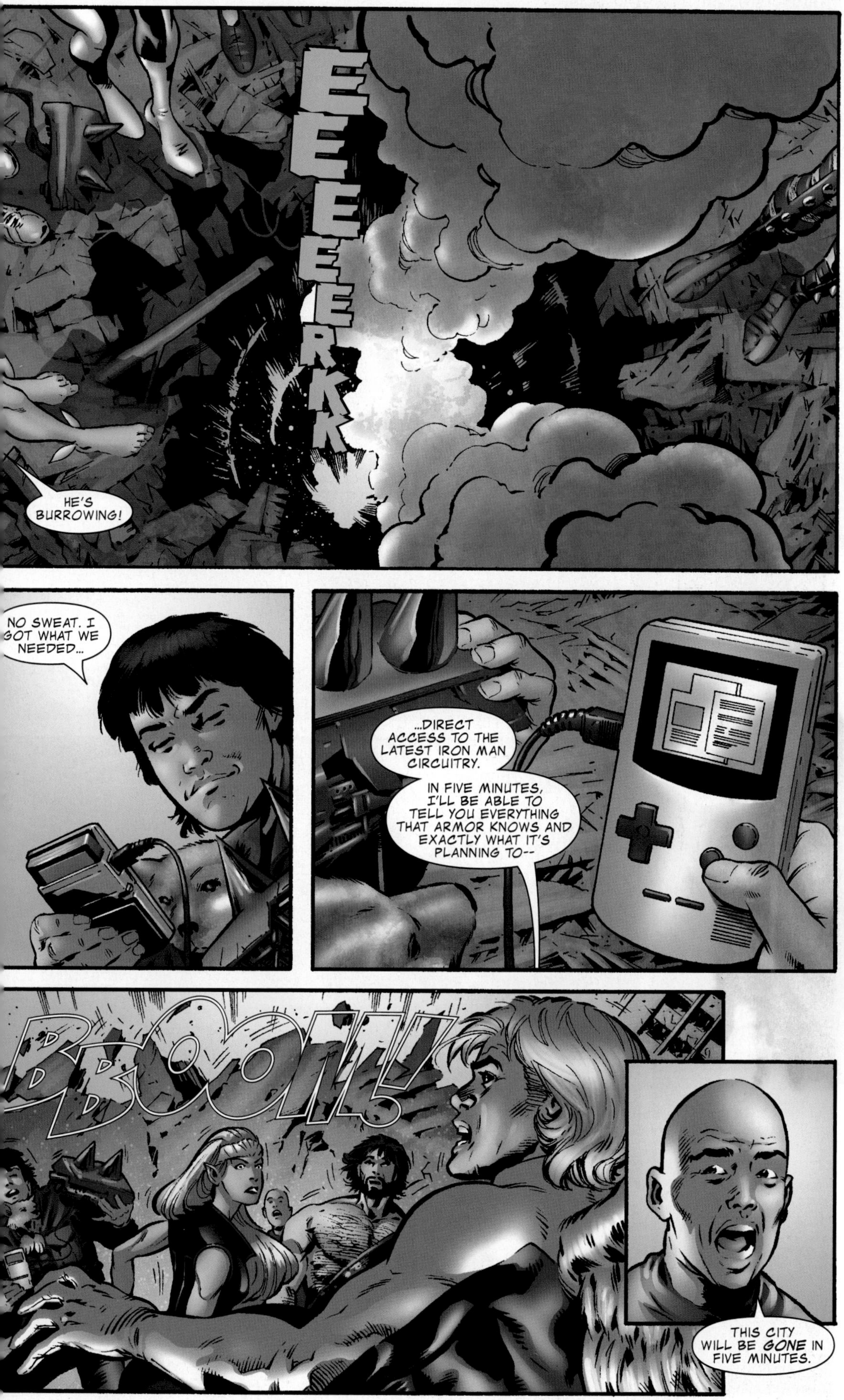
EEEEEERKK
HE'S BURROWING!
NO SWEAT. I GOT WHAT WE NEEDED...
...DIRECT ACCESS TO THE LATEST IRON MAN CIRCUITRY.
IN FIVE MINUTES, I'LL BE ABLE TO TELL YOU EVERYTHING THAT ARMOR KNOWS AND EXACTLY WHAT IT'S PLANNING TO--
BBOOM!
THIS CITY WILL BE GONE IN FIVE MINUTES.

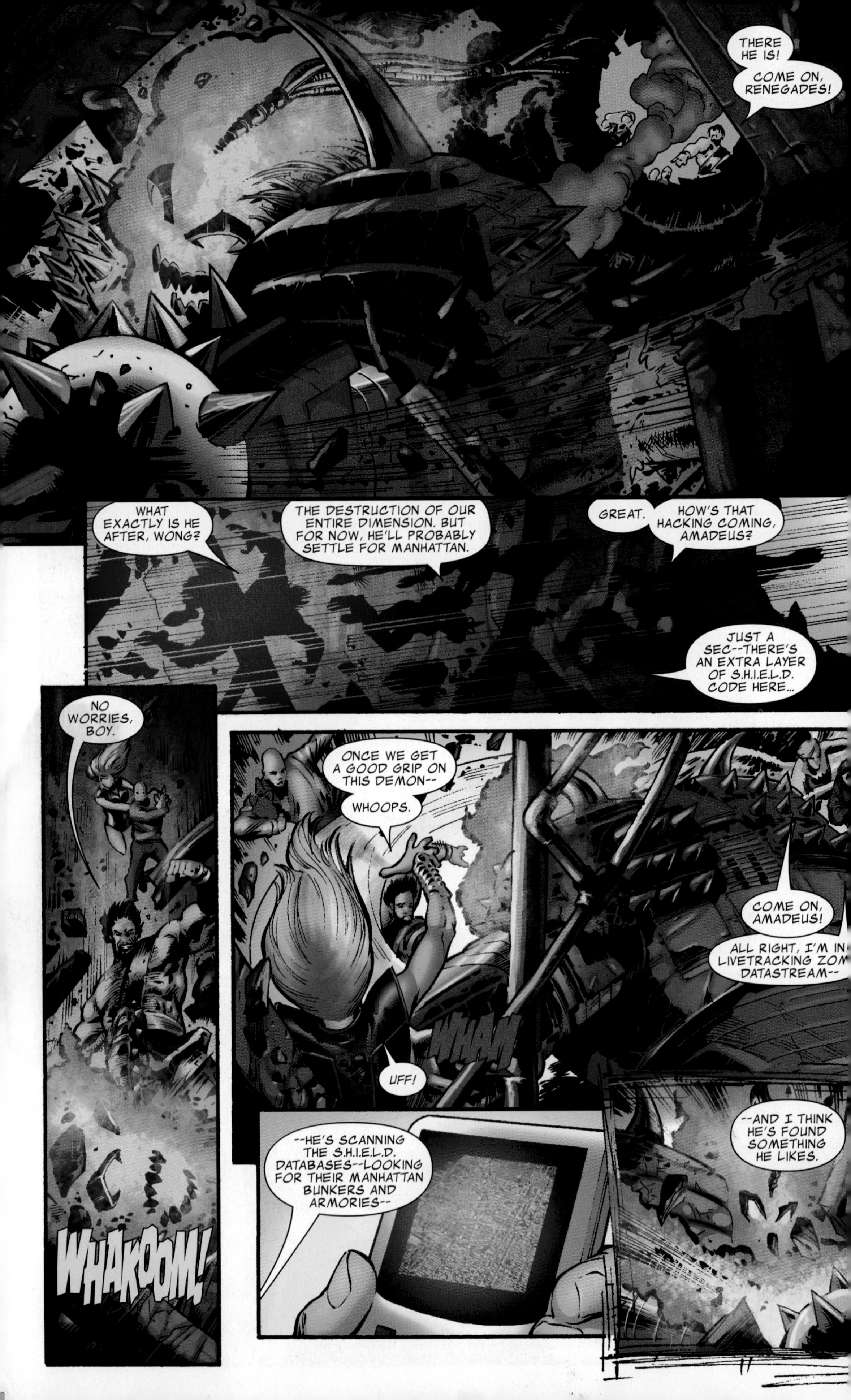

THERE HE IS!
COME ON, RENEGADES!
WHAT EXACTLY IS HE AFTER, WONG?
THE DESTRUCTION OF OUR ENTIRE DIMENSION. BUT FOR NOW, HE'LL PROBABLY SETTLE FOR MANHATTAN.
GREAT.
HOW'S THAT HACKING COMING, AMADEUS?
JUST A SEC--THERE'S AN EXTRA LAYER OF S.H.I.E.L.D. CODE HERE...
NO WORRIES, BOY.
WHAKOOM!
ONCE WE GET A GOOD GRIP ON THIS DEMON--
WHOOPS.
WHAM
UFF!
COME ON, AMADEUS!
ALL RIGHT, I'M IN LIVETRACKING ZOM DATASTREAM--
--HE'S SCANNING THE S.H.I.E.L.D. DATABASES--LOOKING FOR THEIR MANHATTAN BUNKERS AND ARMORIES--
--AND I THINK HE'S FOUND SOMETHING HE LIKES.

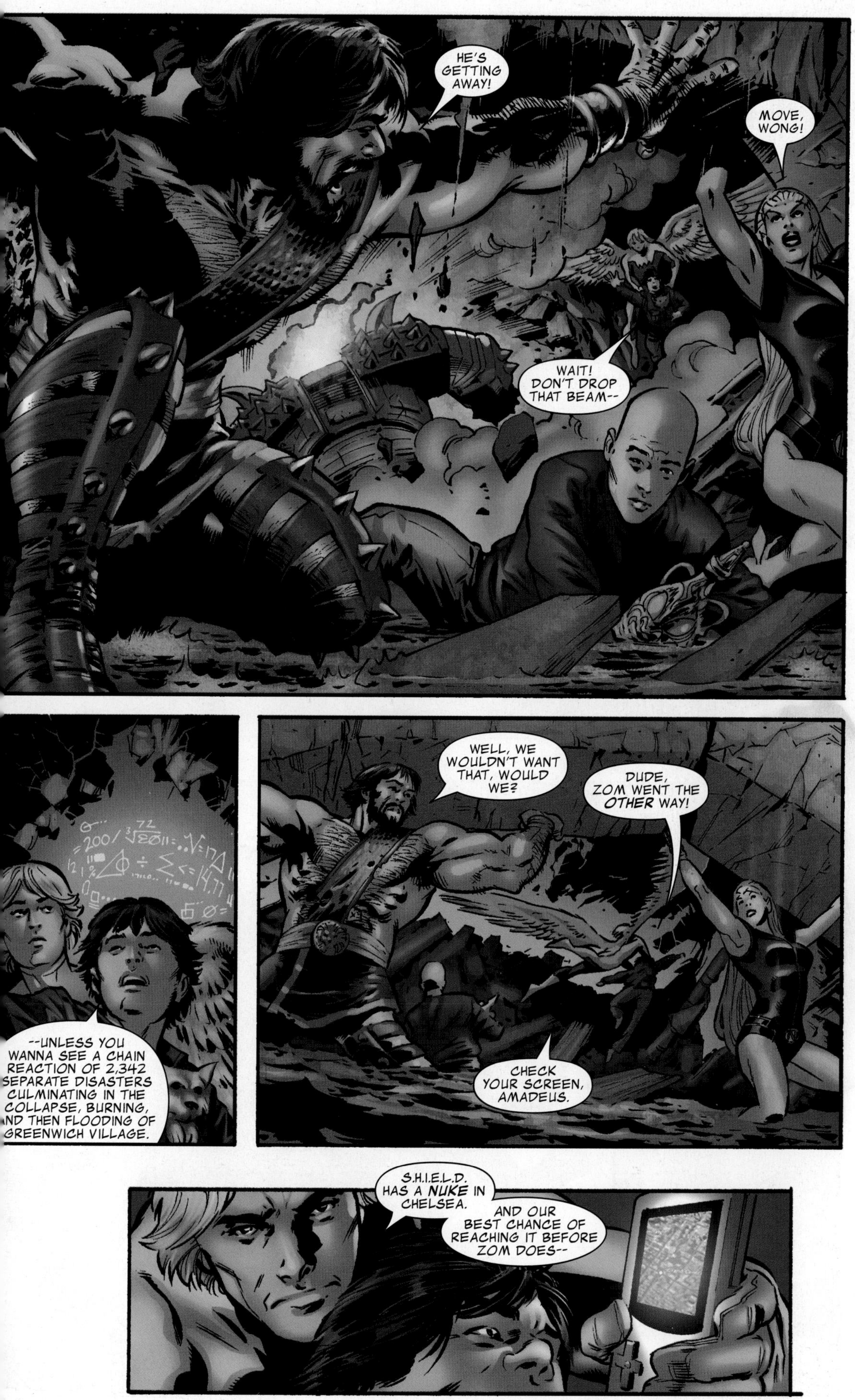
HE'S GETTING AWAY!
MOVE, WONG!
WAIT! DON'T DROP THAT BEAM--
--UNLESS YOU WANNA SEE A CHAIN REACTION OF 2,342 SEPARATE DISASTERS CULMINATING IN THE COLLAPSE, BURNING, ND THEN FLOODING OF GREENWICH VILLAGE.
WELL, WE WOULDN'T WANT THAT, WOULD WE?
DUDE, ZOM WENT THE *OTHER* WAY!
CHECK YOUR SCREEN, AMADEUS.
S.H.I.E.L.D. HAS A *NUKE* IN CHELSEA.
AND OUR BEST CHANCE OF REACHING IT BEFORE ZOM DOES--

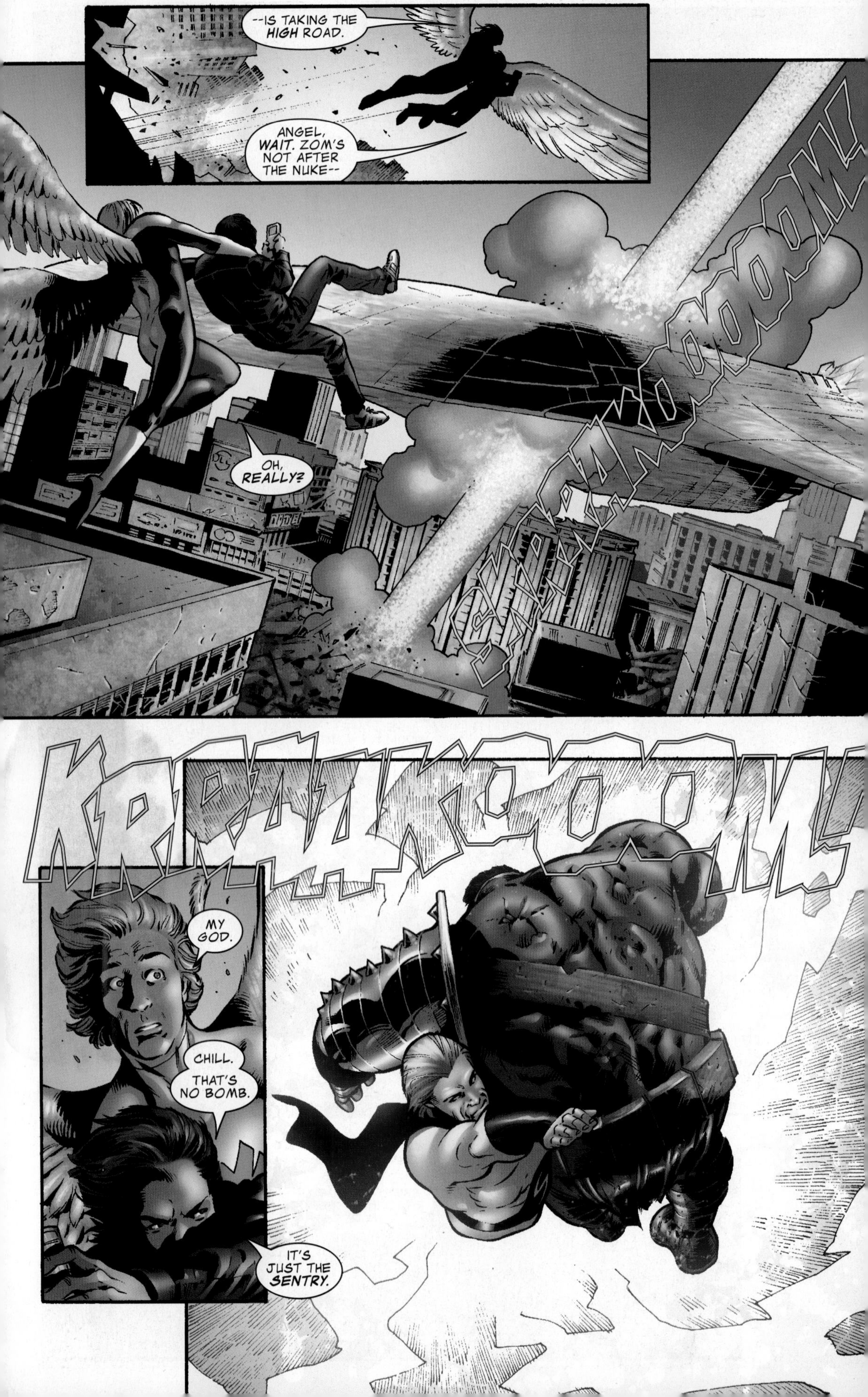
--IS TAKING THE HIGH ROAD.
ANGEL, WAIT. ZOM'S NOT AFTER THE NUKE--
OH, REALLY?
KRAKOOOOOM!
MY GOD.
CHILL.
THAT'S NO BOMB.
IT'S JUST THE SENTRY.

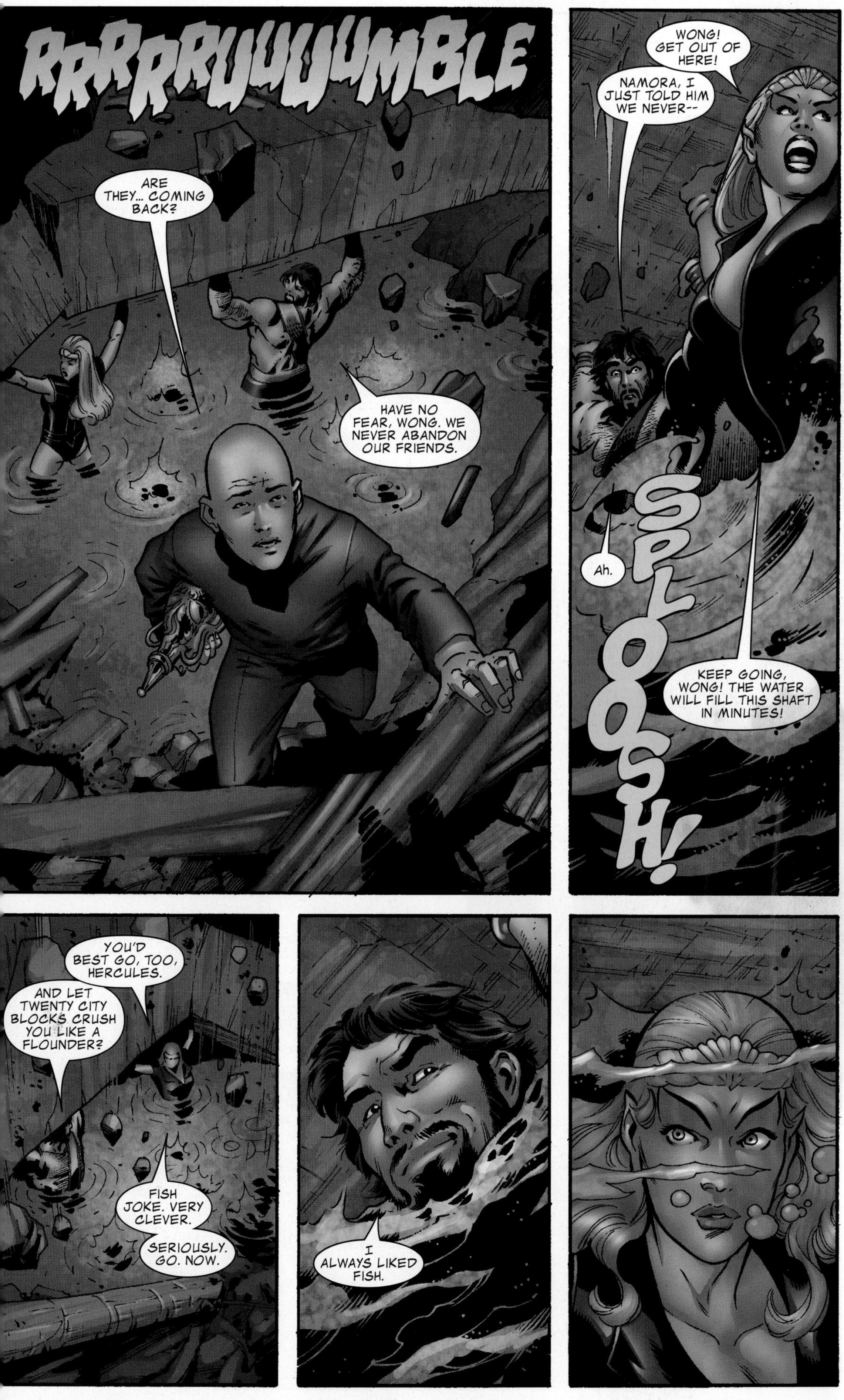
RRRRRUUUUMBLE
ARE THEY... COMING BACK?
HAVE NO FEAR, WONG. WE NEVER ABANDON OUR FRIENDS.
WONG! GET OUT OF HERE!
NAMORA, I JUST TOLD HIM WE NEVER--
Ah.
SPLOOOSH!
KEEP GOING, WONG! THE WATER WILL FILL THIS SHAFT IN MINUTES!
YOU'D BEST GO, TOO, HERCULES.
AND LET TWENTY CITY BLOCKS CRUSH YOU LIKE A FLOUNDER?
FISH JOKE. VERY CLEVER.
SERIOUSLY. GO. NOW.
I ALWAYS LIKED FISH.

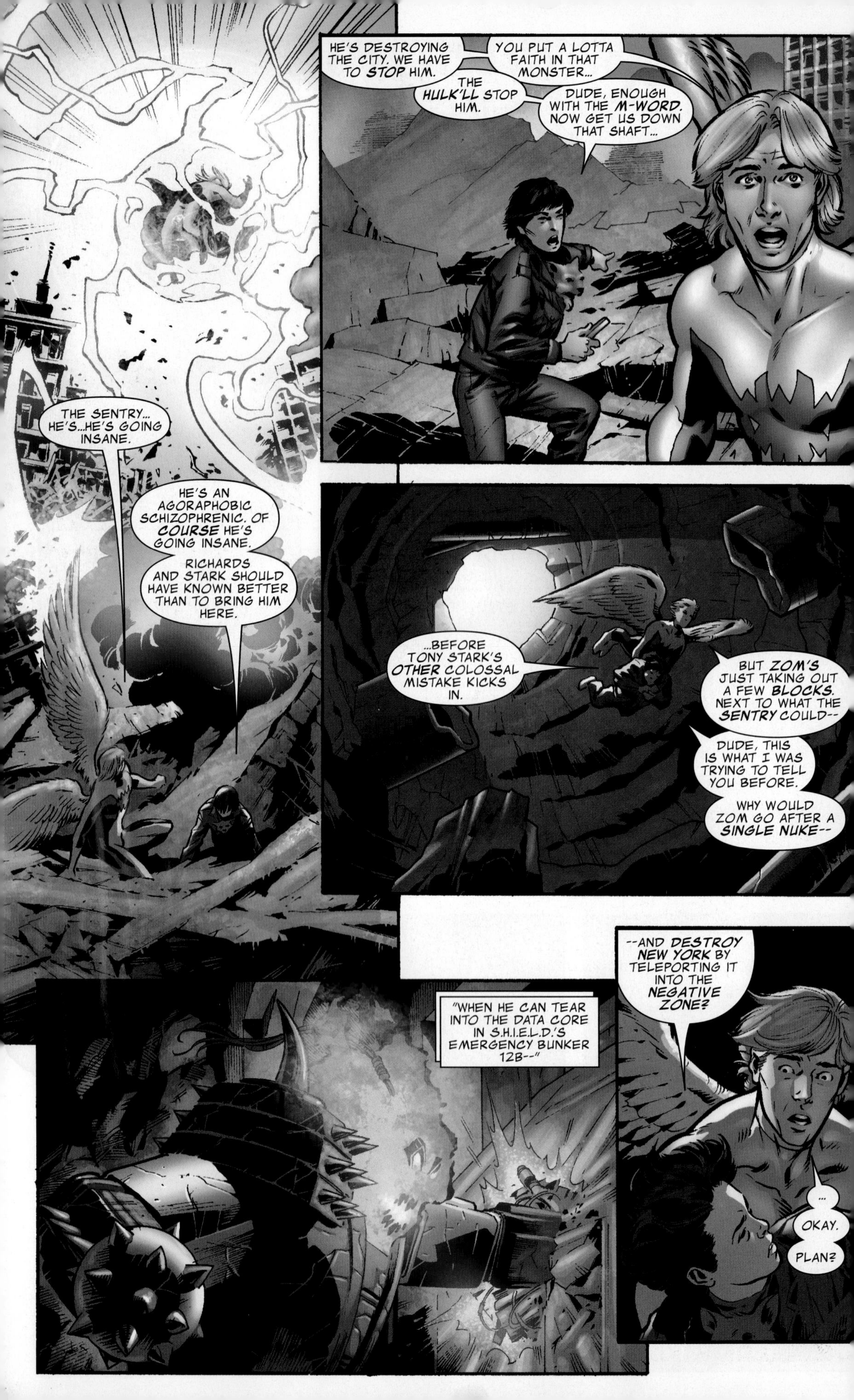
THE SENTRY... HE'S...HE'S GOING INSANE.
HE'S AN AGORAPHOBIC SCHIZOPHRENIC. OF COURSE HE'S GOING INSANE.
RICHARDS AND STARK SHOULD HAVE KNOWN BETTER THAN TO BRING HIM HERE.
HE'S DESTROYING THE CITY. WE HAVE TO STOP HIM.
YOU PUT A LOTTA FAITH IN THAT MONSTER...
THE HULK'LL STOP HIM.
DUDE, ENOUGH WITH THE M-WORD. NOW GET US DOWN THAT SHAFT...
...BEFORE TONY STARK'S OTHER COLOSSAL MISTAKE KICKS IN.
BUT ZOM'S JUST TAKING OUT A FEW BLOCKS. NEXT TO WHAT THE SENTRY COULD--
DUDE, THIS IS WHAT I WAS TRYING TO TELL YOU BEFORE.
WHY WOULD ZOM GO AFTER A SINGLE NUKE--
"WHEN HE CAN TEAR INTO THE DATA CORE IN S.H.I.E.L.D.'S EMERGENCY BUNKER 12B--"
--AND DESTROY NEW YORK BY TELEPORTING IT INTO THE NEGATIVE ZONE?
...
OKAY.
PLAN?

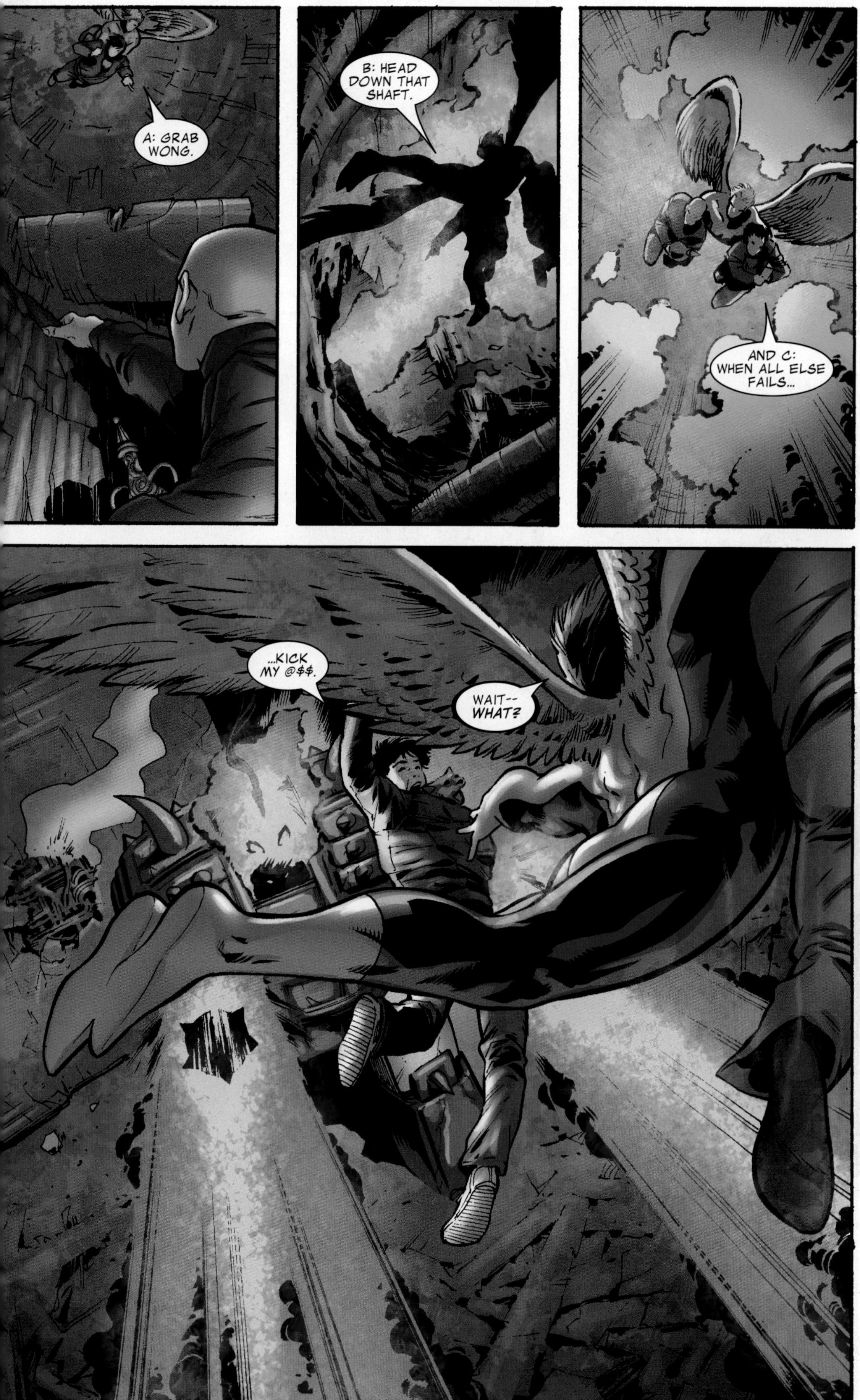
A: GRAB WONG.
B: HEAD DOWN THAT SHAFT.
AND C: WHEN ALL ELSE FAILS...
...KICK MY @$$.
WAIT-- WHAT?

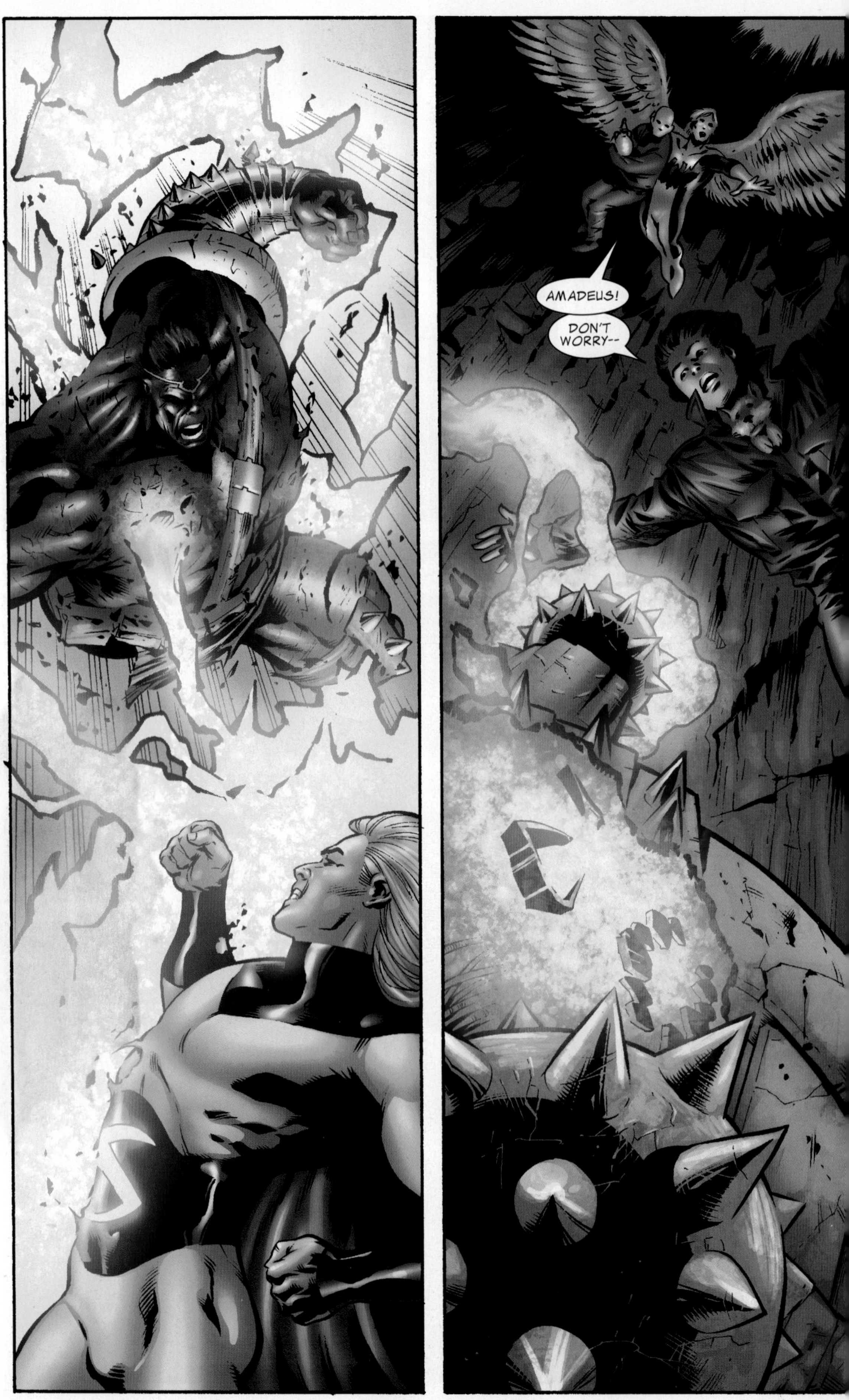
AMADEUS!
DON'T WORRY--

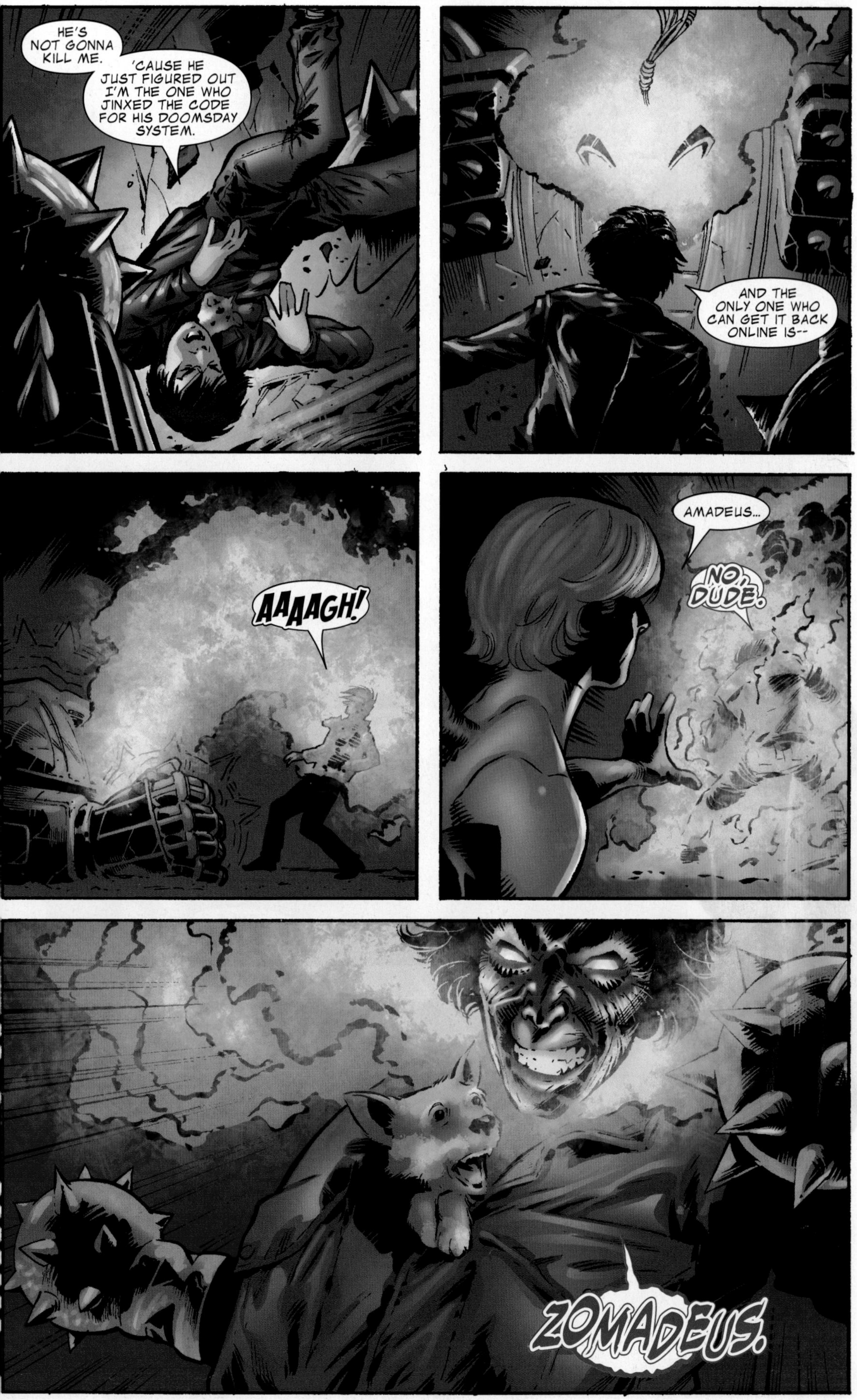
HE'S NOT GONNA KILL ME.
'CAUSE HE JUST FIGURED OUT I'M THE ONE WHO JINXED THE CODE FOR HIS DOOMSDAY SYSTEM.
AND THE ONLY ONE WHO CAN GET IT BACK ONLINE IS--
AAAAGH!
AMADEUS...
NO, DUDE.
ZOMADEUS.

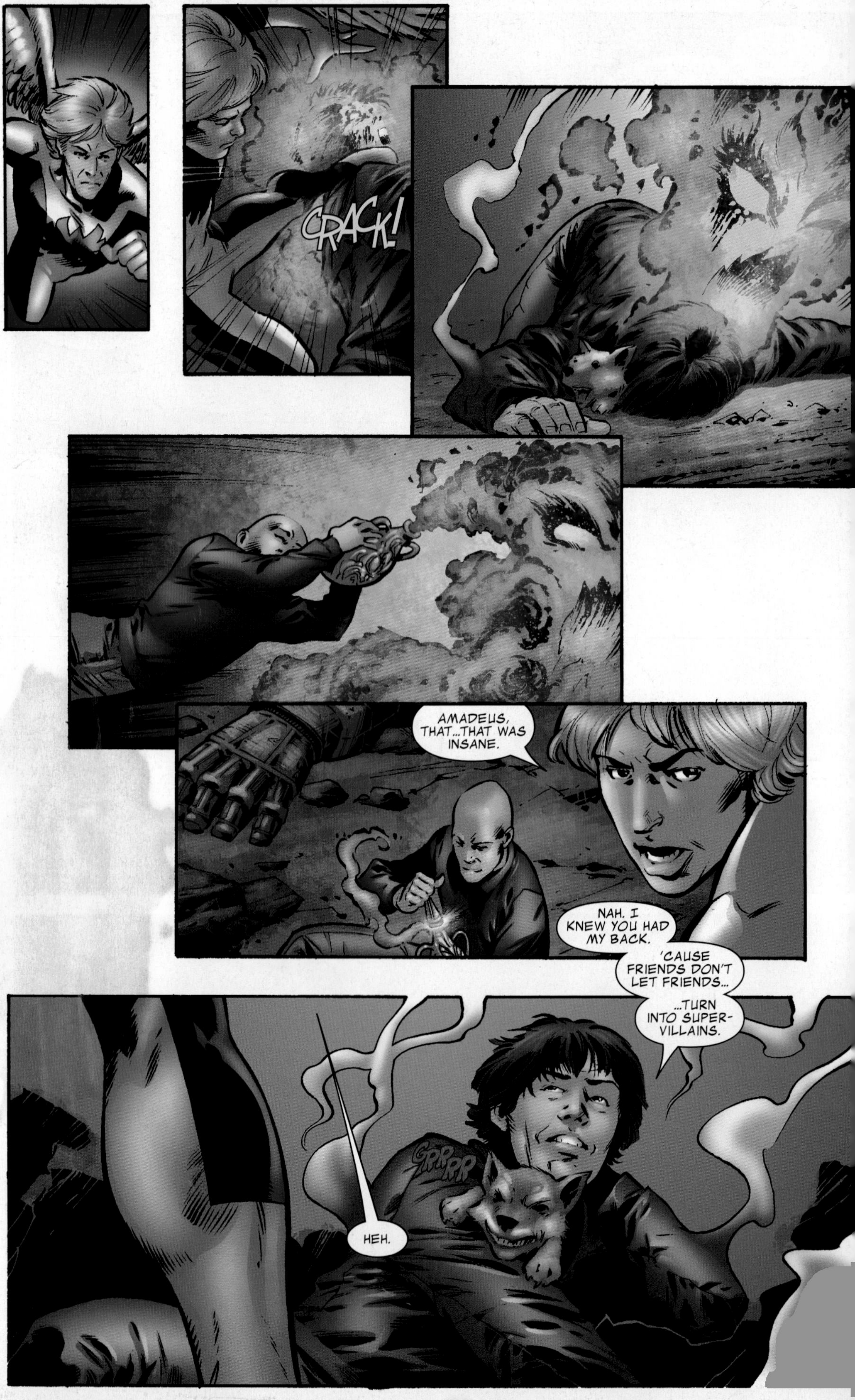
CRACK!
AMADEUS, THAT...THAT WAS INSANE.
NAH. I KNEW YOU HAD MY BACK.
'CAUSE FRIENDS DON'T LET FRIENDS...
...TURN INTO SUPER-VILLAINS.
GRRRR
HEH.

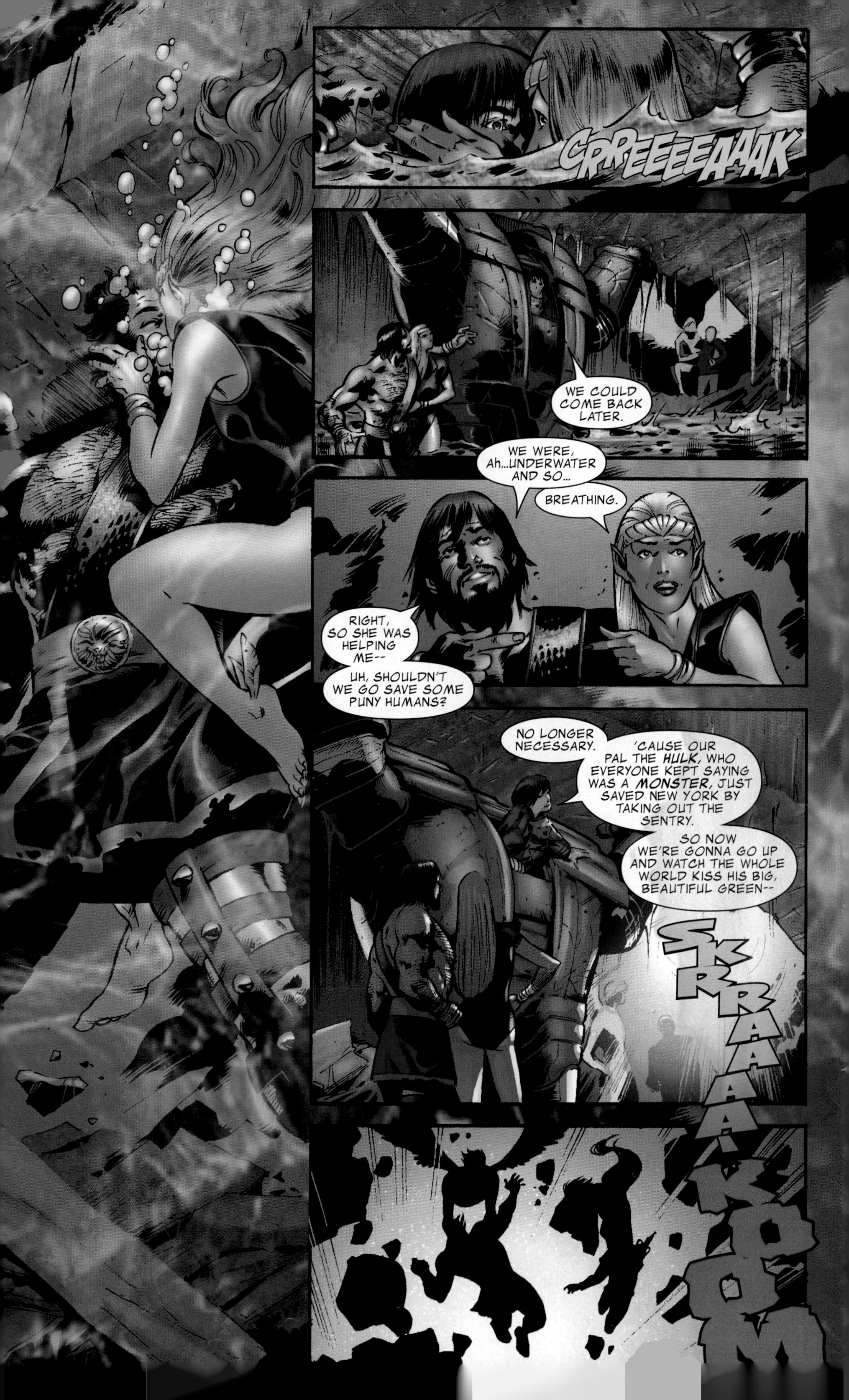
CRREEEEAAAK
WE COULD COME BACK LATER.
WE WERE, Ah...UNDERWATER AND SO...
BREATHING.
RIGHT, SO SHE WAS HELPING ME--
UH, SHOULDN'T WE GO SAVE SOME PUNY HUMANS?
NO LONGER NECESSARY.
'CAUSE OUR PAL THE HULK, WHO EVERYONE KEPT SAYING WAS A MONSTER, JUST SAVED NEW YORK BY TAKING OUT THE SENTRY.
SO NOW WE'RE GONNA GO UP AND WATCH THE WHOLE WORLD KISS HIS BIG, BEAUTIFUL GREEN--
SKRRAAAAKOOM

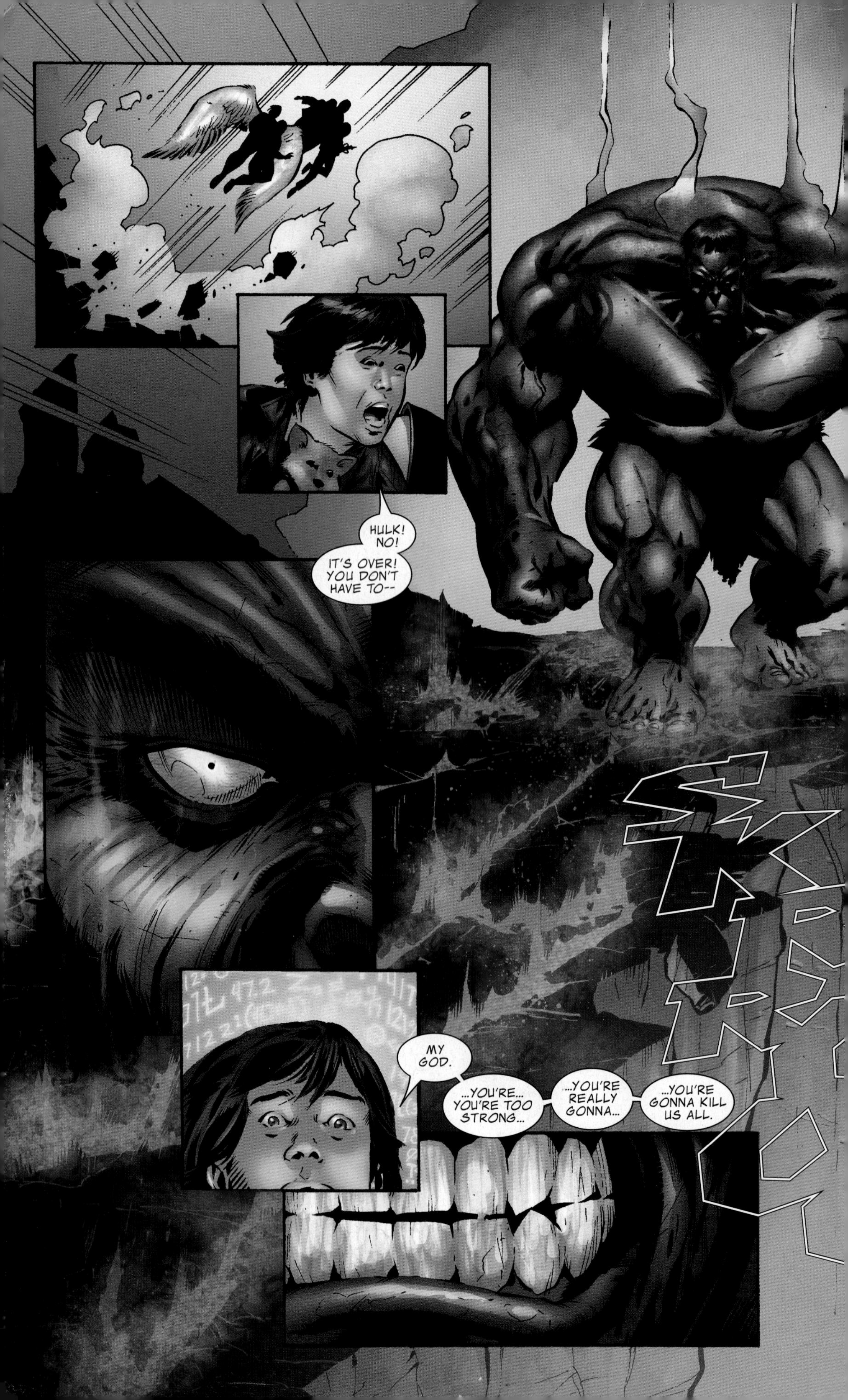
HULK! NO!
IT'S OVER! YOU DON'T HAVE TO--
MY GOD.
...YOU'RE... YOU'RE TOO STRONG...
...YOU'RE REALLY GONNA...
...YOU'RE GONNA KILL US ALL.

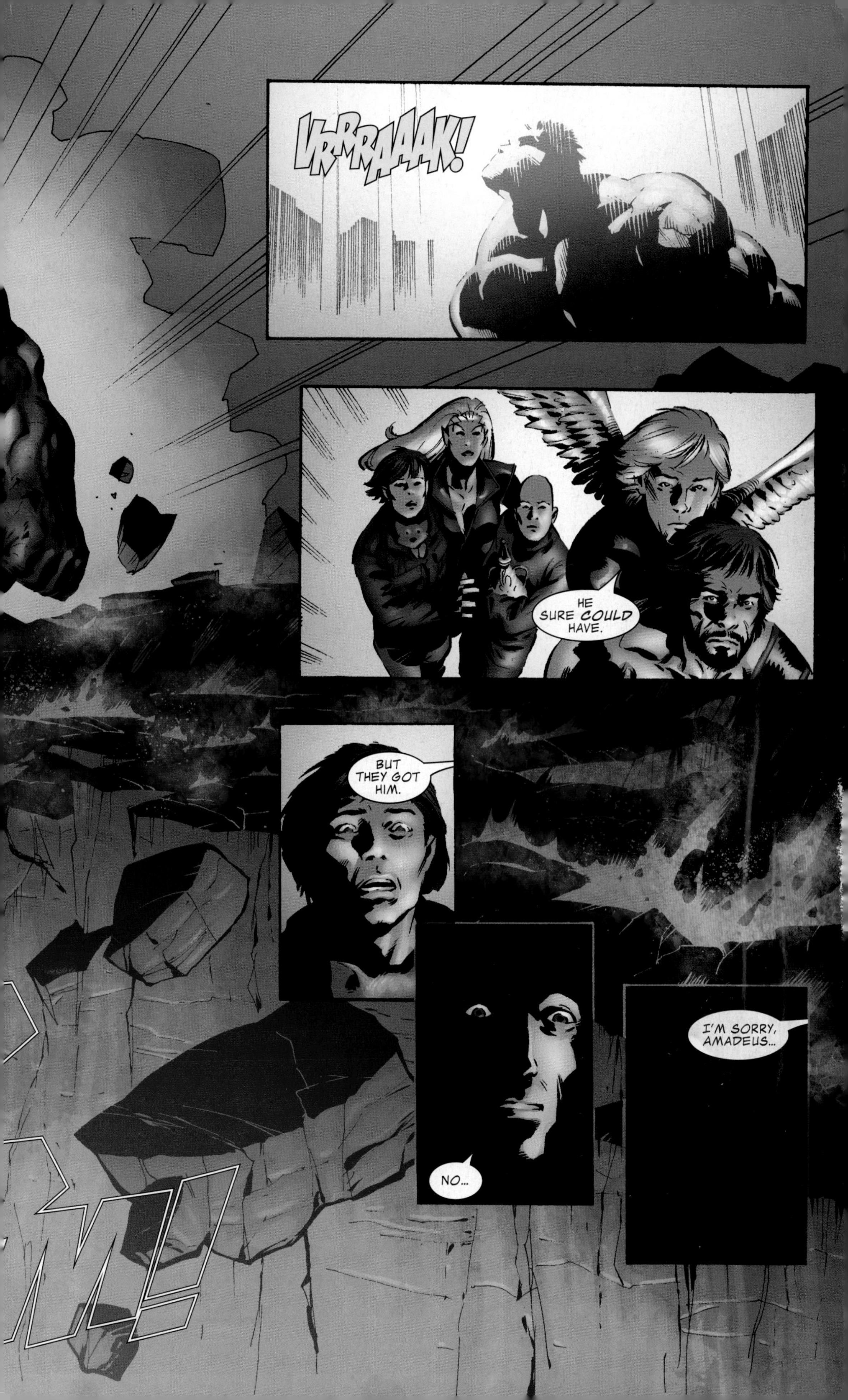
VRRRAAAK!
HE SURE COULD HAVE.
BUT THEY GOT HIM.
NO...
I'M SORRY, AMADEUS...

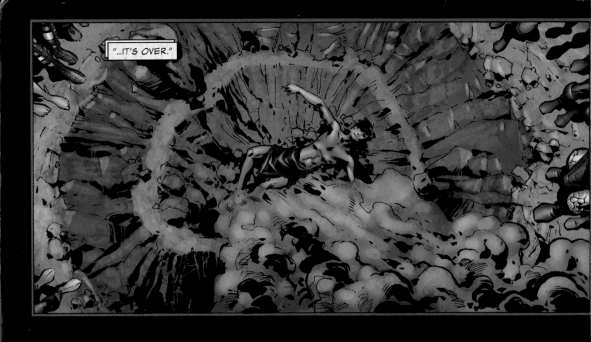

"...IT'S OVER."

YOU SAVED THE WORLD...

...AND YOU WERE THERE FOR YOUR FRIENDS.

YOU SHOULD BE PROUD, BOY.

NOT ALL OF THEM.

THE END.

HISTORY: Mere minutes after achieving the highest score ever on the Excello Soap Company's "Brain Fight" Internet game, earning the title "Mastermind Excello," 16-year-old Amadeus Cho was approached by a woman called Agent Sexton, representing an unidentified agency wishing to train him. Following his refusal, his Arizona home was blown up, killing his parents and sister, but Amadeus escaped, arriving in Jackalope, New Mexico the following morning. Contacting Sexton, he dismissed her claim that a second agency was responsible. Adopting an orphaned coyote pup, Amadeus confronted a helicopter sent by his enemies, deflecting the aim of one attacker's laser gun to distract another attacker, whose misfired missile, whether by accident or design, struck bystander Bruce Banner, triggering his transformation into the Hulk. The Hulk quickly disabled the helicopter and took Amadeus and the pup to safety before departing, earning the boy's undying devotion.

Weeks after the Hulk's disappearance, SHIELD agents targeted Amadeus as a violator of the new Superhuman Registration Act, but Amadeus, having already penetrated SHIELD's computer defenses to learn all he could about the Hulk, destroyed the agents' mini-helicarrier over Coney Island, allowing them time to escape. Returning to New Mexico, he uncovered one of Banner's forgotten bases and hacked into Mr. Fantastic's computer system, learning the Hulk had been shot into space by Mr. Fantastic and others but would doubtlessly return. He relayed data about the Hulk's exile to She-Hulk, who advised him to seek help from the Champions, a super-team that had once misjudged the Hulk and felt they owed him a debt.

Amadeus, accompanied by his coyote pup, recruited former Champions Hercules (Heracles) and Angel (Warren Worthington III), as well as the Atlantean Namora, to pursue the Hulk's interests, which changed dramatically when the Hulk led his Warbound comrades to attack New York. As the Renegades, Amadeus and his allies helped SHIELD restore a measure of safety to the decimated city, although Amadeus, correctly convinced the Hulk would not kill his enemies, failed to persuade the Hulk to end the incursion. Soon afterward, when Dr. Strange used the demon Zom's power to fight the Hulk, the demon's essence partially escaped his control and possessed Iron Man's Hulkbuster armor, which it used to both wreak havoc and learn how to best devastate New York City with SHIELD's resources. Amadeus tricked the demon into entering his own body instead; with no powers of his own, the possessed Amadeus was easily defeated by Angel, and the Zom fragment mystically contained.

REAL NAME: Amadeus Cho
ALIASES: Iolaus, Zomadeus, the Smart Kid, Mastermind Excello
IDENTITY: Publicly known
OCCUPATION: Adventurer/fugitive; former high school student
CITIZENSHIP: USA
PLACE OF BIRTH: Tucson, Arizona
KNOWN RELATIVES: Unidentified parents (deceased), Madame Curie "Maddy" Cho (sister, deceased)
GROUP AFFILIATION: Renegades
EDUCATION: High school dropout; extensively self-educated
FIRST APPEARANCE: Amazing Fantasy #15 (2006)

When the crisis ended, SHIELD took Amadeus and Hercules into custody. Initially cooperating to keep Amadeus from provoking further havoc, Hercules changed his mind when his half-brother Ares, now an Avenger, vowed to humiliate him in government servitude. With Hercules, Amadeus escaped and, intending to hijack the Hulk's spaceship, penetrated the SHIELD base holding it, but a surprise attack from the Black Widow (Natasha Romanoff) almost fatally injured Amadeus' pup. Instead confiscating SHIELD's Behemoth aircraft, a vengeful Amadeus resolved to gain control of every SHIELD facility on Earth and cripple the organization in its entirety.

HEIGHT: 5'6" **WEIGHT:** 117 lbs.
EYES: Black **HAIR:** Black

ABILITIES/ACCESSORIES: Amadeus Cho is allegedly the 7th smartest person on Earth. He can rapidly and without mechanical aid perform mental calculations of almost unimaginable complexity, enabling him to, with minimal stimuli on his part, set multiple physical reactions into motion in his vicinity, forestalling technological and human activity with equal ease; performing multiple calculations in rapid succession costs him immense amounts of energy, requiring him to consume large amounts of food immediately thereafter. He rides a Vespa scooter and customarily carries a phone/radio, Walkman, or other device altered to control nearby electrical signals. He travels with a devoted coyote pup whom he has trained to distract opponents and perform simple search operations.

POWER GRID	1	2	3	4	5	6	7
INTELLIGENCE							
STRENGTH							
SPEED							
DURABILITY							
ENERGY PROJECTION							
FIGHTING SKILLS							

Art by Gary Frank

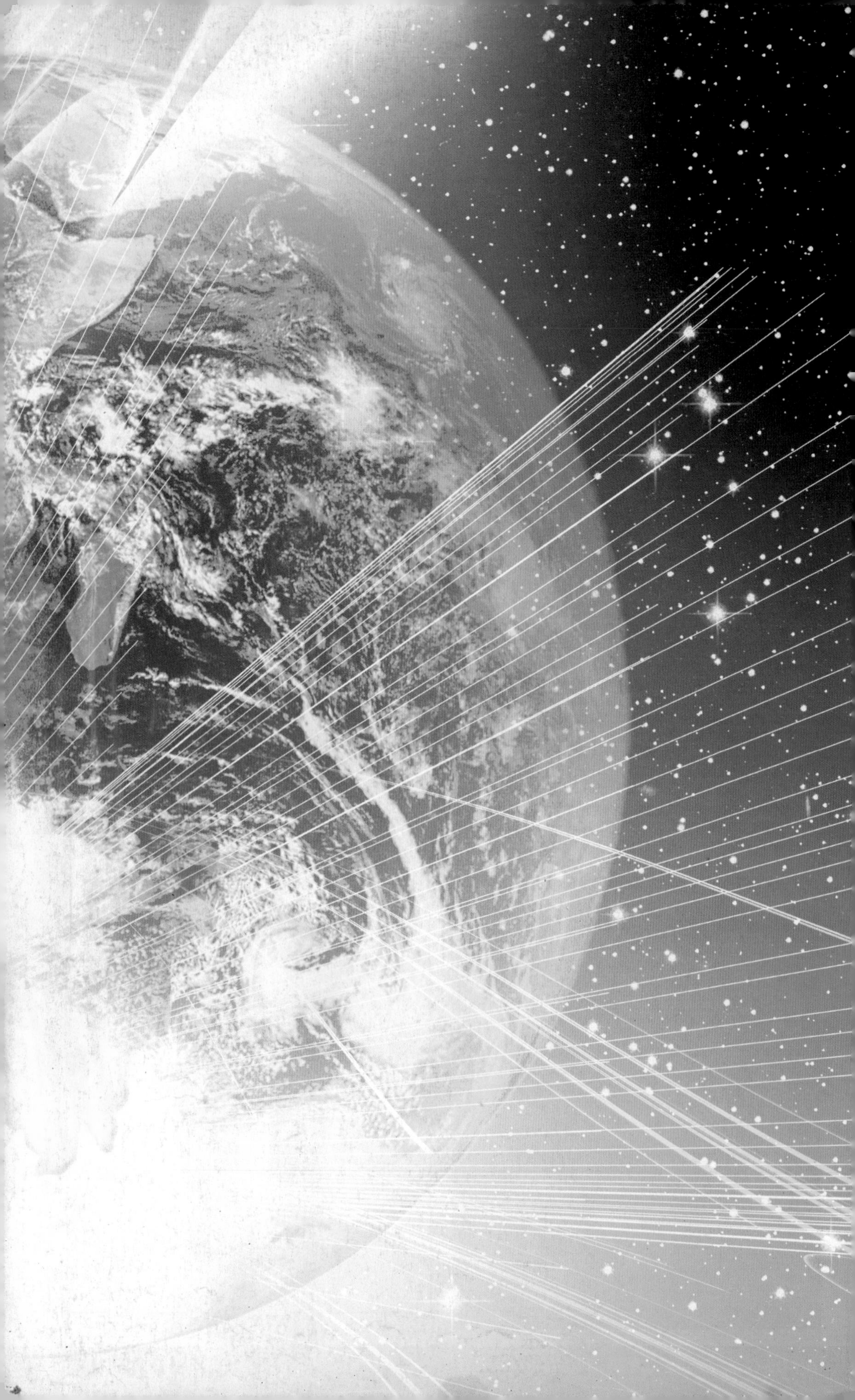